TECHNICAL
READOUT

3058

D1319489

FASA CORPORATION

CONTENTS

BATTLETECH®, 'MECH®, BATTLEMECH®, and MECHWARRIOR® are Registered Trademarks of FASA Corporation. BATTLETECH TECHNICAL READOUT: 3058 is a Trademark of FASA Corporation.

Published by
FASA Corporation
1100 W. Cermak Road
Suite B305
Chicago, IL 60608

FASA Corporation can be reached on America OnLine (E. Mail—FASALou (Earthdawn), FASAInfo (BattleTech, Shadowrun, General Information) or FASA Art (Art Comments)) in the Online Gaming area (Keyword "Gaming"). Via InterNet use <AOL Account Name>@AOL.COM, but please, no list or server subscriptions. Thanks!

Visit FASA on the World Wide Web at http//www.FASA.com

CREDITS

TECHNICAL READOUT: 3058

Design and Writing
Hugh Browne
Chris Hartford
Sam Lewis
Bryan Nystul

Additional Material
Thomas S. Gressman
Christopher Hussey
Rodney Knox
James D. Long
Victor Milán
Blaine L. Pardoe
Anthony Pryor

Development
Bryan Nystul

Development Assistance
Michael Mulvihill

Editorial Staff
Editorial Director
Donna Ippolito
Managing Editor
Sharon Turner Mulvihill
Associate Editors
Diane Piron-Gelman
Rob Cruz

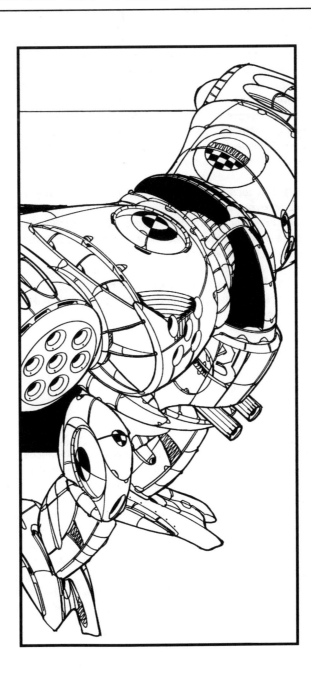

Production Staff
Art Director
Jim Nelson
Project Manager
Jim Nelson
Cover Art
Doug Chaffee
Cover Design
Jim Nelson
Color Plates
Joel Biske
Computer Illustrations
Virtual World Entertainment
Black & White Illustrations
Duane Loose, John Paul Lona
Layout
Mark Ernst
Steve Bryant

Corrected 3rd Printing

Already six years have passed since the invading Clans and the Great Houses signed the Truce of Tukayyid, and the Inner Sphere's fifteen-year breathing space is rapidly diminishing. Recent events in Clan-occupied space signal even more serious trouble—if the Clans' internal warring results in the Crusader faction gaining the upper hand, the Clans may repudiate the truce and resume their war against us well before Truce End. Fortunately, the militaries of the Inner Sphere have taken the initiative in the years since 3052. Their imaginations fueled by the recovery of Star League-era technology and captured Clan OmniMechs, Inner Sphere military designers and manufacturers have developed powerful new BattleMechs and vehicles, resurrected war machines lost to us during the Succession Wars, and significantly upgraded existing designs. Technological breakthroughs in the Draconis Combine have even allowed the DCMS to deploy prototype OmniMechs. Though Inner Sphere manufacturers have not yet succeeded in duplicating Clan weapons, the Kurita OmniMechs can make more efficient and thorough use of battlefield salvage. These and other developments have given us hope that we will face our enemies on a more level field of combat when the Clan War begins again.

The Clans, of course, have also been busy. New OmniMechs are appearing within their ranks, many of them in front-line units. This report includes our latest intelligence on Clan OmniMechs, both new models and additional observations of those described in earlier reports. It also covers Inner Sphere BattleMechs and vehicles, both new designs and machines from the days of the Star League. For analysts and commanders interested in current military technology, this technical readout is a vital reference tool.

As always, my staff and I gratefully acknowledge the support and assistance of Precentor Martial Anastasius Focht, whose suggestion it was that we include original ComStar BattleMech designs in this report. We also thank the legions of ComStar personnel whose observations and painstaking research make up this book. Without their efforts, this work would not have been possible.

—Merle Jimmus
Demi-Precentor V-Sigma
ComStar Archives, Terra
25 January 3058

GAME NOTES

This book presents several units designated as Inner Sphere OmniMechs. These units use Inner Sphere weapons and equipment, but have a modular construction that allows technicians to create a number of different weapons and equipment configurations. When creating configurations for these 'Mechs, use the **Outfitting an OmniMech** rules on page 106 of the **BattleTech Compendium: The Rules of Warfare**. Inner Sphere OmniMech pods do not automatically include CASE, but CASE can be added to torso locations if the appropriate tonnage and space is allocated.

When using Inner Sphere OmniMechs in an extended campaign, keep in mind that the attachment points for their weapon pods have been constructed in such a way that only a minor adaptation allows these points to accept Clan weapon pods. An undamaged component from a Clan OmniMech pod can be installed on an Inner Sphere OmniMech with no addition to the repair difficulty (p. 95, **BattleTech Compendium: The Rules of Warfare**). Damaged Clan components must be repaired before they can be installed; in this case, the standard +4 modifier applies.

CONVENTIONAL VEHICLES

VEHICLES

The aftermath of the Fourth Succession War saw a renaissance in arms technology, with numerous techniques, components and methodologies lost since the fall of the Star League coming back into mainstream use. The brief but bitterly fought War of 3039 prompted the first purposeful use of these technologies, with the main efforts directed predominantly toward new BattleMech designs and improved BattleMech systems. In the decade of relative peace that followed, demand for new and better military machines declined, and Inner Sphere arms manufacturers saw little need to rush their development.

The arrival of the Clans in late 3049 touched off a new arms race. Because this fearsome new enemy did not use vehicles in combat, most of the military research and development involved BattleMechs, with smaller but substantial research efforts directed toward battle armor, aerofighters and naval vessels. Research into vehicle upgrades remained almost non-existent until after the Battle of Tukayyid, largely because of the general perception that vehicles are more fragile and less versatile than their giant BattleMech cousins. To a certain extent this conventional military wisdom is true—however, the difference in effectiveness between 'Mechs and vehicles is not as great as MechWarriors or the media tend to believe. The highly successful defense of Tukayyid, in which the Com Guard fielded combined-arms units of BattleMechs, armored vehicles and infantry, demonstrated that conventional vehicles can play an important role in the fight against the Clans if used properly.

Basic vehicle design principles have changed little since the latter years of the twentieth century, making design and construction a much faster and simpler process for vehicles than for BattleMechs. This greatly reduces their cost, allowing militaries to purchase numerous vehicles for the price of a single BattleMech. On a number of occasions, the sheer numbers of vehicles in given units have proved devastatingly effective.

In the years since the Battle of Tukayyid, a number of new and upgraded vehicle designs have appeared. Modern technology has begun to address certain flaws inherent in standard vehicle construction, with ferro-fibrous armor and anti-missile systems greatly improving the odds of a vehicle surviving a battle. The increased effectiveness of modern weapons and the now-widespread use of fusion power plants have also helped to dramatically reduce the performance gap between vehicles and BattleMechs.

The following designs represent many such upgraded vehicles of all weight classes and combat roles. The absence of upgraded naval or support craft in this technical briefing reflects modern military requirements—as the Clans do not engage such units in combat, there is little to be gained by upgrading them.

Whether the use of upgraded vehicles will play a major part in halting the Clan invaders, or even taking the war to them, remains to be seen. With the Truce of Tukayyid looking increasingly fragile, the storm may break sooner than expected, and we can only hope that the Inner Sphere's military establishments have done enough to ensure our survival.

—Igarashi Miya
Precentor VI-Lambda/Omega
ComStar Archives, Terra
19 January 3058

SPRINT SCOUT HELICOPTER

Mass: 10 tons
Movement Type: VTOL
Power Plant: Galas Lightpower 80 Fusion
Cruising Speed: 140 kph
Flank Speed: 216 kph
Armor: Star Slab/1 Ferro-Fibrous
Armament:
   None
Manufacturer: Michaelson Heavy Industries
   Primary Factory: Ruchbah
Communications System: Johnston Wide Band
Targeting and Tracking System: OptiSight-12 with
   Beagle Active Probe and TAG

OVERVIEW

The Clan enemy's advantage in mobility prompted Inner Sphere militaries to seek alternatives to light BattleMechs for reconnaissance duty. Michaelson Heavy Industries designed the Sprint Scout VTOL to meet this need. Created primarily for speed, the Sprint also supports state-of-the-art electronic equipment. It is gaining favor across the Clan front as a capable scout vehicle.

CAPABILITIES

The Sprint's nose-mounted Beagle probe, which is capable of defeating all but the most sophisticated countermeasures, enables the Sprint to easily locate hidden units. The probe is wired directly into the VTOL's Johnston Wide Band comm system, which instantly relays the enemy's whereabouts to a command unit for swift battlefield response. The Sprint also carries a TAG system, which enables a Sprint pilot to spot for artillery units from safe behind friendly lines.

One of the fastest choppers in its class, the Sprint can outrun enemy ground forces easily. In fact, the Sprint's speed provides its main form of defense. Because the design is intended as a reconnaissance vehicle, the Sprint is unarmed. The weight savings helps provide the Sprint with the remarkable speed that distinguishes it from other VTOLs. For the same reason, the Sprint is armor-light—only one ton of ferro-fibrous plating covers the entire craft.

DEPLOYMENT

The Sprint was designed in 3052 as a support vehicle for units facing the Clans. Originally deployed with Federated Commonwealth forces, large numbers of the VTOL have recently been sold to the Draconis Combine military. The Sprint can now be found in almost every garrison unit on the borders of Clan-held space.

VARIANTS

Units with ample recon support have created a Sprint variant that acts as a quick-response troop transport by removing the Sprint's sensors to make room for infantry. Another variant popular in the Draconis Combine replaces the TAG system with a C3 slave unit. Typically, these variants are used as spotters for 'Mech and ground-vehicle fire. An additional variant replaces the Sprint's TAG with a single medium laser. These VTOLs serve as mobile raiders that can locate and harass enemy units until reinforcements arrive.

Type: Sprint Scout Helicopter
Technology Base: Inner Sphere
Movement Type: VTOL
Tonnage: 10

Equipment		Mass
Internal Structure:		1
Engine:	80	4
Type:	Fusion	
Cruising MP:	13	
Flank MP:	20	
Equipment		**Mass**
Heat Sinks:	10	0
Control Equipment:		.5
Lift Equipment:		1
Power Amplifier:		0
Armor Factor:	18	1

	Armor Value
Front	7
R/L Side	3/3
Rear	3
Rotor	2

Weapons and Ammo	Location	Tonnage
Beagle Active Probe	Front	1.5
TAG	Front	1

SPRINT SCOUT HELICOPTER

MAULTIER HOVER APC

VEHICLES

Mass: 15 tons
Movement Type: Hover
Power Plant: Magna 50 Internal Combustion
Cruising Speed: 97 kph
Flank Speed: 151 kph
Armor: Durallex Light Ferro-Fibrous
Armament:
 1 Pinard Reaper Streak SRM Rack
Manufacturer: Taurus Territorial Industries
 Primary Factory: Sterope
Communications System: Neil 6000-x
Targeting and Tracking System: TracTex Alpha-1

OVERVIEW

Like its larger cousin the Maxim, this SLDF design can transport an entire platoon of infantry and apparently saw extensive action during the second half of the 26th century. The design was thought to be lost forever until a young Taurian farmer on Celeano stumbled on the remains of a Star League storehouse while plowing his fields in 3019. His discovery provided the Taurian Concordat with sophisticated weapons, vehicles, technological information and several operational Maultiers. Concordat ruler Thomas Calderon, leery of his large neighbor the Federated Suns, ordered news of the discovery withheld. Rumors of it escaped, but few people took them seriously.

CAPABILITIES

Concordat scientists studied the recovered equipment and attempted to replicate the designs. The

Maultier was one of the simplest, and the scientists found it relatively straightforward to copy.

Built around a conventional chassis, the Maultier used a 50-series ICE engine—relatively easy to obtain even in the Periphery—that gave it a top speed of around 150 kph. This excellent speed allowed it to deploy infantry troops more quickly than most other vehicles, minimizing the time it had to spend in the combat zone.

The Maultier's targeting and communications systems were also comparable to those produced in the Concordat and could easily be replaced. However, the vehicle's armaments posed more of a problem. The Concordat lacked the technological know-how to duplicate ferro-fibrous armor until the early 3040s, and the sophisticated Streak missile launcher had to be replaced with a conventional system until Pinard managed to duplicate the Streak system in early 3054.

DEPLOYMENT

The Taurian Defense Forces have been using the Maultier as an infantry transport since before the Fourth Succession War, mainly in actions against pirates. It also played a key role in an incident that nearly touched off a civil war, which happened during a botched coup attempt against Thomas Calderon in 3055. Resentment had been building against the increasingly unstable Calderon. When Calderon loyalists attempted to arrest government ministers who had called for his resignation, almost two dozen Maultiers of Marshal Hadji Doru's Taurian Guards Corps delivered infantry to key points in the capital to prevent the arrests. The speed of the Maultiers allowed Doru's troops to take effective control of the capital before the loyalist troops were even aware of what was happening. Why Doru did not consolidate his control and force Protector Calderon from office remains one of the unanswered questions of history.

Type: Maultier Hover APC
Technology Base: Inner Sphere
Movement Type: Hover
Tonnage: 15

Equipment		Mass
Internal Structure:		1.5
Engine:	50	3
Type:	ICE	
Cruising MP:	9	
Flank MP:	14	
Heat Sinks:	0	0
Control Equipment:		1
Lift Equipment:		1.5
Power Amplifier:		0
Turret:		0
Armor Factor:	45	2.5

	Armor Value
Front	15
R/L Side	10/10
Rear	10

Weapons and Ammo	Location	Tonnage
Streak SRM 2	Front	1.5
Ammo (SRM) 50	Body	1
Infantry	Body	3

MAULTIER HOVER APC

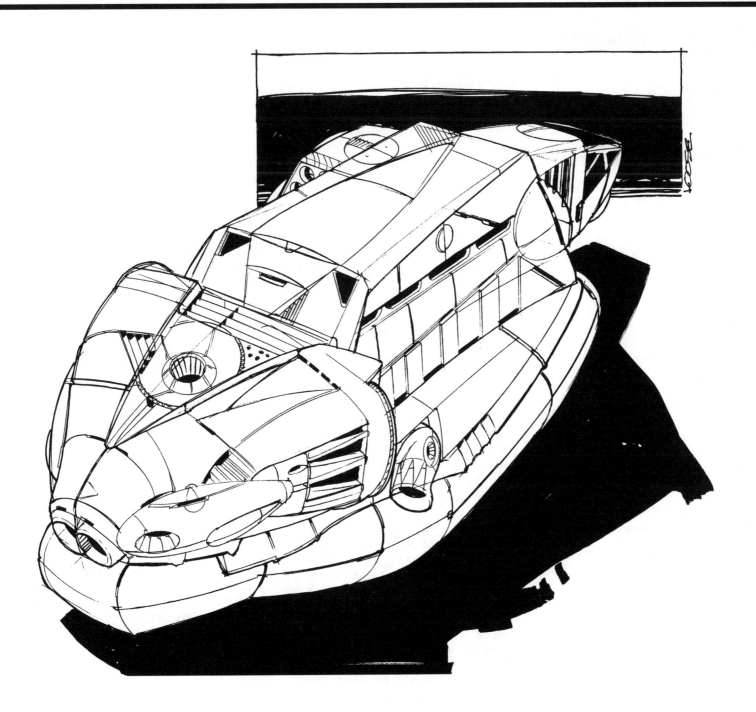

CENTIPEDE SCOUT CAR

Mass: 20 tons
Movement Type: Hover
Power Plant: Vox Type 75 Internal Combustion
Cruising Speed: 86 kph
Flank Speed: 130 kph
Armor: ProtecTech 6
Armament:
  1 Defiance B3M Medium Laser
  1 Zippo Vehicular Flamer
Manufacturer: Gienah Combat Vehicles/Red
  Devil Industries
  Primary Factory: Gienah/Pandora (Lancaster)
Communications System: Scuti Dualcom
Targeting and Tracking System: Beagle Active Probe

OVERVIEW

The loss of the Joint Equipment Systems factory on Alshain to Clan Ghost Bear in late 3051 robbed the Inner Sphere of its source of Skulker scout vehicles. Gienah Combat Vehicles, manufacturer of the PackRat patrol vehicle, saw a market and decided to develop an alternative to the Skulker.

Gienah originally planned to simply upgrade the Skulker design, but chose an alternative course once they realized they would have to retool their manufacturing process to create a Skulker-based vehicle. On the advice of Dr. Vanessa England, head of the Centipede design team, Gienah chose a more radical redesign. Dr. England's proposed Centipede replaced the Skulker's wheeled drive system with a hover unit, which required additional lifting gear but eliminated the

need for the Skulker's bulky GM Classic power plant. Production of the new vehicle began in early 3053.

CAPABILITIES

The use of a hover system allows the Centipede to travel much faster than its progenitor, though it also limits the vehicle's ability to deal with difficult ground. The AFFC's military procurement department was initially unsure of the Centipede's viability, but test deployments with numerous front-line units proved the vehicle's effectiveness.

The Centipede's main weapon is a fixed-mount Defiance B3M medium laser, situated just below the driver's compartment. The fixed arc of this weapon limits its effectiveness, but the Centipede is designed as a scout unit rather than a fighting vehicle. If caught unprepared by hostile fire, the Centipede's driver can easily use the vehicles speed and maneuverability to flee out of harm's way. The addition of a flamer, similar to that on the PackRat, provides limited anti-infantry protection for the entry hatch, situated between the twin drive-fans at the rear of the vehicle.

DEPLOYMENT

Test deployment of the Centipede to AFFC units began in early 3054, with units going to troops stationed on the Clan and Marik–Liao borders. In May of 3054 the First Free Worlds League Guards raided the world of Saiph in the Sarna March, and the seriously overmatched First Battalion of the Fifth Lyran Guards threw its brand-new Centipedes into the fray.

The Lyran troops fought a running battle for more than a week, eventually falling back to the northern port city of Hangzhou. The Fifth Lyrans were able to reach Hangzhou more or less intact almost entirely because of the superb reconnaissance information provided by the Centipedes' Beagle active probes, which allowed the Lyrans to react almost instantly to Marik maneuvers. Once the beleaguered Lyran troops reached the port, the Centipedes traveled over the waters of the Hangzhou Wan River to spy out the enemy's rear area. The Lyran Guards held out for another two weeks, until the arrival of the First Kestrel Grenadiers forced the Marik forces to withdraw.

The Centipede is now a standard vehicle in the Lyran Alliance Armed Forces, and a number remain in service with the AFFC.

VARIANTS

The Red Devil plant on Pandora began production of the Centipede in mid-3053, but because of supply problems this variant uses the locally produced but unreliable Jones 75 engine. The failure rate of this drive, estimated at 15 percent, contributed greatly to Red Devil's poor reputation.

Type: Centipede Scout Car
Technology Base: Inner Sphere
Movement Type: Hover
Tonnage: 20

Equipment		Mass
Internal Structure:		2
Engine:	75	4
Type:	ICE	
Cruising MP:	8	
Flank MP:	12	
Heat Sinks:	3	3
Control Equipment:		1
Rotor Tonnage/Lift Equipment:		2
Power Amplifier:		.1
Turret:		0
Armor Factor:	56	3.5

	Armor Value
Front	14
R/L Side	14/14
Rear	14

Weapons and Ammo	Location	Tonnage
Medium Laser	Front	1
Flamer (Vehicle)	Rear	.5
Ammo (Flamer) 20	Body	1
Beagle Active Probe	Front	1.5

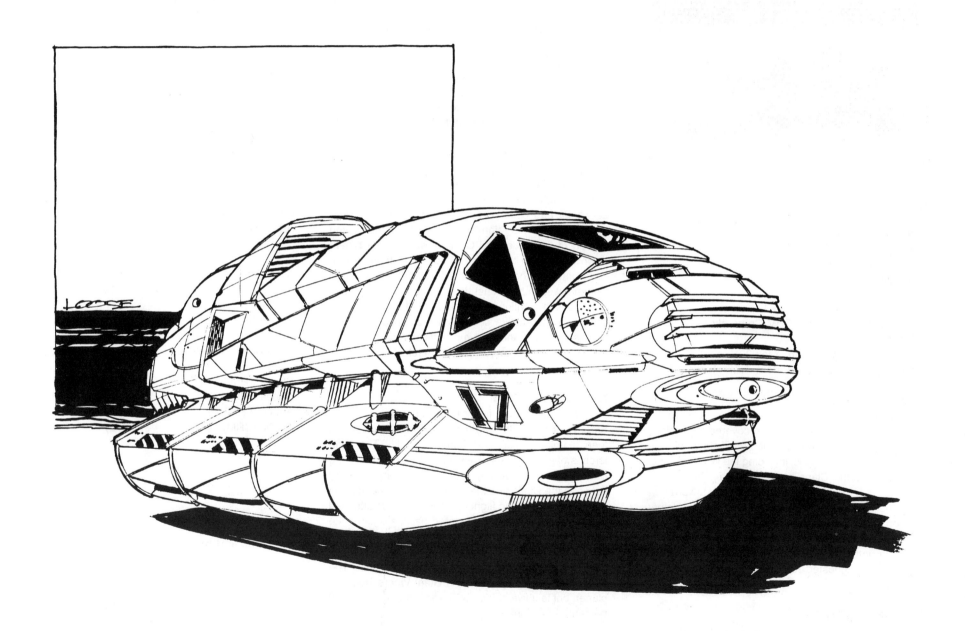

VEHICLES

Mass: 20 tons
Movement Type: VTOL
Power Plant: Lockheed 70 Micro-Fusion
Cruising Speed: 108 kph
Flank Speed: 162 kph
Armor: Kallon Unity Weave
Armament:
    1 LongFire V LRM-5
    2 Hovertec SRM-2 Streak Launchers
Manufacturer: Lockheed-CBM Corporation
    Primary Factory: Furillo
Communications System: Xilex-2010
Targeting and Tracking System: N&D Handsfree

OVERVIEW

In July 3048, Lockheed-CBM's Sandpiper research team proposed using recovered technology to enhance the performance and battlefield survivability of a number of vehicles, including the Warrior VTOL. The arrival of the Clans put a temporary halt to this scheme, as Lockheed turned all its efforts toward providing parts for upgrading BattleMechs. The Sandpiper division was scaled down, and most of its staff released. After the truce, Lockheed-CBM resumed its research into vehicle upgrades and implemented Sandpiper's suggested refit of the Warrior and other vehicles.

CAPABILITIES

The most notable change to the Warrior was the inclusion of a Lockheed-70 fusion plant, which was considerably lighter than the old ICE engine. The weapons systems were similarly revamped—the designers replaced the TharHes 4-pack missile launchers with a pair of Hovertec Streak launchers, and the chin-mounted SarLon autocannon with a Longfire V long-range missile system. The Hovertec system ensures than any short-range missiles fired by the Warrior will hit their target, while the LongFire LRM launcher provides a lightweight alternative to the old autocannon system.

The addition of Kallon Unity Weave armor has boosted the craft's protection against incoming fire, though the fragile rotor remains a weak point in the design. Until the invasion of the Sarna March, Lockheed had been receiving supplies of this armor composite from the Talon-Wernke system in the Davion portion of the Federated Commonwealth. The breakdown of order in the Sarna March and strained relations between the Lyran Alliance and the Federated Commonwealth have cast doubts on Lockheed's ability to obtain continued supplies of this composite. Unless an alternative source can be secured in the next few months, the next run of Warriors will use the less effective Longanecker PlastiSteel of the original design.

DEPLOYMENT

The new Warrior first saw action against a Clan Steel Viper raid on the world of New Exford in what was then a unified Federated Commonwealth. The Clan force swiftly outflanked New Exford's sole defending BattleMech unit, leaving only vehicles and infantry between the Clans and the granaries of the capital city of Woodborough. The flight of six Warrior H8s attached to the vehicle unit made repeated passes against the attacking force of OmniMechs and Elementals, delaying the Steel Viper unit long enough for the BattleMech unit to regroup and organize a counterattack. The defenders eventually drove the Steel Vipers from the planet, but lost five of the six Warriors and a total of 60 percent of the vehicles.

Type: Warrior H8 Attack Helicopter
Technology Base: Inner Sphere
Movement Type: VTOL
Tonnage: 20

Equipment		Mass
Internal Structure:		2
Engine:	105	5.5
Type:	Fusion	
Cruising MP:	10	
Flank MP:	15	
Heat Sinks:	0	10
Control Equipment:		1
Lift Equipment:		2
Power Amplifier:		0
Armor Factor:	45	2.5

	Armor Value
Front	15
R/L Side	10/10
Rear	8
Rotor	2

Weapons and Ammo	Location	Tonnage
LRM 5	Front	2
Streak SRM 2	Front	1.5
Streak SRM 2	Front	1.5
Ammo (LRM) 24	Body	1
Ammo (SRM) 50	Body	1

VEHICLES

Mass: 25 tons
Movement Type: Hover
Power Plant: Nissan 95 Internal Combustion
Cruising Speed: 97 kph
Flank Speed: 151 kph
Armor: Star Slab/3
Armament:
   1 LongFire V LRM-5
Manufacturer: Kressly Warworks
   Primary Factory: Epsilon Eridani
Communications System: Angst Clear Channel 3
Targeting and Tracking System: BlazeFire Sight
   Lock

OVERVIEW

Kressly Warworks designed the Blizzard in response to the need for a faster platoon transport. Standard infantry transports had proved inadequate in the face of the rapid Clan advances, as the Federated Commonwealth discovered at great cost during the Clan War. Because the AFFC lacked speedy troop transports, countless ground troopers were stranded behind Clan lines and captured.

In designing the Blizzard, Kressly aimed for a vehicle that could move troops as swiftly and effectively as the famed Maxim transport but at a lower cost. The finished prototype met almost all of Kressly's expectations—the Blizzard could carry more troops and move faster than the Maxim. However, the Blizzard did not offer nearly as much protection as the Maxim. As a result, sales of the Blizzard remained soft until the

eruption of war in the Sarna March brought the vehicle renewed notice.

CAPABILITIES

The swift Blizzard transport can carry an entire platoon of motorized or jump infantry; a simple modification of its cargo compartment allows it to carry up to two full platoons of standard foot infantry. Designed with infantry in mind, this hover transport offers extremely comfortable seating. The seats can be converted to beds for transporting up to fourteen wounded soldiers off the battlefield. The Blizzard's maximum speed of more than 130 kph allows it to reach most battle zones in seconds, and troops can disembark swiftly and efficiently from its multiple exit hatches. This focus on speed and comfort, however, comes at the expense of weapons and armor protection. The Blizzard's armor is adequate, but not exceptional. Its single turret-mounted, long-range missile launcher provides only token harassment fire against approaching units.

DEPLOYMENT

So far, the Blizzard has appeared mainly within the boundaries of the Chaos March. The Federated Commonwealth and Lyran Alliance have expressed interest in the design but have yet to deploy the vehicle. The Blizzard may end up just about anywhere; Kressly's only factory is located on the so-called Trader's World of Epsilon Eridani, and the company does not discriminate against any buyers.

VARIANTS

Because Kressly has not had much success with the Blizzard until recently, no known variants exist. Kressly promotes the craft's large cargo capacity as a strong selling point, and so is disinclined to tamper with that design element.

Type: Blizzard Hover Transport
Technology Base: Inner Sphere
Movement Type: Hover
Tonnage: 25

Equipment		Mass
Internal Structure:		2.5
Engine:	95	6
Type:	ICE	
Cruising MP:	9	
Flank MP:	14	
Heat Sinks:	0	0
Control Equipment:		1.5
Lift Equipment:		2.5
Power Amplifier:		0
Turret:		0.5
Armor Factor:	48	3

	Armor Value
Front	10
R/L Side	10/10
Rear	9
Turret	9

Weapons and Ammo	Location	Tonnage
LRM 5	Turret	2
Ammo (LRM) 24	Body	1
Infantry	Body	6

BLIZZARD HOVER TRANSPORT

CAVALRY ATTACK HELICOPTER

VEHICLES

Mass: 25 tons
Movement Type: VTOL
Power Plant: Michaelson 110 Internal Combustion
Cruising Speed: 108 kph
Flank Speed: 162 kph
Armor: Star Slab/3
Armament:
　1 Harpoon SRM-6 Rack
　3 Holly SRM Derringers
Manufacturer: Michaelson Heavy Industries
　Primary Factory: Ruchbah
Communications System: Garret Supremesound
Targeting and Tracking System: Garret D2j

OVERVIEW

The Cavalry attack helicopter is one of Michaelson Heavy Industries' new rapid relief/assault VTOL designs. Since its debut in 3054, the Cavalry has seen limited but always effective use. The chopper played a vital part in the escape of more than a regiment of infantry from Clan Steel Viper forces when that Clan retook the world of Twycross. In that rescue effort, a lance of Cavalrys slowed the advance of the Viper 'Mechs long enough for the AFFC troopers to board their armored personnel carriers and retreat.

CAPABILITIES

The sleek Cavalry packs a deadly punch. Multiple SRM racks deliver a lethal barrage of missiles, and this speedy chopper can maneuver quickly enough to take its best shot and retreat before the enemy can return fire. MechWarriors operating in the Chaos March have learned to fear the appearance of lances of Cavalry copters on the battlefield because they often carry inferno rounds in their SRM launchers. A forest can quickly become a blazing funeral pyre for any 'Mech unlucky enough to get caught in the crossfire.

The Cavalry's critics note the chopper's drawbacks. With limited ammunition and no secondary weapons systems, the craft may become defenseless in an extended battle. Michaelson executives stress that the Cavalry is designed for brief hit-and-run engagements rather than as a front-line attack chopper, and they point to its flawless service record as evidence of the design's soundness.

The Cavalry's armor protection is more than adequate for its one-man crew. Heavy armor layers on the nose of the craft allow it to take a hit from weapons as heavy as a Clan PPC and keep flying. As with most VTOLs, the Cavalry's rotor is its weakest point, but Michaelson has armored this vital piece of equipment as heavily as possible.

DEPLOYMENT

The Cavalry is too new a design to have seen much use in the regular units of the AFFC. The Federated Commonwealth has purchased several, but most of the Cavalry's sales have been to nobles in the Draconis and Sarna Marches. The Cavalry has proved its worth over and over on the fields of the Chaos March.

VARIANTS

Michaelson offers one variant of the Cavalry, reducing its armor in order to add another Holly SRM-2 rack. Interested buyers, however, must balance the advantages offered by increased firepower against the VTOL's increased vulnerability to damage.

Type: Cavalry Attack Helicopter
Technology Base: Inner Sphere
Movement Type: VTOL
Tonnage: 25

Equipment		Mass
Internal Structure:		2.5
Engine:	110	7
Type:	ICE	
Cruising MP:	10	
Flank MP:	15	
Heat Sinks:	0	0
Control Equipment:		1.5
Lift Equipment:		2.5
Power Amplifier:		0
Armor Factor:	56	3.5

	Armor Value
Front	20
R/L Side	13/13
Rear	8
Rotor	2

Weapons and Ammo	Location	Tonnage
SRM 6	Front	3
Ammo (SRM 6) 15	Body	1
SRM 2	Front	1
SRM 2	Front	1
SRM 2	Front	1
Ammo (SRM 2) 50	Body	1

CAVALRY ATTACK HELICOPTER

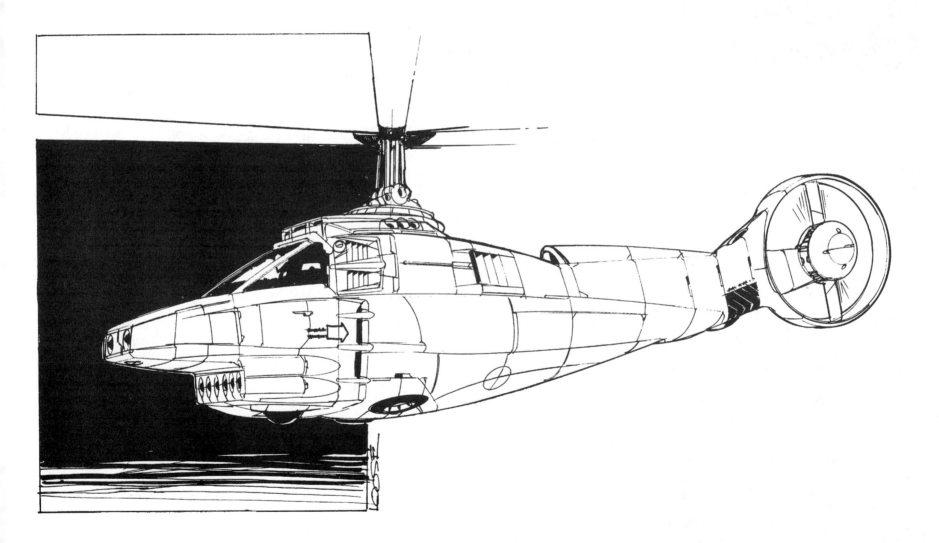

KESTREL VTOL

VEHICLES

Mass: 25 tons
Movement Type: VTOL
Power Plant: 160 Internal Combustion
Cruising Speed: 130 kph
Flank Speed: 194 kph
Armor: ProTech 4
Armament:
 2 Blackwell B75 Machine Guns
Manufacturer: Blackwell Corporation
 Primary Factory: Outreach
Communications System: Dalban StarLink Classic
Targeting and Tracking System: Garret E2b

OVERVIEW

The Kestrel was the third combat vehicle commissioned from Blackwell by Wolf's Dragoons in 3007. Despite the fact that the design for the vehicle's basic air frame is more than 50 years old, the Kestrel remains one of the Inner Sphere's premier special-operation VTOLs.

CAPABILITIES

As a basic combat transport helicopter, the Kestrel is mediocre. It is adequately but not strongly armored, its speed is average, and its armament is relatively light. In addition, its cargo capacity is oversized for a squad and undersized for a platoon. This necessitates splitting up units prior to making an air assault, hampering unit integrity. These flaws, however, seem far less problematic when the vehicle is used for special operations. Indeed, certain features of the Kestrel

make it a particularly good choice for a special-operations role.

The Kestrel's main rotor is made up of five thin blades. When running, these blades make a high-pitched, fanlike whispering sound rather than the traditional whop-whop-whop of four-bladed rotors. Under normal atmospheric conditions, observers cannot hear the Kestrel approaching until it is within 300 meters or less of their position. Normal background noises often further conceal the subdued sounds of the Kestrel's rotors, making the vehicle virtually indistinguishable from wind in the trees.

The Kestrel's avionics are also specially designed to allow it to operate at extremely low altitudes at all hours of the night. Refueling pods give it a virtually unlimited radius of operation. The Kestrel's multifuel turbine gives it the ability to use almost any class of hydrocarbon-based fuel. But most important, the Kestrel's full-cockpit thermal imaging systems, internal and satellite navigation systems, and laser terrain-avoidance system make the design a prime choice for covert insertions and extractions.

DEPLOYMENT

To date, only the Seventh Commando of Wolf's Dragoons has been known to use the Kestrel. While no one can say for certain that the Kestrel was tailor-made for operations performed by the Dragoons unit, its cargo capacity does exactly match the lift requirements for the Seventh Commando LRRP units that operate deep behind enemy lines for extended periods of time.

Type: **Kestrel VTOL**
Technology Base: Inner Sphere
Movement Type: VTOL
Tonnage: 25

Equipment		Mass
Internal Structure:		2.5
Engine:	160	12
Type:	ICE	
Cruising MP:	12	
Flank MP:	18	
Heat Sinks:	0	0
Control Equipment:		1.5
Lift Equipment:		2.5
Armor Factor:	24	1.5

	Armor Value
Front	8
R/L Side	5/5
Rear	4
Rotor	2

Weapons and Ammo	Location	Tonnage
Machine Gun	Front	.5
Machine Gun	Front	.5
Ammo (100) MG	Body	.5
Infantry	Body	3.5

KESTREL VTOL

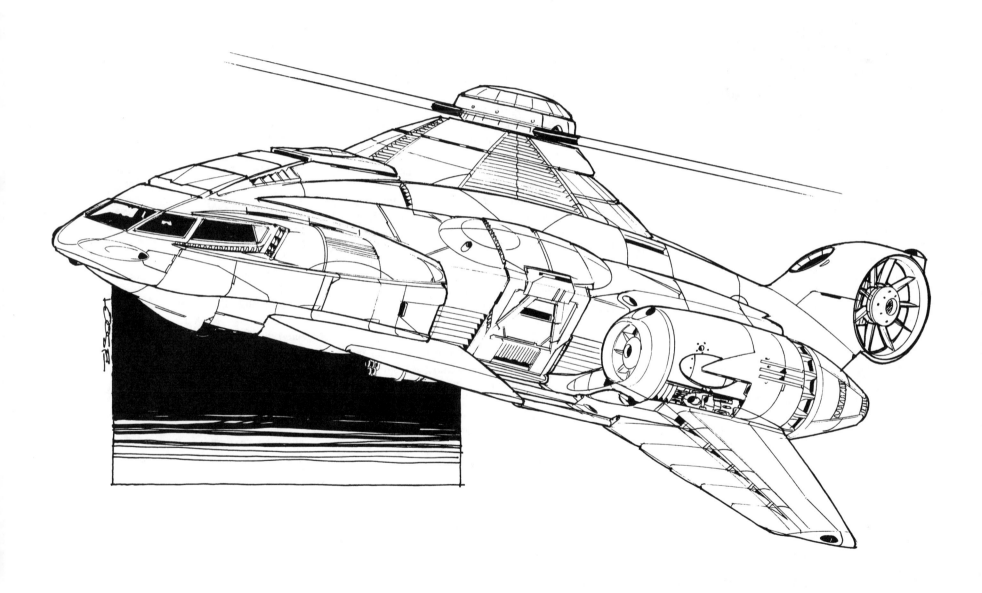

VEHICLES

Mass: 30 tons
Movement Type: Tracked
Power Plant: GM 180 Fusion
Cruising Speed: 65 kph
Flank Speed: 97 kph
Armor: ProTech 6
Armament:
    5 tons of pod space available
Manufacturer: Blackwell Corporation
    Primary Factory: Outreach
Communications System: Dalban StarLink II
Targeting and Tracking System: Garret Fib

OVERVIEW

One of the three vehicle types commissioned by Wolf's Dragoons from Blackwell in 3007, Blackwell's production of the Badger remains shrouded in mystery. When originally contracted by the Dragoons, Blackwell was not even able to keep up with replacement actuator orders. Blackwell had no designs or in-house design staff capable of designing and testing a combat vehicle. But less than a year later, Blackwell was turning out Dragoon combat vehicles at the rate of five per month and still had enough excess capacity to fill orders for Peregrine VTOLs.

In hindsight, most observers speculate that the Dragoons supplied Blackwell with the technical specs and machinery needed to produce the Badger. By doing so, the Dragoons created a secure and independent source of spare parts and vehicles that freed them from the need to return to the Clan homeworlds for replacement vehicles and parts. The modular nature of the Badger's weapons system, strikingly similar to the modular systems used in Clan OmniMechs, seems to confirm this theory.

CAPABILITIES

The Badger is a tracked vehicle used in terrain that precludes the use of hovercraft. The Badger is deployed in an offensive capacity only rarely, because it is handicapped by a light weapon load, lack of ammunition, and comparatively light armor. Typically, the Dragoons use Badgers as infantry transports. The vehicle's lasers provide ample fire support for dismounted infantry troops in such situations.

The spacious interior of the Badger also makes the vehicle well-suited to transport infantry because the interior greatly reduces fatigue for the embarked infantry. Rather than riding in a cramped, ill-ventilated space, wedged between boxes of ammo and rations, infantry troops in a Badger may recline in comfortable seats and store gear in specially designed interior stowage areas. Though some may scoff at such creature comforts, the difference between rested troops and those fatigued by an uncomfortable cross-country journey often spells the difference between defeat and victory.

DEPLOYMENT

The Dragoons have withdrawn the Badger from front-line service and reassigned most to Home Guard units. Others have been converted to ammo supply vehicles. Additionally, the Dragoons lost many Badgers on Luthien, and some observers speculate that Kurita troops salvaged enough of them to outfit a company.

Type: **Badger Tracked Transport**
Technology Base: Inner Sphere
Movement Type: Tracked
Tonnage: 30

Equipment		Mass
Internal Structure:		3
Engine:	180	10.5
Type:	Fusion	
Cruising MP:	6	
Flank MP:	9	
Heat Sinks:	10	0

Equipment		Mass
Control Equipment:		1.5
Lift Equipment:		0
Power Amplifier:		0
Turret:		1
Armor Factor:	80	5

	Armor Value
Front	20
R/L Side	18/18
Back	16
Turret	8

Fixed Equipment	Location	Tonnage
Infantry	Body	4

Weapons and Ammo	Location	Tonnage
Primary Configuration		
Medium Laser	Turret	1
Medium Laser	Turret	1
Medium Laser	Turret	1
SRM 2	Front	1
Ammo (SRM) 50	Body	1
Alternate Configuration A		
SRM 2	Turret	1
SRM 2	Turret	1
SRM 2	Turret	1
SRM 2	Front	1
Ammo (SRM) 50	Body	1
Alternate Configuration B		
SRM 4	Turret	2
SRM 4	Front	2
Ammo (SRM) 25	Body	1
Alternate Configuration C		
LRM 5	Turret	2
LRM 5	Front	2
Ammo (LRM) 24	Body	1

Weapons and Ammo	Location	Tonnage
Alternate Configuration D		
Medium Laser	Turret	1
Medium Laser	Turret	1
Medium Laser	Turret	1
Small Laser	Right	.5
Small Laser	Left	.5
Heat Sink	Body	1
Alternate Configuration E		
Small Laser	Turret	.5
Small Laser	Turret	.5
Small Laser	Turret	.5
Small Laser	Turret	.5
Small Laser	Turret	.5
Small Laser	Turret	.5
Small Laser	Front	.5
Small Laser	Right	.5
Small Laser	Left	.5
Small Laser	Rear	.5

GALLEON LIGHT TANK

Mass: 30 tons
Movement Type: Tracked
Power Plant: 210 GTEM Fusion
Cruising Speed: 76 kph
Flank Speed: 119 kph
Armor: Jolassa 328 Ferro-Fibrous
Armament:
    2 Hellion-V Medium Lasers
    1 Priestly 600p Medium Pulse Laser
Manufacturer: Brooks Incorporated
    Primary Factory: Irian
Communications System: Maxell 500
    Communication System
Targeting and Tracking System: Beagle Active
    Probe

OVERVIEW

Brooks Incorporated began producing the Galleon in 2892 and seemed prepared to support full production for many years. When the Andurien War ended, however, Thomas Marik immediately began to upgrade the Free Worlds League armed forces, concentrating his efforts on the Marik Militia. Because the Captain-General and many of his commanders considered the Galleon to be a relatively light, fragile unit, they cut back orders for the vehicle in favor of more heavily armed designs and so severely disrupted Brooks Incorporated's business.

In an attempt to regain their previous profit levels, Brooks submitted an improved design to the FWL procurement department, then waited nearly three years for the military to respond. Limited production of the

new Galleon began in 3043, with the Free Worlds League deploying several for evaluation. The shakedown run resulted in a request for a number of modifications, and so full-scale production did not commence until 3048.

CAPABILITIES

By exchanging the 180 GTEM internal combustion engine for a 210 GTEM fusion power plant, Brooks added 46 kph to the Galleon's top speed. Brooks further improved the vehicle by upgrading its armor to a ferro-fibrous composite manufactured by Jolassa.

The revised weapons systems replaces the two small lasers with a second medium laser and a medium pulse laser. Though this version of the Galleon possessed speed, armor and firepower far superior to the original, the FWL procurement department remained dissatisfied. As its final concession, Brooks added a Beagle active probe to the vehicle's sensor suite. The final result was a superior scout tank.

DEPLOYMENT

Though Brooks sold Galleons to both the Federated Commonwealth and Draconis Combine, which used the tank during the war against the Clans, the Free Worlds League only began to use its Galleons within the last year of the invasion. Their superior speed allowed the tank units to dash into sensor range of the defending forces, scan their defenses, and then withdraw before coming under sustained fire, a tactic successfully repeated many times in the campaign to recapture worlds lost to the Federated Commonwealth during the Fourth Succession War. For example, Galleons were included in the force used to recapture Oliver, and their capabilities allowed the FWL forces to exploit weaknesses in the Third NAIS Cadre's defenses, ultimately making the Davion troops' situation untenable and forcing them to withdraw.

Type: Galleon Light Tank
Technology Base: Inner Sphere
Movement Type: Tracked
Tonnage: 30

Equipment		Mass
Internal Structure:		3
Engine:	210	13.5
Type:	Fusion	
Cruising MP:	7	
Flank MP:	11	
Heat Sinks:	10	0
Control:		1.5
Lift Equipment:		0
Power Amplifier:		0
Turret:		.5
Armor Factor:	108	6

	Armor Value
Front	25
R/L Side	18/18
Back	19
Turret	28

Weapons and Ammo	Location	Tonnage
Medium Laser	Left	1
Medium Laser	Right	1
Medium Pulse Laser	Turret	2
Beagle Active Probe	Front	1.5

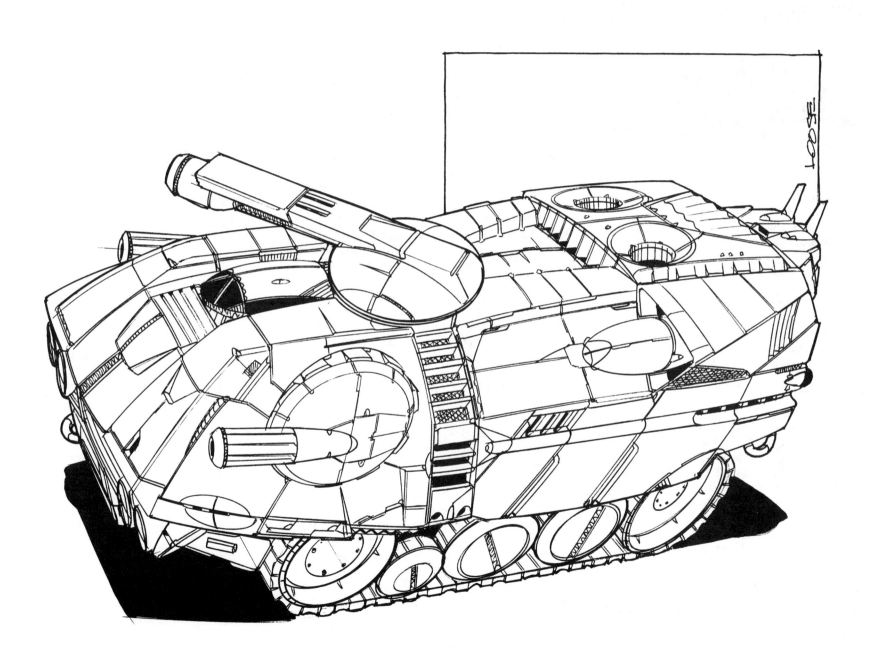

VEHICLES

Mass: 30 tons
Movement Type: VTOL
Power Plant: DAV 160 Gas Turbine
Cruising Speed: 108 kph
Flank Speed: 162 kph
Armor: Lexington Ltd High Grade
Armament:
 2 ScatterGun Light Machine Guns
Manufacturer: New Earth Trading Company
 Primary Factory: New Earth
Communications System: Johnston Q Rotor 2
Targeting and Tracking System: None (manual gunners)

OVERVIEW

The Karnov tilt-rotor design has been in service for hundreds of years. In 2920, New Earth Trading Company (NETC) began distributing the Karnov to the Inner Sphere, though they received their entire supply of these vehicles from ComStar. When ComStar revealed the existence of the Com Guard in the early 3030s, they took that opportunity to requisition more of the VTOL units for their own troops. NETC responded to this reduced inventory by building its own manufacturing plant, which came online in late 3043. These facilities brought the availability of the Karnov back to pre-3030 levels. The battle with the Clans on Tukayyid forced the Com Guard to devote all its resources to rebuilding, and ComStar abandoned its arrangement with NETC. Forced to rely solely on their new plant for production, NETC turned this potential setback into an advantage by setting a design team to work creating

customized Karnov units. The most exciting version to date incorporates recovered technology.

CAPABILITIES

The upgraded Karnov is somewhat slower than the original design. NETC reduced the power plant to a DAV 160, accepting a slight reduction in performance to create room for increased defenses and cargo capacity.

Other than upgrading the vehicle's armor, NETC's most important defensive alteration to the Karnov was the addition of ScatterGun light machine guns on either side of the unit. Manned by single gunners firing without electronic aids, the machine guns serve to defend a vehicle loading or unloading in a combat zone. This innovation offers a welcome change to relying on the protection of friendly forces operating in the area and has greatly reduced the number of Karnovs lost to enemy infantry. The largely unprotected rotors still represent the vehicle's most vulnerable area.

The addition of universal hardpoints to the enlarged cargo bay allows the bay to be reconfigured for a wide range of cargo, including conventional or power armored infantry and light vehicles.

DEPLOYMENT

The upgraded Karnov first became available in 3055, seeing action that year in a number of units. The 23rd Arcturan Guards produced the most notable action in a raid against Sudeten. Hauptmann-General Killson used a number of Karnovs in an operation to drop small teams of infantry behind Clan lines, units assigned to perform sabotage and cause general disruption. After these small-unit actions destroyed a Star of the Eighth Falcon Regulars, Star Colonel Ravill Pryde ordered the Inner Sphere teams hunted down. The Karnovs went back into action, successfully retrieving nearly a third of the troops from the rendezvous points. Now wary of the declared "non-combatant" status of the Karnov, the Jade Falcons attacked a number of the vehicles as they attempted to land, destroying eight of the seventeen Karnov UR transports assigned to the Guards.

Type: **Karnov UR Transport**
Technology Base: Inner Sphere
Movement Type: VTOL
Tonnage: 30

Equipment		Mass
Internal Structure:		3
Engine:	160	12
Type:	ICE	
Cruising MP:	10	
Flank MP:	15	
Heat Sinks:	0	0
Control:		1.5
Power Amplifier:		0
Lift Equipment:		3
Armor Factor:	27	1.5

	Armor Value
Front	7
R/L Side	6/6
Back	6
Rotor	2

Weapons and Ammo	Location	Tonnage
Machine Gun	Left	.5
Machine Gun	Right	.5
Ammo (MG) 200	Body	1
Cargo	Body	7

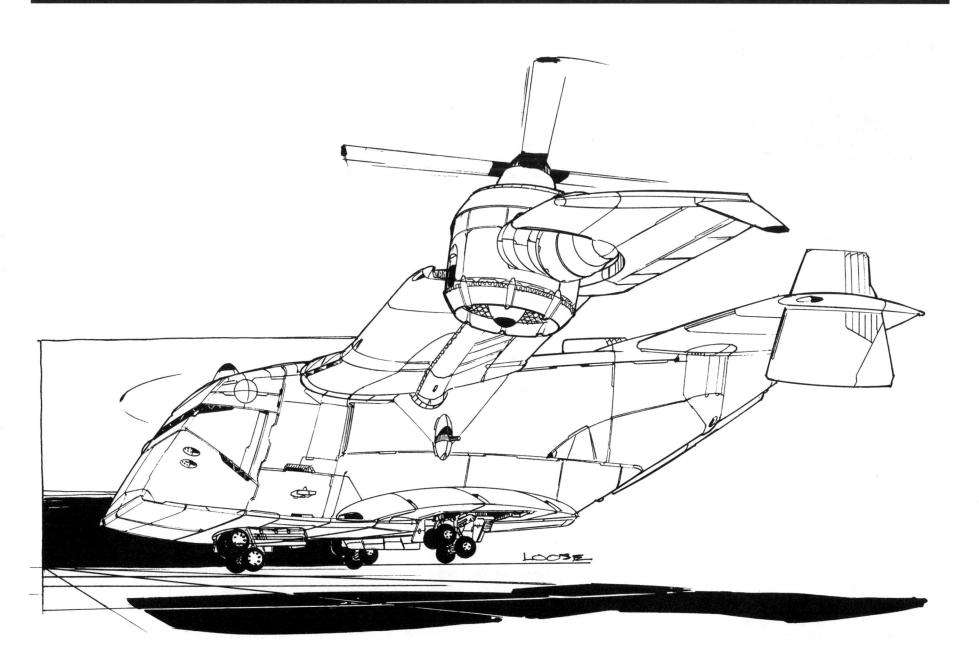

VEHICLES

Mass: 30 tons
Movement Type: VTOL
Power Plant: DAV 220 Fusion
Cruising Speed: 130 kph
Flank Speed: 194 kph
Armor: ProTech Medium
Armament:
  2 Larkin SRM-4 Launchers
  2 Blackwell B75 Machine Guns
Manufacturer: Blackwell Corporation
  Primary Factory: Outreach
Communications System: Dalban StarLink IIa
Targeting and Tracking System: Garret E2b

OVERVIEW

Another product of Blackwell Corporation, the Peregrine was originally commissioned by Wolf's Dragoons but was quickly made available for sale to any buyer. This VTOL saw wide use throughout the Inner Sphere in the arsenals of Houses Kurita, Liao, and Marik during the 3020s, and Wolf's Dragoons never did press it into general service in their units. They found the Peregrine mechanically unreliable, poorly protected and expensive—one Dragoons pilot reportedly claimed that it "flew like a brick." By 3028, the "Wolf's Dragoons mystique" surrounding the vehicle had been burned away in the fire of hard-fought combat, and the Inner Sphere Houses had placed their Peregines into reserve depots or assigned them to local police forces.

CAPABILITIES

The Peregrine was designed to escort transports during air assaults. Keeping in mind the need for such a vehicle to provide suppressive fire across a landing zone, the Peregrine's designers gave it impressive short-range firepower: dual SRM launchers and mini-guns. Unfortunately, these weapons' ranges are so short that the vehicle must move inside the range of small-arms fire to use them effectively. The machine is too thinly armored to sustain even a reasonable level of damage, and so Peregrine losses in battles became phenomenally high.

Another major design flaw was the use of an internal flywheel rather than a traditional tail rotor to combat the torque from the vehicle's main rotor. Several Peregrine pilots were killed during hard emergency landings, which tended to cause the flywheel to break free of its mountings, tear through the fusion plant and smash into the cockpit.

Maintenance of the Peregrine's fusion plant posed its own hazards for technicians, who had to wear Level 1 protective garments to keep themselves safe while working. Poorly designed access hatches made routine maintenance physically difficult to carry out, and procedures for preventative maintenance were overly complex. In one particularly egregious case, changing a certain belt every 100 flight hours required the disassembly and removal of the fusion plant and rotor system.

DEPLOYMENT

The Peregrine's many problems caused all House militaries to withdraw it from active service. Many Peregrines belonging to the Kurita Civilian Guidance Corps saw action during the Clan War, but reportedly fared no better against the Clans than against Inner Sphere opponents.

Type: Peregrine Attack VTOL
Technology Base: Inner Sphere
Movement Type: VTOL
Tonnage: 30

Equipment		Mass
Internal Structure:		3
Engine:	220	15
Type:	Fusion	
Cruising MP:	12	
Flank MP:	18	
Heat Sinks:	10	0
Control Equipment:		1.5
Lift Equipment:		3
Power Amplifier:		0
Armor Factor:	8	.5

	Armor Value
Front	2
R/L Side	2/2
Rear	1
Rotor	1

Weapons and Ammo	Location	Tonnage
Machine Gun	Front	.5
Machine Gun	Front	.5
SRM 4	Left	2
SRM 4	Right	2
Ammo (MG) 200	Body	1
Ammo (SRM) 25	Body	1

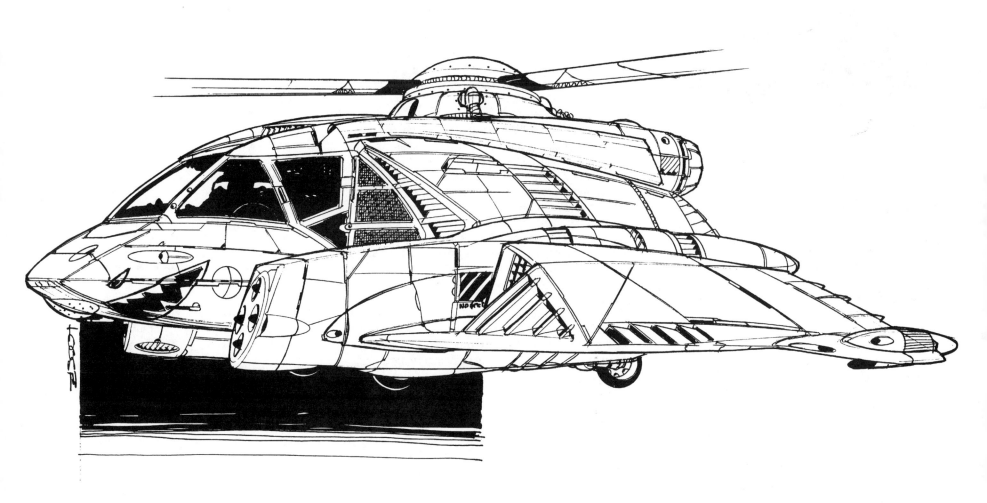

VEHICLES

Mass: 30 tons
Movement Type: VTOL
Power Plant: Michaelson-Omni 40 Internal Combustion
Cruising Speed: 65 kph
Flank Speed: 97 kph
Armor: StarSlab 3
Armament:
   1 Poland Main Model C Gauss Rifle
Manufacturer: Michaelson Heavy Industries
   Primary Factory: Ruchbah
Communications System: Garret Supremesound
Targeting and Tracking System: Garret D2j

OVERVIEW

The Yellow Jacket gunship is Michaelson Heavy Industries' newest design. A deadly craft, the Yellow Jacket provides one of the most mobile fire-support platforms in existence. Though it carries only one weapon, the Yellow Jacket is capable of sustained fire, which makes a lance of these helicopters one of the most lethal forces an enemy can face. This new design has sparked interest in the Federated Commonwealth and the Lyran Alliance. Field tests being conducted in the Chaos March are expected to prove the effectiveness of this chopper.

CAPABILITIES

The Yellow Jacket is built around the Poland Model C Gauss rifle. This massive weapon, which constitutes the bulk of the craft's weight, can hurl rounds at speeds up to Mach 2.2. The Yellow Jacket carries enough ammunition to remain on the field for extended sorties, wreaking havoc on enemy lines.

Though not as fast as most VTOLs, the Yellow Jacket still has greater speed than most BattleMechs and OmniMechs. The Gauss rifle's long range combined with the Yellow Jacket's respectable speed keep the vehicle relatively safe, as does its heavy armor. Like the Cavalry VTOL, the Yellow Jacket can take a direct hit to its nose from a Clan PPC and keep flying.

DEPLOYMENT

Sales for the Yellow Jacket started high and have continued to climb. Most of the early models went to garrison forces in the Sarna March, where they are still in use. The AFFC has also used the craft on the Clan border and achieved solid results, sparking more interest in the design around the Inner Sphere, but this interest has yet to materialize into major orders. Michaelson Heavy Industries frequently uses footage from skirmishes in the Chaos March to help close sales of the Yellow Jacket.

VARIANTS

The single existing variant of the Yellow Jacket replaces almost a ton of armor with more ammunition for the Gauss rifle. Michaelson does not recommend this variant but will supply it at customer request.

Type: **Yellow Jacket Gunship**
Technology Base: Inner Sphere
Movement Type: VTOL
Tonnage: 30

Equipment		Mass
Internal Structure:		3
Engine:	40	2
Type:	ICE	
Cruising MP:	6	
Flank MP:	9	
Heat Sinks:	0	0
Control Equipment:		1.5
Lift Equipment:		3
Power Amplifier:		0
Armor Factor:	56	3.5

	Armor Value
Front	20
R/L Side	13/13
Rear	8
Rotor	2

Weapons and Ammo	Location	Tonnage
Gauss Rifle	Front	15
Ammo (Gauss) 16	Body	2

VEHICLES

Mass: 35 tons
Movement Type: Tracked
Power Plant: Doorman 140
Cruising Speed: 43 kph
Flank Speed: 65 kph
Armor: Star Slab/4 Ferro-Fibrous
Armament:
2 Coventry Star Fire LRM Racks
Manufacturer: Defiance Industries
Primary Factory: Hesperus
Communications System: TharHes Mini-Talk
Targeting and Tracking System: TharHes AGART
with Artemis FCS

OVERVIEW

In 3053, with 'Mech production increasing rapidly, Defiance Industries redesigned their popular Hunter light support tank. The design team made use of modern technology to increase the vehicle's firepower at the original Hunter's reasonable price.

CAPABILITIES

In the new Hunter, the original's large missile rack has been replaced with a pair of smaller Star Fire launchers mounted one above the other. Both of these launchers are equipped with the Artemis fire-control system, and they can deliver larger numbers of missiles into the target zone with devastating accuracy. To make room for the Artemis units, the vehicle's designers removed some armor and the defensive flamer. The armor, though lower in overall tonnage, is ferro-fibrous rather than standard, and so the degree of protection remains substantially the same.

DEPLOYMENT

Full production of the new Hunter has only recently begun—the first new Hunters arrived in Federated Commonwealth units in early 3055. Most of the tanks delivered went to Lyran units, and with the recent split in the Federated Commonwealth these Hunters now belong to the Lyran Alliance. Some analysts have suggested a hidden agenda at work in some ranks of the AFFC's procurement division, but no evidence exists to support these allegations.

Testing of the new Hunter highlighted a flaw in the design that has affected deployment of the vehicles. During a mock battle, a group of Hunters bombarding an enemy position received warning that a fast scout lance was moving their way. The Hunters fired several volleys at the approaching 'Mechs, causing slight damage, and then began to withdraw. However, the tanks' reduced speed allowed the pursuing 'Mechs to close on the tanks and inflict severe damage on the vehicles. As a result, field deployments of Hunters usually pair them with guard units that excel at medium- and close-range combat.

Type: Hunter Light Support Tank
Technology Base: Inner Sphere
Movement Type: Tracked
Tonnage: 35

Equipment		Mass
Internal Structure:		3.5
Engine:	140	7.5
Type:	Fusion	
Cruising MP:	4	
Flank MP:	6	
Heat Sinks:	10	0
Control Equipment:		2
Lift Equipment:		0
Power Amplifier:		0
Turret:		0
Armor Factor:	72	4

	Armor Value
Front	28
R/L Side	15/15
Back	14

Weapons and Ammo	Location	Tonnage
LRM 15	Front	7
Artemis IV FCS	Front	1
LRM 15	Front	7
Artemis IV FCS	Front	1
Ammo (LRM) 16	Body	2

HUNTER LIGHT SUPPORT TANK

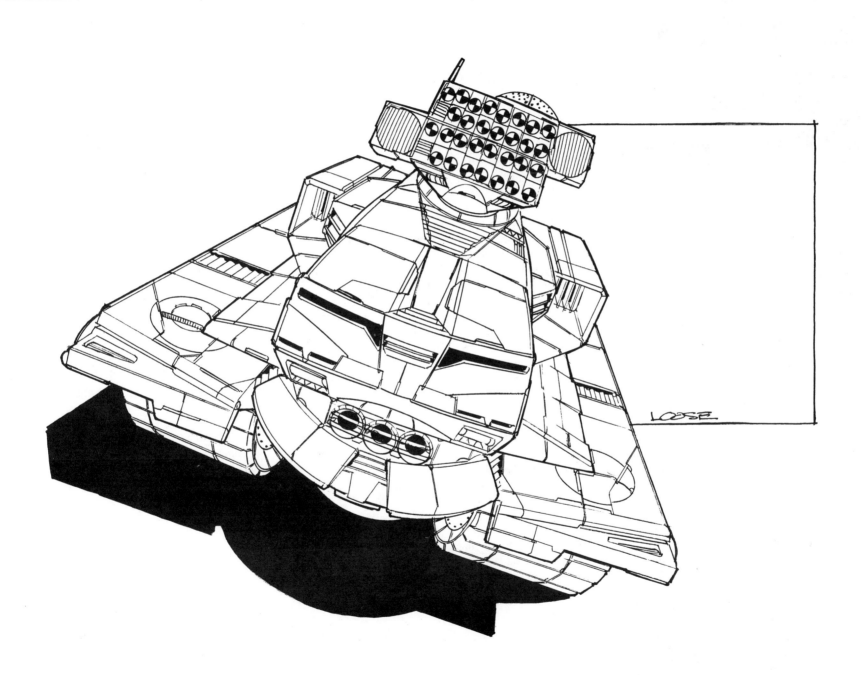

PEGASUS SCOUT HOVERTANK

VEHICLES

Mass: 35 tons
Movement Type: Hover
Power Plant: Scarborough 105 Fusion
Cruising Speed: 86 kph
Flank Speed: 130 kph
Armor: Protec 12 Ferro-Fibrous
Armament:
　1 Victory Heartbeat Medium Pulse Laser
　2 Valiant Pilum SRM Racks
Manufacturer: Scarborough Manufacturers
　Primary Factory: Al Na'ir
Communications System: Scarborough Talky 3 with
　Guardian ECM
Targeting and Tracking System: Scarborough
　Tracky 3 with Beagle Active Probe and TAG

OVERVIEW

A popular and successful light reconnaissance vehicle used by the armies of all the Successor States, the Pegasus was an ideal candidate for upgrading after the truce. The High Command of the Draconis Combine Mustered Soldiery commissioned Scarborough Manufacturers of Al Na'ir to bring the Pegasus in line with rediscovered Star League-era technologies. When the DCMS asked that the Pegasus be provided with the latest electronics to enhance its reconnaissance role, Scarborough reluctantly informed the High Command that their facility could not provide that specific high-tech equipment. Taking advantage of the détente between House Kurita and House Davion, Scarborough negotiated for parts with

two Federated Commonwealth manufacturers of state-of-the-art weapons and electronics: Valiant Systems and Wunderland Enterprises. This partnership has allowed the Scarborough plant to revamp their electronics division and incorporate the requested modifications.

CAPABILITIES

The designers of the Pegasus made room for all their modifications by replacing the tank's ICE engine with a compact fusion engine. The DCMS wanted the new Pegasus to have a sophisticated electronics package, and the new design delivers. Wunderland and Scarborough engineers created the Tracky 3 targeting system with Beagle active probe and TAG, which allow the Pegasus to scout ahead and locate concealed enemy forces and then call down artillery fire. The Guardian ECM suite fitted to the vehicle's communications array effectively disrupts enemy systems.

The Pegasus is not designed for a stand-up fight—it uses its impressive top speed of 130 kph to conduct hit-and-fade operations. The Pegasus is fast enough to outrun virtually any opponent. Those it cannot escape must face its twin turreted short-range missile racks. The Pegasus also uses a pulse laser to defend itself when cornered. Six-and-a-half tons of Protec 12 ferro-fibrous armor give this vehicle adequate protection for its intended role.

DEPLOYMENT

Scarborough has agreed to supply Pegasus vehicles to the AFFC in return for the help of Federated Commonwealth manufacturers, and the Pegasus is beginning to turn up in AFFC and DCMS units. The Pegasus fulfills its mission best when paired with artillery assets so that it can instantly call down fire on any enemy it finds.

Type: Pegasus Scout Hovertank
Technology Base: Inner Sphere
Movement Type: Hover
Tonnage: 35

Equipment		Mass
Internal Structure:		3.5
Engine:	105	5.5
Type:	Fusion	
Cruising MP:	8	
Flank MP:	12	
Heat Sinks:	10	0
Control Equipment:		2
Lift Equipment:		3.5
Power Amplifier:		0
Turret:		1
Armor Factor:	116	6.5

	Armor Value
Front	30
R/L Side	20/20
Rear	20
Turret	26

Weapons and Ammo	Location	Tonnage
SRM 6	Turret	3
SRM 6	Turret	3
Ammo (SRM) 15	Body	1
Medium Pulse Laser	Front	2
TAG	Front	1
Guardian ECM	Body	1.5
Beagle Active Probe	Front	1.5

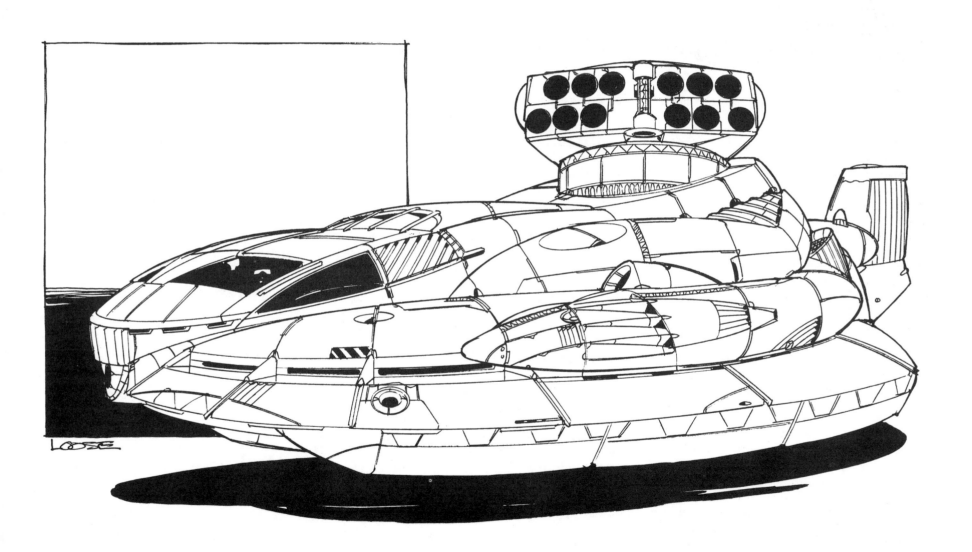

PEGASUS SCOUT HOVER TANK

PLAINSMAN MEDIUM HOVERTANK

VEHICLES

Mass: 35
Movement Type: Hover
Power Plant: 140 Internal Combustion
Cruising Speed: 97 kph
Flank Speed: 150 kph
Armor: Star Slab/3
Armament:
   2 Harvester 20K SRM-6 Launchers
   1 Harvester 2K SRM-2 Launcher
Manufacturer: Pinard Protectorates Limited
   Primary Factory: Pinard
Communications System: Olmstead 30
Targeting and Tracking System: Maxell TA55

OVERVIEW

Created as part of Wolf's Dragoons 3030 rearmament program, the Plainsman is a solid tank design from Pinard Protectorates Limited. The Plainsman's high speed and striking power make up for its lack of armor, though some crews complain about the vehicle's vulnerability.

CAPABILITIES

Reliability is the hallmark of the Plainsman. The designers purposely avoided cutting-edge weapons and components in favor of proven, field-tested technologies. The Earthwerks turbine is a bit bulky and rattles a bit while spooling up to speed, but it can work for more than 5,000 hours without failure and seems to need no more than a prayer of thanks as its daily preventive-maintenance routine. The Star Slab armor is the same type that went to war with Kerensky, but it is not susceptible to micro-cracks as were the newer ferro-fibrous armors when they were first deployed. The Plainsman's Harvester SRMs can cleanly fire salvos even when the tubes are full of mud and dirt. The Plainsman's robust build and utter dependability has made it beloved by its crews, who tend to forgive the thinness of its armor for a hovertank of its class.

During the War of 3039, a Federated Commonwealth home guard militia company on Sadalbaria was ordered to exchange their unserviceable Pegasus hovertanks for Plainsmen. Having delivered their vehicles to a salvage yard, the skeleton crew of drivers and commanders were walking across the spaceport tarmac toward their dozen brand-new Plainsmen when the alert sirens went off—the Second Shin Legion was making a combat drop onto the field. The militiamen ran to the Plainsmen and started them up. With only half the normal crew and no familiarity with the new vehicles, the militia company went into battle against the elite troops of the Draconis Combine. It took two full companies of DCMS 'Mechs 30 minutes to drive off the militia. All of the Plainsmen suffered significant damage—missile launchers sheared off, skirts riddled with holes, engines smoking and shaking, armor holed—but all twelve Plainsmen left the spaceport with all twenty-four crewmen still alive. Even under the most adverse circumstances, the Plainsman acquitted itself well.

DEPLOYMENT

The Plainsman is currently used by second-echelon troops in the Lyran Alliance, Free Worlds League and Draconis Combine. A recon company attached to the Second Shin Legion also deploys the vehicle.

Type: Plainsman Medium Hovertank
Technology Base: Inner Sphere
Movement Type: Hover
Tonnage: 35

Equipment		Mass
Internal Structure:		3.5
Engine:	140	10
Type:	ICE	
Cruising MP:	9	
Flank MP:	13	
Heat Sinks:	0	0
Control Equipment:		2
Lift Equipment:		3.5
Power Amplifier:		0
Turret:		1
Armor Factor:	80	5

	Armor Value
Front	18
R/L Side	16/16
Rear	12
Turret	18

Weapons and Ammo	Location	Tonnage
SRM 6	Turret	3
SRM 6	Turret	3
SRM 2	Front	1
Ammo (SRM 6) 30	Body	2
Ammo (SRM 2) 50	Body	1

PLAINSMAN MEDIUM HOVERTANK

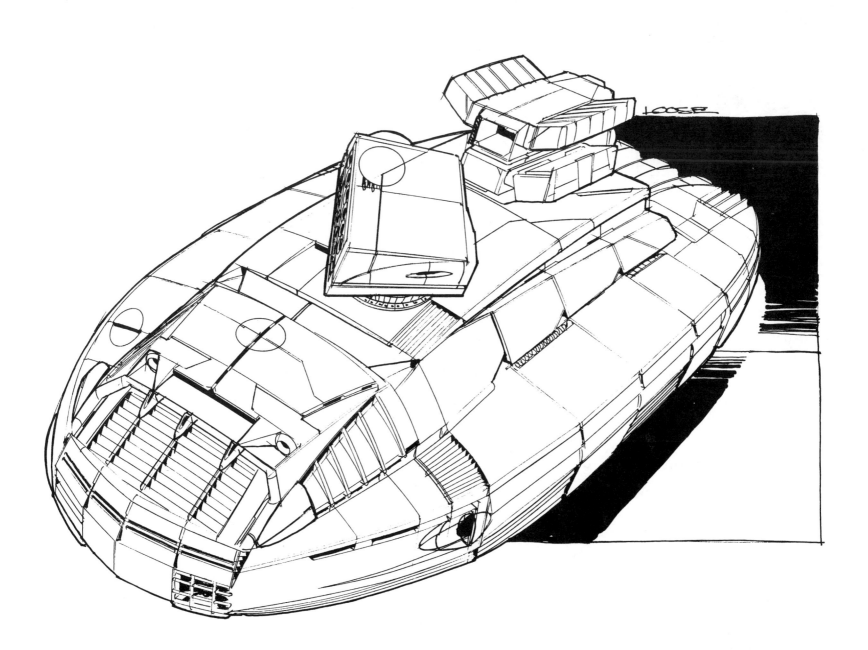

STRIKER LIGHT TANK

VEHICLES

Mass: 35 tons
Movement Type: Wheeled
Power Plant: InterFus 155
Cruising Speed: 54 kph
Flank Speed: 86 kph
Armor: Valiant Scutum Ferro-Fibrous
Armament:
 1 Valiant Arbalest LRM Rack
 2 Valiant Javelin Streak SRM Racks
Manufacturer: Valiant Vehicles
 Primary Factory: Johnsondale
Communications System: Wunderland XXXV-1
 Series
Targeting and Tracking System: Wunderland XXXV-
 1 Series with Artemis FCS

OVERVIEW

With the Striker light tank, Valiant Vehicles set out to produce a tank design that would maximize the potential of a wheeled vehicle. Nearly all experts agree that Valiant succeeded admirably by ingeniously combining the low cost of a wheeled chassis with high-quality weapons and electronics systems. The economical Striker attracted many budget-conscious buyers immediately, and after the design proved effective on the battlefield Valiant immediately began working on a refitted version of the Striker. The upgraded Striker retains the original design's attractive combination of low cost and advanced weaponry and electronics, which makes it a popular tank throughout the Inner Sphere.

CAPABILITIES

To make the most of the Striker's capabilities, the designers replaced the original design's internal combustion engine with a more compact fusion engine. Though more expensive, the new engine freed up room for extra equipment. To increase the number of missiles that the Striker could deliver on target, the designers provided the new Striker with an Artemis-slaved LRM-15 rack as its primary weapons system. This addition effectively doubled the long-range firepower of the new Striker.

For short-range defense, a pair of Valiant Javelin Streak SRM systems replaced the original SRM-6. The Streak system provides the same firepower on average as the SRM-6, but the new system uses ammunition much more efficiently and thereby allows for extended field operations. Finally, Valiant Systems provided the Striker with its own brand of ferro-fibrous armor, giving the tank a fair chance of survival on the modern battlefield.

DEPLOYMENT

Though Valiant Vehicles usually offers its products exclusively to the AFFC, an undisclosed number of Strikers have been sold to the DCMS. As yet the refitted Striker has seen no action, though this may soon change. The AFFC has reinforced garrisons along the Capellan border with large numbers of Strikers.

VARIANTS

The only known Striker variant replaces the Artemis FCS with a Narc beacon and reduces the size of the LRM launcher. Adherents claim that this change allows other units to use the Striker's targeting information. Critics, however, maintain that the variant Striker would have to get too close to the enemy in order to function well.

Type: Striker Light Tank
Technology Base: Inner Sphere
Movement Type: Wheeled
Tonnage: 35

Equipment		Mass
Internal Structure:		3.5
Engine:	155	8.5
Type:	Fusion	
Cruising MP:	5	
Flank MP:	8	
Heat Sinks:	10	0
Control Equipment:		2
Lift Equipment:		0
Power Amplifier:		0
Turret:		1
Armor Factor:	125	7

	Armor Value
Front	28
R/L Side	25/25
Rear	21
Turret	26

Weapons and Ammo	Location	Tonnage
LRM 15	Turret	7
Artemis FCS	Turret	1
Ammo (LRM) 8	Body	1
Streak SRM 2	Turret	1.5
Streak SRM 2	Turret	1.5
Ammo (SRM) 50	Body	1

STRIKER LIGHT TANK

GOBLIN INFANTRY SUPPORT VEHICLE

Mass: 45 tons
Movement Type: Tracked
Power Plant: Fireheart 180 Fusion
Cruising Speed: 43 kph
Flank Speed: 65 kph
Armor: Durallex Light Ferro-Fibrous
Armament:
1 Sutel Precision Line Large Pulse Laser
2 Johnston Miniguns
1 Harpoon-6 SRM Racks
1 MainFire Point-Defense Anti-Missile System
Manufacturer: Johnston Industries
Primary Factory: New Syrtis
Communications System: CommuTech XL
Targeting and Tracking System: BlazeFire Tracker
with Range Check

OVERVIEW

Based on an obscure 20th-century concept, the original Goblin was a unique design—a tank with integral infantry support. Though it generally fared well on the battlefield, Goblin engagements with power-suited infantry during the Clan War prompted Johnston Industries to redesign the tank. The new Goblin is classed as an infantry-support vehicle intended to transport and support up to a platoon of infantry. A prototype saw action with the AFFC during the last months of the Clan War, and full production began in early 3053.

CAPABILITIES

The new Goblin features weapons systems reconfigured to provide optimal infantry support. A large Sutel pulse laser replaces the original design's BlazeFire laser, trading range for accuracy. Together with a Harpoon-6 missile system, the Sutel provides effective firepower against power-armored troops. A pair of miniguns serve as a last line of defense.

The refitted Goblin also makes extensive use of new armor compounds that provide 30 percent more protection than the original armor. The substitution of a light fusion engine for the LongWay ICE power plant also enabled the Goblin designers to increase the vehicle's overall armor tonnage. The additional armor, combined with the new MainFire anti-missile system, has drastically increased the Goblin's battlefield survivability. Unfortunately, the limited ammunition supply for the AMS restricts its use to the first or second volley directed against the vehicle.

DEPLOYMENT

The refitted Goblin first saw action on the world of Hsien during recent action in the Sarna March. Marik forces destroyed the aerospace assets of the Second Federated Commonwealth RCT, enabling regiments of McCarron's Armored Cavalry to drop onto the planet and strike at the Second RCT's ground forces. The Second had been using the new Goblin for more than four years, and the unit's commander, Marshal Thome, was intimately familiar with their capabilities.

The Marshal threw most of the Goblins into the battle that took place in the city of Chengde, where bitter street fighting devastated units on both sides. The close-quarters urban battle made an ideal test for the Goblins and their infantry; though attrition gradually reduced their numbers, they managed to inflict considerable damage on the mercenary troops. When hostilities officially ended in mid-December, only seven out of twenty-four Goblins remained operational.

Type: Goblin Infantry Support Vehicle
Technology Base: Inner Sphere
Movement Type: Tracked
Tonnage: 45

Equipment		Mass
Internal Structure:		4.5
Engine:	180	10.5
Type:	Fusion	
Cruising MP:	4	
Flank MP:	6	
Heat Sinks:	10	0
Control Equipment:		2.5
Lift Equipment:		0
Power Amplifier:		0
Turret:		1
Armor Factor:	170	9.5

	Armor Value
Front	40
R/L Side	32/32
Rear	26
Turret	40

Weapons and Ammo	Location	Tonnage
Large Pulse Laser	Turret	7
2 Machine Guns	Front	1
Ammo (MG)100	Body	.5
SRM 6	Turret	3
Ammo (SRM)15	Body	1
Anti-Missile System	Front	.5
Ammo (Anti-Missile)12	Body	1
Infantry	Body	3

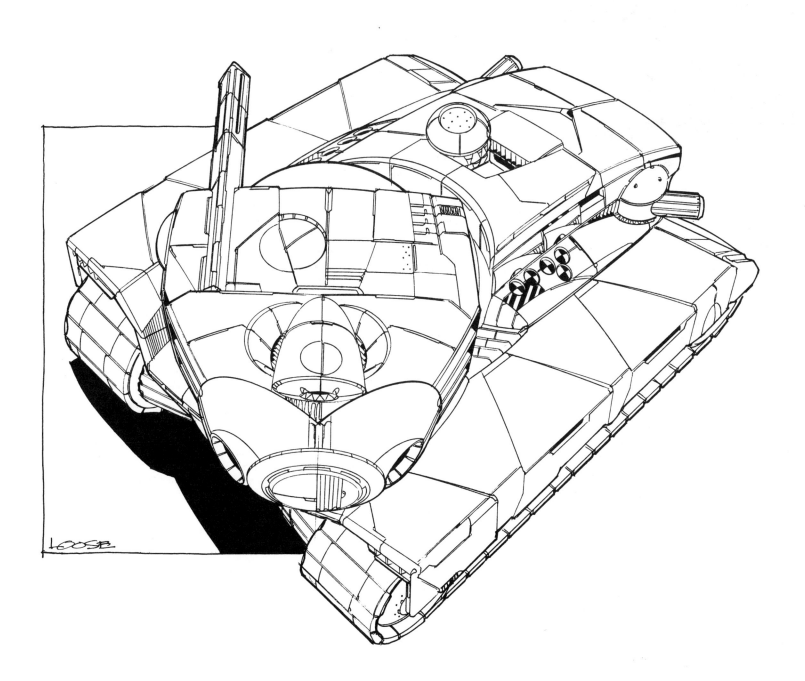

REGULATOR HOVERTANK

VEHICLES

Mass: 45 tons
Movement Type: Hover
Power Plant: GM 170
Cruising Speed: 97 kph
Flank Speed: 151 kph
Armor: Hellespont Lite Ferro-Fibrous
Armament:
    1 Inokuma Gauss Rifle
Manufacturer: Aldis Industries
    Primary Factory: Betelgeuse
Communications System: Olmstead 37
Targeting and Tracking System: Virtutrak S1

OVERVIEW

Because so many of the Capellan Confederation's BattleMech production facilities had fallen into the hands of the Federated Commonwealth during the Fourth Succession War, Capellan military designers turned their attention toward the creation of effective conventional vehicles. The Regulator is an impressive result of these efforts. The Regulator first saw action during the recent conflict between the Federated Commonwealth and the Liao–Marik alliance.

CAPABILITIES

This swift and agile tank carries a massive Inokuma Gauss rifle capable of devastating most targets with one or two shots. Using its superior speed and maneuverability, the Regulator can train this weapon on the relatively weak side and rear facings of BattleMechs, using the rifle's devastating power to maximum effect.

Powered by a fusion engine and protected by ferro-fibrous armor, the Regulator is a state-of-the-art vehicle that incorporates many of the technologies recovered in the past few years. The sophisticated Virtutrak targeting system allows the vehicle to track up to fifteen targets simultaneously and provides the Regulator gunner with a pseudo-360-degree viewing system comparable to that provided by most BattleMechs.

DEPLOYMENT

The Regulator saw its first action when Capellan troops landed on the Federated Commonwealth world of Tsingtao in support of a popular uprising. Guerrilla raids had effectively paralyzed the local government, allowing the rebels to seize control of several population centers. The garrison commander of Tsing City, Captain Amanda King, managed to extricate her 'Mech forces and march to engage the enemy troops advancing from the south.

On seeing that the Liao force consisted of vehicles, Captain King ordered her BattleMechs to pick off the vehicles with their long-range weapons. As a large portion of the Liao force consisted of Pegasus-and Scimitar-class vehicles with primarily short-range weapons, this strategy should have paid off. However, the Capellan forces also included a lance of Regulators that the Commonwealth battle computers had failed to identify. The Regulators' powerful main guns outranged the guns of the garrison 'Mechs. The tanks cost the garrison force three 'Mechs, including the commander's *Javelin*. Captain King's second-in-command, Lieutenant Harrington, called for his unit to retreat into the nearby Lambley Forest.

Type: Regulator Hovertank
Technology Base: Inner Sphere
Movement Type: Hover
Tonnage: 45

Equipment		Mass
Internal Structure:		4.5
Engine:	170	9
Type:	Fusion	
Cruising MP:	9	
Flank MP:	14	
Heat Sinks:	10	0
Control Equipment:		2.5
Lift Equipment:		4.5
Power Amplifier:		0
Turret:		1.5
Armor Factor:	108	6

	Armor Value
Front	30
R/L Side	16/16
Rear	16
Turret	30

Weapons and Ammo	Location	Tonnage
Gauss Rifle	Turret	15
Ammo (Gauss) 16	Body	2

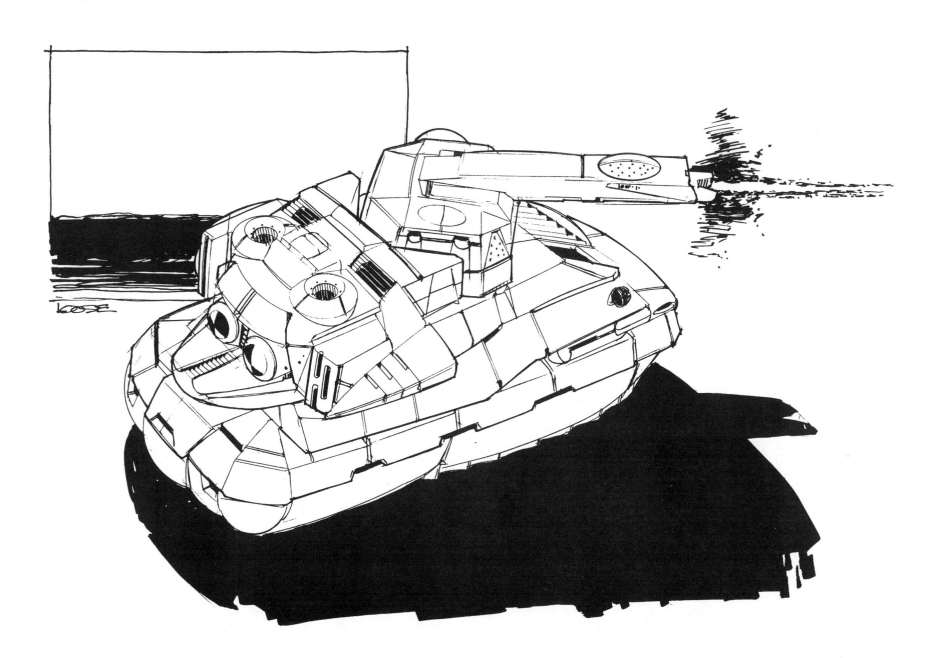

BANDIT HOVERCRAFT

VEHICLES

Mass: 50 tons
Movement Type: Hover
Power Plant: VOX 215 Fusion
Cruising Speed: 97 kph
Flank Speed: 151 kph
Armor: ProTech 5
Armament:
    7 tons of pod space available
Manufacturer: Blackwell Corporation
    Primary Factory: Outreach
Communications System: Dalban StarLink II
Targeting and Tracking System: Garret E5a

OVERVIEW

Major Sean Rutherford, head of Wolf's Dragoons' Contract Operations Group, contacted the president of the Blackwell Corporation in January 3007 to negotiate a contract for production of combat vehicles and replacement parts. Three vehicles were commissioned: the Kestrel VTOL transport, the Badger APC and the Bandit hovercraft. Blackwell, then a minor manufacturer of actuator parts and 'Mech components, grew dramatically in the intervening years—and that growth remains difficult to explain. Throughout the Inner Sphere, the early quarter of the century was characterized by water raids, technology losses and scrupulous salvage operations. The machinery and tools required to expand an industrial facility to the extent that Blackwell did were not available on the open market, and no records exist that suggest Blackwell received the spoils from some other vanquished facility.

Nevertheless, the first Bandit was delivered to the Dragoons in March 3008 and this vehicle has been in exclusive Dragoon service ever since.

CAPABILITIES

The Bandit has served the Dragoons well. The major advantage of the Bandit is its versatility, with at least seven significant known variants in existence. Like the Badger, the Bandit's weaponry is modular in nature and can be very quickly reconfigured in the field as circumstances require. It is rumored (with an admittedly low level of reliability) that Dragoon techs have become adept at remounting different weapon systems on Bandits after allowing enemy recon patrols to glimpse the vehicles, to add a further level of confusion to the battle once the enemy is engaged.

DEPLOYMENT

The Bandit is only found in service with Wolf's Dragoons. Until 3055, the Bandit was the standard APC for half of all of the Dragoons' infantry units. With the unit's recent reorganization, the Dragoons threw much of its infantry resources toward outfitting its troops with battle suits. Because battle-suited infantry do not need personnel carriers, the Bandit is now found exclusively with the Dragoons' Support Command and Home Guard.

Type: **Bandit Hovercraft**
Technology Base: Inner Sphere
Movement Type: Hover
Tonnage: 50

Equipment		Mass
Internal Structure:		5
Engine:	215	14.5
Type:	Fusion	
Cruising MP:	9	
Flank MP:	14	
Heat Sinks:	10	0
Control Equipment:		2.5
Lift Equipment:		5
Power Amplifier:		0
Turret:		1
Armor Factor:	176	11

	Armor Value
Front	42
R/L Side	40/40
Rear	32
Turret	22

Fixed Equipment	Location	Tonnage
Infantry	Body	4

Weapons and Ammo	Location	Tonnage
Primary Configuration		
Medium Laser	Turret	1
Medium Laser	Turret	1
Medium Laser	Turret	1
Machine Gun	Front	.5
Ammo (MG) 100	Body	.5
SRM 2	Front	1
SRM 2	Front	1
Ammo (SRM) 50	Body	1
Alternate Configuration A		
1 PPC	Turret	7
Alternate Configuration B		
2 SRM 4	Turret	4
1 SRM 2	Front	1
Ammo (SRM) 25	Body	1
Ammo (SRM) 50	Body	1
Alternate Configuration C		
2 SRM 6	Turret	6
Ammo (SRM) 15	Body	1
Alternate Configuration D		
3 LRM 5	Turret	6
Ammo (LRM) 24	Body	1
Alternate Configuration E		
1 LRM 10	Turret	5
1 Medium Laser	Front	1
Ammo (LRM) 12	Body	1

BANDIT HOVERCRAFT

Weapons and Ammo	Location	Tonnage	Weapons and Ammo	Location	Tonnage
Alternate Configuration F			*Alternate Configuration G*		
1 Large Laser	Turret	5	2 Medium Lasers	Turret	2
1 Medium Laser	Front	1	6 Small Lasers	Front	3
1 Heat Sink	Body	1	2 Heat Sinks	Body	2

VEHICLES

Mass: 50 tons
Movement Type: Hover
Power Plant: Strand 265 XL Fusion
Cruising Speed: 108 kph
Flank Speed: 162 kph
Armor: Star Slab/11.5 Type HVA
Armament:
    1 Sunglow Type 2 Large Laser
    1 Diverse Optics Type 18 Medium Laser
    1 Delta Dart LRM 10-Pack
Manufacturer: Alpha Trading Corporation
    Primary Factory: Perdition
Communications System: O/P AIR900
Targeting and Tracking System: RCA Instatrac Mk.
    XII

OVERVIEW

Financed by the continued brisk sales of Alpha Trading Corporation's J. Edgar Light Hovertank, the Fulcrum is fast, maneuverable and easy to maintain. The first four prototypes of this vehicle rolled off the production lines in 3056 and performed so well in all tests that Alpha Trading received orders for 500 of them in a mere four months. Alpha Trading has already filled these orders and is gearing up its plant to build another 1,000 Fulcrum hovertanks.

CAPABILITIES

Built for rugged endurance and easy maintenance, the Fulcrum is well-armed and armored. An XL engine gives the Fulcrum a top speed of 175 kph, mak-

ing it a tough target to hit. The new engine is simple to maintain, with access panels on the rear deck and in the main compartment. The engine can also be replaced in the field. In fact, during testing a team of techs removed a defective engine and installed a new one in less than three hours.

The Fulcrum is equipped to carry out a variety of missions, though its primary missions are reconnaissance and fast strikes. The Fulcrum's weapons are simple but effective. The Sunglow large laser and the Delta Dart LRM-10 have been used for hundreds of years and have a respectable reputation throughout the Inner Sphere and the Periphery. A medium laser rounds out the Fulcrum's weapons. So far, the only complaint about the Fulcrum's firepower is the fact that it only carries one ton of LRM ammo—in a long battle, the supply runs out fairly quickly.

To hide the Fulcrum from enemy forces and allow it to screen friendly units, the designers installed a Guardian ECM suite. The vehicle also carries TAG and so can act as a spotter for units equipped with the Arrow IV missile system. The Fulcrum's armor is specially designed for hover vehicles—the bulk of the Fulcrum's ten tons of armor cover the front and the turret. Finally, the craft's eleven heat sinks allow the Fulcrum to fire its energy weapons almost constantly without the risk of overheating.

DEPLOYMENT

The Fulcrum has yet to see combat, though the Lyran Alliance has stationed several lances of Fulcrums along its borders with the Free Worlds League and the Periphery.

Type: Fulcrum Heavy Hovertank
Technology Base: Inner Sphere
Movement Type: Hover
Tonnage: 50

Equipment		Mass
Internal Structure:		5
Engine:	265	10.5
Type:	XL Fusion	
Cruising MP:	10	
Flank MP:	15	
Heat Sinks:	11	1
Control Equipment:		2.5
Lift Equipment:		5
Power Amplifier:		0
Turret:		1.5
Armor Factor:	160	10

	Armor Value
Front	46
R/L Side	27/27
Rear	20
Turret	40

Weapons and Ammo	Location	Tonnage
Large Laser	Turret	5
Medium Laser	Turret	1
LRM 10	Turret	5
Ammo (LRM) 12	Body	1
Guardian ECM	Body	1.5
TAG	Front	1

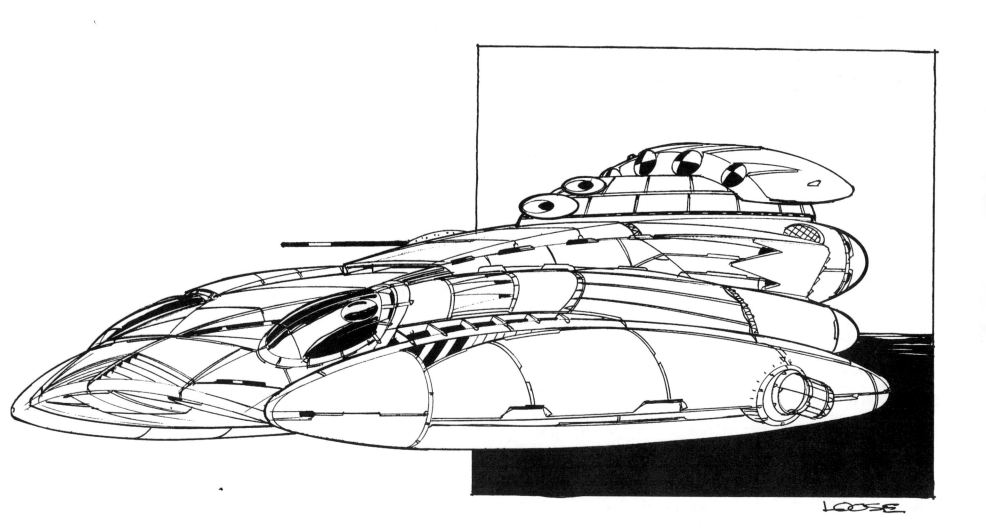

MAXIM HEAVY :OVER TRANSPORT

VEHICLES

Mass: 50 tons
Movement Type: Hover
Power Plant: Powertech 165 Highlift
Cruising Speed: 86 kph
Flank Speed: 130 kph
Armor: ProtecTech 6
Armament:
　1 Telos-6 SRM Launcher
　2 LongFire V LRM Launchers
　2 Guided Technologies Streak-2 Missile
　　Launchers
　2 Bulldog Miniguns
Manufacturer: Scarborough Manufacturing
　Primary Factory: Al Na'ir
Communications System: Scarborough Talky 2
Targeting and Tracking System: Scarborough
　Tracky 1 with TAG

OVERVIEW

The Maxim's maneuverability and unique weapons mix have made it one of the most respected vehicles on the modern battlefield. Its popularity as an infantry carrier led Theodore Kurita of the Draconis Combine to choose the Maxim for conversion to a power-armored infantry transport, and he commissioned Scarborough Manufacturers to develop and produce the upgraded design.

CAPABILITIES

The refit uses ferro-fibrous technology and additional armor on the LRM mounts and the turret to increase the armor protection of the Maxim. The modified weapons array includes Streak missile launchers and a TAG system that enables a Maxim crew to act as spotters for supporting Arrow-IV fire. In addition, Scarborough added firmpoints to the infantry compartment for securing battle-armored troops during the high-speed dash across the battlefield, and enlarged the main door to accommodate the bulky armor suits.

DEPLOYMENT

During the Battle for Luthien, the DCMS used several units of Maxims to hunt down and kill Stars of OmniMechs and Elementals that had outflanked the DCMS's main position. One such unit encountered a medium Star consisting of two *Black Hawks*, a *Fenris* and two *Lokis*. The DCMS commander ordered half his company to provide LRM covering fire while the rest deployed their troops.

The initial barrage did little damage to the Clan Star, and the OmniMechs quickly moved to crush the Inner Sphere infantry troops. The anti-infantry pods carried by several of the OmniMechs proved devastatingly effective, causing many casualties. The Maxims, however, performed brilliantly. They destroyed three Clan 'Mechs with SRM fire and crippled a fourth with a ramming attack.

VARIANTS

The fire-support variant of the Maxim replaces the original design's SRM launchers and TAG unit with a turret-mounted LRM-15 and two tons of ammunition. The anti-personnel variant replaces the original design's side-mounted Streak SRMs with machine guns for use in areas patrolled by enemy infantry.

Type: Maxim Heavy Hover Transport
Technology Base: Inner Sphere
Movement Type: Hover
Tonnage: 50

Equipment		Mass
Internal Structure:		5
Engine:	165	12
Type:	ICE	
Cruising MP:	8	
Flank MP:	12	
Heat Sinks:	10	0
Control Equipment:		2.5
Lift Equipment:		5
Power Amplifier:		0
Turret:		1
Armor Factor:	108	6

	Armor Value
Front	25
R/L Side	23/23
Rear	16
Turret	21

Weapons and Ammo	Location	Tonnage
SRM 6	Turret	3
Ammo (SRM) 15	Body	1
Streak SRM 2	Left	1.5
Streak SRM 2	Right	1.5
Ammo (Streak SRM) 50	Body	1
LRM 5	Front	2
LRM 5	Front	2
Ammo (LRM) 24	Body	1
Machine Gun	Turret	.5
Machine Gun	Turret	.5
Ammo (MG) 100	Body	.5
Infantry	Body	3
TAG	Turret	1

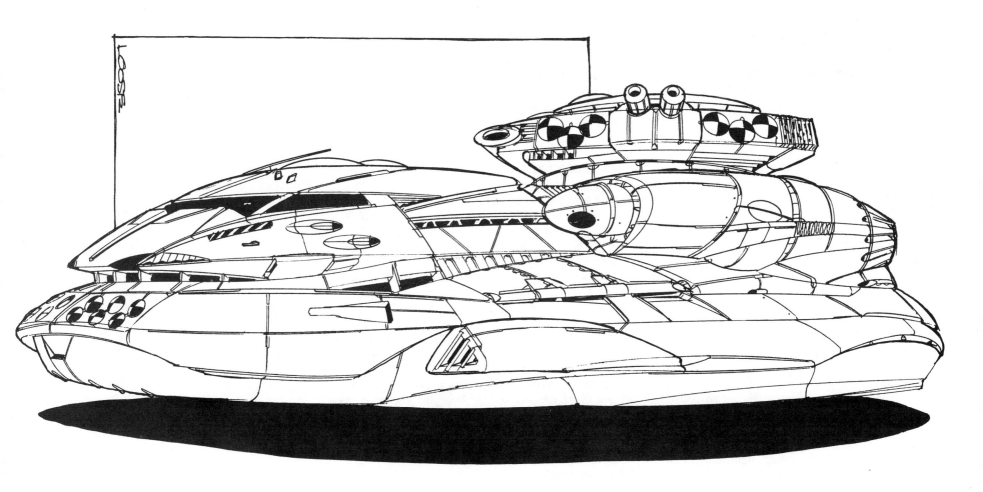

VEDETTE MEDIUM TANK

VEHICLES

Mass: 50 tons
Movement Type: Tracked
Power Plant: Locom-Pack 250 InterComBust
Cruising Speed: 54 kph
Flank Speed: 86 kph
Armor: Hellespont Lite
Armament:
   1 Imperator Ultra Class 5 Autocannon
Manufacturer: Hellespont Industrials
   Primary Factory: Sian
Communications System: ComStar Rover
Targeting and Tracking System: ComStar Test-2

OVERVIEW

Though originally produced exclusively by the New Earth Trading Company, the sheer simplicity of the Vedette's design created a demand for the vehicle that could only be met by licensing the design to third-party manufacturers. One of these manufacturers was Hellespont Industrials of Sian, one of the largest producers of armored fighting vehicles in the Capellan Confederation. Hellespont received large orders for the Vedette from the Capellan military in the wake of the Fourth Succession War, which left Capellan BattleMech units devastated and forced the Capellans to augment their forces with conventional vehicles. Though new technology was in short supply in the Confederation during this period, Hellespont experimented with a number of vehicle upgrades, including a revamped Vedette.

CAPABILITIES

The new Vedette is a simple, cost-effective upgrade that features performance and survivability considerably superior to its progenitor. To increase the tank's survivability, Hellespont gained additional armor tonnage by removing the light machine gun and replacing the standard armor with the locally produced ferro-fibrous Hellespont Lite. This modification provides the tank with 20 percent more armor protection. Hellespont also exchanged the Armstrong J11 autocannon for an Imperator Ultra series gun. This improvement in firepower allows the crew to attack with an increased rate of fire and at greater ranges than previously possible.

DEPLOYMENT

The first upgraded Vedettes rolled out from the Hellespont plant in October 3054. The design saw its first field action nearly a year later with Christobal's Regiment, part of McCarron's Armored Cavalry. The Regiment had been stationed on Harloc when the planet came under raiding attacks by the Arcadians, a mercenary unit under contract to the St. Ives Compact. For the better part of a week the Regiment pursued the Arcadians without success. Then the Arcadian commander, apparently unfamiliar with the planet's terrain, led his force high into the Owen Stanley mountains, unaware that the area was accessible by only one pass. In response, the Regiment commander set an ambush by ordering his Vedettes to dig in along the sides of the pass. When the Arcadians attempted to exit the area, the Regiment 'Mechs forced them through the pass, where the Vedettes engaged them. Seven Vedettes and their crews were destroyed in the fighting, but not before they destroyed an equal number of enemy 'Mechs.

VARIANTS

The New Earth Trading Company is manufacturing an upgraded version of the Vedette that is very similar in design to the Hellespont variant. In addition to mounting the Ultra gun, the NETC version keeps the machine gun and half ton of ammunition and replaces the standard armor with ferro-fibrous, marginally improving the tank's level of protection.

Type: Vedette Medium Tank
Technology Base: Inner Sphere
Movement Type: Tracked
Tonnage: 50

Equipment		Mass
Internal Structure:		5
Engine:	250	25
Type:	ICE	
Cruising MP:	5	
Flank MP:	8	

Equipment		Mass
Heat Sinks:	0	0
Control Equipment:		2.5
Lift Equipment:		0
Power Amplifier:		0
Turret:		1
Armor Factor:	116	6.5

	Armor Value
Front	25
R/L Side	21/21
Rear	24
Turret	25

Weapons and Ammo	Location	Tonnage
Ultra AC/5	Turret	9
Ammo (AC) 20	Body	1

VEDETTE MEDIUM TANK

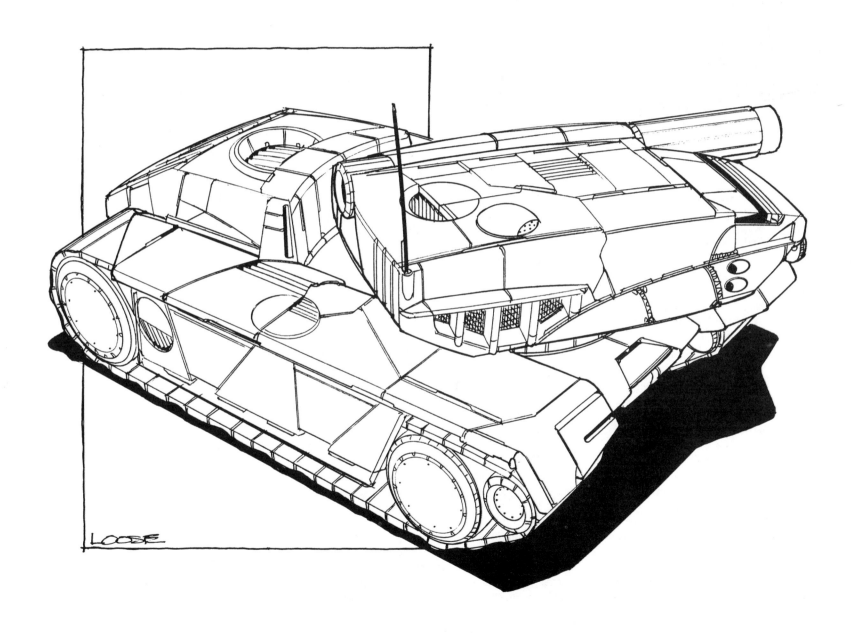

LOOSE

SRM/LRM CARRIER

VEHICLES

Mass: 60 tons
Movement Type: Tracked
Power Plant: InterComBust 180 (SRM),
   InterComBust 120 (LRM)
Cruising Speed: 32 kph (SRM), 22 kph (LRM)
Flank Speed: 54 kph (SRM), 32 kph (LRM)
Armor: Lexington Ltd. High Grade
Armament:
   SRM: 9 Holly SRM VI
      1 Doering Electronics Glowworm NARC
      System
   LRM: 3 FarFire LRM Racks
Manufacturer: Quickcell Company
   Primary Factory: Oliver
Communications System: Communicator (with C[3]
   link on LRM)
Targeting and Tracking System: FireScan with
   IndirecTrack (and Artemis FCS on LRM)

OVERVIEW

In the period immediately following the Truce of Tukayyid, the AFFC once again began to improve their conventional units and regimental combat teams, this time concentrating on better equipping their troops. The commission of new and improved versions of the standard long- and short-range missile carriers was an important part of this effort. The first new SRM carriers rolled off the production line in late 3054, with the first new LRM carriers appearing approximately a year later.

The Federated Commonwealth had relied on Quickcell, based on the planet Oliver, for regular supplies of missile carriers for many years. It is ironic,

then, that having invested billions of C-bills in the development of these new vehicles, the Federated Commonwealth lost both Oliver and Quickcell to the Free Worlds League in the recent Marik–Liao invasion of the Sarna March. Captain-General Marik intends to allow Quickcell to honor its contracts with the Federated Commonwealth, but will most assuredly extract a price from his rival for that concession.

CAPABILITIES

Though the improved SRM carrier has changed little from the original design, Quickcell's modifications offer a substantial improvement in performance. Lexington Ltd. High Grade armor replaces the conventional plating mounted on the original version, providing slightly improved protection. Replacing one SRM launcher with a Doering Electronics Glowworm NARC system and installing more sophisticated seeker-heads on the missiles provides a higher on-target hit rate.

The LRM carrier underwent a more drastic overhaul. Quickcell replaced the original power plant with an InterComBust 120, reducing the vehicle's speed but freeing enough tonnage to attach an Artemis system to each of the FarFire launchers. The extra space also increases the available ammunition by three tons. Advanced C[3] targeting electronics round out the LRM carrier's redesign, allowing the vehicle to perform as part of a linked fire-network. Like the SRM carrier, the improved LRM vehicle makes use of Lexington High Grade armor.

DEPLOYMENT

Over the past few years, these vehicles have been used in a number of engagements, against both Clan and Inner Sphere opponents. The First Kathil Uhlans used a number of LRM carriers in their defense of Koniz, where the vehicles' improved accuracy and endurance effectively broke Clan formations.

One of the most notable uses of the SRM carrier occurred in late 3057, when Marik troops attacked the world of Devil's Rock. The largest share of the fighting took place on the streets of Forest City, with engagement ranges often shrinking to less than 100 meters. The Federated Commonwealth defenders used a

lance of SRM carriers as hunter-killers, attacking Marik 'Mechs from ambush and often killing or crippling whole units with the first volley. The four SRM carriers accounted for two lances of Marik 'Mechs in approximately four hours fighting.

Type: **SRM Carrier**
Technology Base: Inner Sphere
Movement Type: Tracked
Tonnage: 60

Equipment		Mass
Internal Structure:		6
Engine:	180	14
Type:	ICE	
Cruising MP:	3	
Flank MP:	5	
Heat Sinks:	0	0
Control Equipment:		3
Lift Equipment:		0
Power Amplifier:		0
Turret:		0
Armor Factor:	54	3

	Armor Value
Front	14
R/L Side	14/14
Rear	12

Weapons and Ammo	Location	Tonnage
SRM 6	Front	3
SRM 6	Front	3
SRM 6	Front	3
SRM 6	Front	3
SRM 6	Front	3
SRM 6	Front	3
SRM 6	Front	3
SRM 6	Front	3
SRM 6	Front	3
Ammo (SRM) 45	Body	3
Narc Missile Beacon	Front	3
Ammo (Narc) 6	Body	1

SRM/LRM CARRIER

Type: **LRM Carrier**
Technology Base: Inner Sphere
Movement Type: Tracked
Tonnage: 60

Equipment		Mass
Internal Structure:		6
Engine:	120	8
Type:	ICE	
Cruising MP:	2	
Flank MP:	3	
Heat Sinks:	0	0
Control Equipment:		3
Lift Equipment:		0
Power Amplifier:		0
Turret:		0
Armor Factor:	54	3

	Armor Value
Front	14
R/L Side	14/14
Rear	12

Weapons and Ammo	Location	Tonnage
LRM 20	Front	10
Artemis IV FCS	Front	1
LRM 20	Front	10
Artemis IV FCS	Front	1
LRM 20	Front	10
Artemis IV FCS	Front	1
Ammo (LRM) 36	Body	6
C3 Slave	Body	1

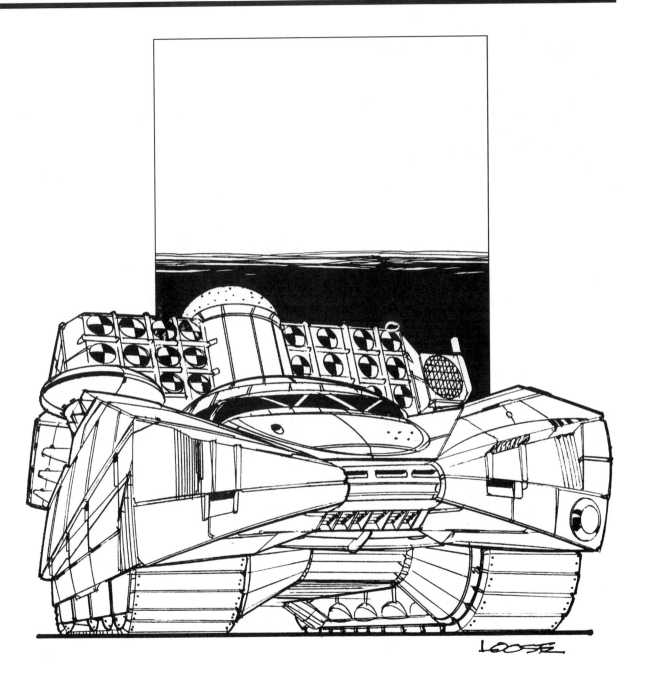

MANTICORE HEAVY TANK

VEHICLES

Mass: 60 tons
Movement Type: Tracked
Power Plant: Pitban 240 Fusion
Cruising Speed: 43 kph
Flank Speed: 65 kph
Armor: Durallex Super Ferro-Fibrous
Armament:
  1 TharHes Thunderbolt-12 Large Pulse Laser
  1 TharHes Reacher-10 LRM Rack
  1 TharHes Maxi SRM Rack
  1 Defiance Sting Streak SRM-2 Rack
Manufacturer: Defiance Industries
  Primary Factory: Hesperus
Communications System: TharHes Muse 54-58K
Targeting and Tracking System: TharHes TargiTrack
  with Artemis

OVERVIEW

Long regarded as a powerful infantry weapon, the Manticore has grown even more deadly thanks to improvements made possible by technological advancements. The team responsible for crafting a redesign of this trusted unit focused on two goals: to identify the vehicle's maximum strategic potential, andto reach that potential with minimal alteration from the original to allow easy upgrades on existing Manticores. Their solution was to make the weapons systems more effective by finding ways to deliver more ordnance on target.

CAPABILITIES

The designers chose to retain the original design's power plant and basic chassis, which forced them to economize on weight elsewhere in the unit. Rather than sacrificing systems, they made the weapons systems more energy efficient. The new Manticore's main weapon is a TharHes Thunderbolt large pulse laser. Though the laser lacks the range of the original PPC, increased accuracy evens out the balance. Artemis fire-control systems improve the accuracy of both the short- and long-range missile racks, resulting in more missiles hitting their targets. Placed in the vehicle's turret, these three weapons enjoy excellent fields of fire. The front of the Manticore carries a Defiance Sting Streak missile rack. Because this system replaced a laser, the design team was able to remove heat sinks to gain needed space.

For increased survivability, Defiance increased the Manticore's protection by upgrading its armor to Durallex Super ferro-fibrous.

DEPLOYMENT

The first Manticores issued went to Lyran Royal Guard units, where they were used mainly for ceremonial duties. As active units began purchasing the Manticore, Defiance produced a field refit kit to allow those units to upgrade to the new design. If, as expected, hostilities between the Great Houses resume in earnest, sales of the redesigned Manticore may grow exponentially.

VARIANTS

Because the Manticore represents a relatively modern design, Defiance Industries feels no real need to offer variants in the near future. Though they have been considering the benefits of replacing the pulse laser with a LB 10-X autocannon, they feel that weapon would require the sacrifice of too much other firepower to offer a true improvement.

Type: **Manticore Heavy Tank**
Technology Base: Inner Sphere
Movement Type: Tracked
Tonnage: 60

Equipment		Mass
Internal Structure:		6
Engine:	240	17.5
Type:	Fusion	
Cruising MP:	4	
Flank MP:	6	
Heat Sinks:	10	0
Control Equipment:		3
Lift Equipment:		0
Power Amplifier:		0
Turret:		2
Armor Factor:	179	10

	Armor Value
Front	43
R/L Side	34/34
Rear	26
Turret	42

Weapons and Ammo	Location	Tonnage
Large Pulse Laser	Turret	7
LRM 10	Turret	5
Artemis IV FCS	Turret	1
Ammo (LRM) 12	Body	1
SRM 6	Turret	3
Artemis IV FCS	Turret	1
Ammo (SRM) 15	Body	1
Streak SRM 2	Front	1.5
Ammo (Streak SRM) 50	Body	1

MANTICORE HEAVY TANK

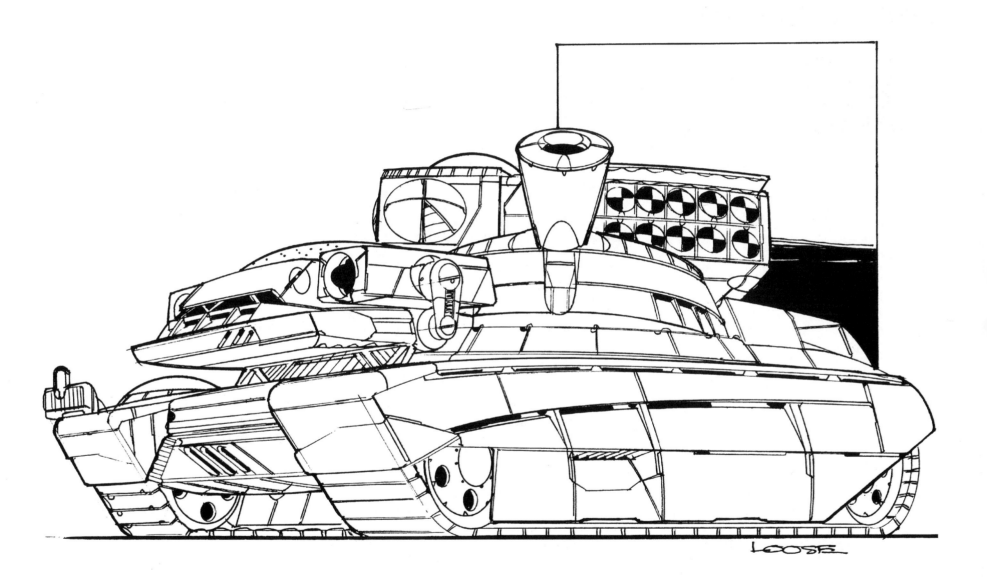

PO HEAVY TANK

VEHICLES

Mass: 60 tons
Movement Type: Tracked
Power Plant: Ceres 240 Internal Combustion
Cruising Speed: 43 kph
Flank Speed: 65 kph
Armor: Starshield Type V
Armament:
　1 Ceres Arms Model T Class 10 Autocannon
　2 Maxi Mini Machine Guns
Manufacturer: Ceres Metal Industries
　Primary Factory: Menke, St. Ives
Communications System: CeresComm Model 37-P
Targeting and Tracking System: Ceres/Maladev 3

OVERVIEW

The end of the Fourth Succession War devastated the Capellan Confederation. Having lost more than half its star systems and most of its industrial base, the Capellan military was left desperate for new war materiel to rebuild its conventional forces. The young Chancellor, Romano Liao, recognized her realm's plight and quickly commissioned Ivan Maladev, an up-and-coming military weapons designer and student of twentieth-century Russian history, to address the crisis.

The Capellan military needed weapons fast, but because Romano's sister Candace Liao took a sizable portion of both state and family funds when she defected to the Federated Commonwealth, the new weapons also needed to be inexpensive. Taking a page from Russian history, Maladev designed a tank that packed a hefty punch and was built using sturdy, economical

parts. The most important design specification, however, was that all the components for the new tank were manufactured in what remained of the Confederation.

The military approved the tank and rushed the design from the drawing board to full-scale production in a record fourteen months. Chancellor Liao named the new tank the Po for the mischievous and vengeful spirit of Chinese tradition, and used her new units to brutally and brilliantly fend off an invasion mounted jointly by the Duchy of Andurien and the Magistracy of Canopus.

CAPABILITIES

The Po is built around the rugged and dependable Ceres 240 internal combustion engine, which gives the tank a maximum flank speed of 65 kph. Simply constructed with reliable components, the Po offers easy maintenance in the field. The Po makes its main punch with the Ceres Arms Model T Class 10 autocannon. A weapon with an excellent combat record, the Model T makes the Po a serious combat threat to light and medium 'Mechs. Two Maxi Mini machine guns—one turret-mounted alongside the autocannon and another mounted in a ball joint on the front of the Po—constitute the tank's secondary weapons.

Ten and half tons of armor provide respectable protection for a heavy tank. Along with its ease of maintenance and decent firepower, this protection makes the Po a popular poor man's version of the Rommel/Patton tank. Despite the jokes deriding the Po as a wannabe of better-known units, it has become the principal combat vehicle on Capellan worlds lacking 'Mech units.

DEPLOYMENT

Since 3038, Ceres has sold the Po to mercenary and House units throughout the Inner Sphere. In an ongoing attempt to bolster its depleted armor units, House Marik continues to purchase the lion's share of all Po tanks that roll off the production lines. The tank's brisk sales keep badly needed C-bills pouring into the Capellan treasury.

Type: Po Heavy Tank
Technology Base: Inner Sphere
Movement Type: Tracked
Tonnage: 60

Equipment		Mass
Internal Structure:		6
Engine:	240	23
Type:	ICE	
Cruising MP:	4	
Flank MP:	6	
Heat Sinks:	0	0
Control Equipment:		3
Lift Equipment:		0
Power Amplifier:		0
Turret:		1.5
Armor Factor:	168	10.5

	Armor Value
Front	40
R/L Side	32/32
Rear	30
Turret	34

Weapons and Ammo	Location	Tonnage
AC/10	Turret	12
Machine Gun	Turret	.5
Machine Gun	Front	.5
Ammo (AC) 20	Body	2
Ammo (MG) 200	Body	1

PO HEAVY TANK

TOKUGAWA HEAVY TANK

VEHICLES

Mass: 60 tons
Movement Type: Wheeled
Power Plant: Nissan 220
Cruising Speed: 43 kph
Flank Speed: 65 kph
Armor: Star Slab/2
Armament:
    2 Diverse Optics Type 20p Medium Pulse Lasers
    1 Imperator Code Red LB 10-X Autocannon
    1 Ayukawa "Slapper" SRM-6 Launcher
Manufacturer: Buda Imperial Vehicles, Bulldog
Enterprises
    Primary Factories: Luthien (Buda), Proserpina
    (Bulldog)
Communications System: Sipher CommSys 1
Targeting and Tracking System: TargiTrack 717 with
    Artemis FCS

OVERVIEW

The first Tokugawa heavy tanks were designed by the DCMS Procurement Division and manufactured at numerous sites throughout the Draconis Combine during the First Succession War. By the 31st century, the number of firms manufacturing the design had dwindled to one—Buda Imperial Vehicles of Luthien. To remedy this situation, Gunji-no-Kanrei Theodore Kurita commissioned Bulldog Enterprises of Proserpina to produce Tokugawas. The first Bulldog Enterprises Tokugawa appeared in 3046. Shortly after the Combine's defeat of the Clans on Luthien, Buda and Bulldog began a joint research project to create an improved Tokugawa. Research continued until 3053, with the first new Tokugawa rolling out from the Buda plant in November of that year.

CAPABILITIES

A Nissan 220 fusion unit powers the upgraded Tokugawa. This compact power plant enables the Tokugawa to carry an impressive arsenal of weapons systems, which includes a pair of Diverse Optics Type 20p pulse lasers. These lasers provide effective firepower within 180 meters. The design's arsenal also features a turret-mounted Ayukawa "Slapper" SRM unit fitted with an Artemis FCS.

But perhaps the most impressive weapon the vehicle carries is the Imperator Code Red autocannon, which can fire a diverse range of ammunition. The Imperator system can be purchased only from Imperator Automatic Weaponry in the Free Worlds League, which has led some observers to speculate that Imperator has been instructed by Thomas Marik to provide Buda and Bulldog "favored buyer" status.

DEPLOYMENT

A number of new Tokugawas have been shipped to units along the Clan frontier, though the largest concentration remains on Luthien itself. So far, observers can confirm only a single instance of the Tokugawa having seen action—in the defense of Kilmarnock against Clan Nova Cat. In that engagement, forces attached to the First Amphibian LAG used Tokugawas to contain Clan battle-armored infantry units.

Type: Tokugawa Heavy Tank
Technology Base: Inner Sphere
Movement Type: Wheeled
Tonnage: 60

Equipment		Mass
Internal Structure:		6
Engine:	220	15
Type:	Fusion	
Cruising MP:	4	
Flank MP:	6	
Heat Sinks:	10	0
Control Equipment:		3
Lift Equipment:		0
Power Amplifier:		0
Turret:		1.5
Armor Factor:	168	10.5

	Armor Value
Front	40
R/L Side	33/33
Rear	26
Turret	36

Weapons and Ammo	Location	Tonnage
2 Medium Pulse Lasers	Front	4
LB 10-X AC	Turret	11
Ammo (LB 10-X) 30	Body	3
SRM 6	Turret	3
Artemis IV FCS	Turret	1
Ammo (SRM) 30	Body	2

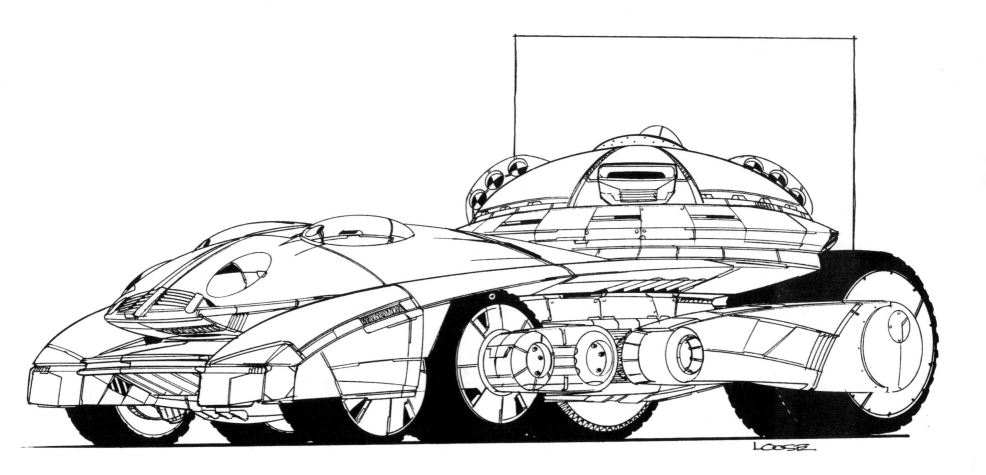

PILUM HEAVY TANK

VEHICLES

Mass: 70 tons
Movement Type: Wheeled
Power Plant: InterFus 260 Fusion
Cruising Speed: 43 kph
Flank Speed: 65 kph
Armor: Valiant Scutum Ferro-Fibrous
Armament:
  2 Valiant Arbalest LRM Racks
  2 Valiant Javelin Streak SRM Racks
  2 Valiant Ruby Dart Medium Pulse Lasers
Manufacturer: Valiant Vehicles
  Primary Factory: Johnsondale
Communications System: Wunderland XXV-2 Series
Targeting and Tracking System: Wunderland XXV-2
  with Artemis FCS

OVERVIEW

The Pilum heavy tank represents Valiant Vehicles' attempt to follow up the success of their Striker design. Most simply, the Pilum was designed as a heavier version of the Striker. This approach has enabled Valiant to use Striker components in the new design and keep the cost of the Pilum relatively low. In fact, Valiant even took the unusual step of using a wheeled chassis for the Pilum, making it the first known wheeled 70-ton tank. Though this design choice elicited criticism from military observers, the success of the Striker convinced Valiant to go ahead with the wheeled chassis.

CAPABILITIES

The Pilum's InterFus 260 fusion power plant provides the tank with an impressive flanking speed of 65 kph. The Pilum's pair of turret-mounted Valiant Arbalest missile racks, slaved to an Artemis IV fire-control system, make it well suited for long-range support duty. For short-range protection, the Pilum carries a pair of turret-mounted Valiant Javelin Streak short-range missile racks and a pair of Valiant Ruby Dart medium pulse lasers mounted in the front of the vehicle.

Like many long-range support vehicles, the Pilum is lightly armored for its weight. However, the Pilum's Valiant Scutum ferro-fibrous armor partially compensates for this potential drawback.

DEPLOYMENT

Technical problems on the new production line at Valiant's Johnsondale factory had delayed distribution of the Pilum, but troubleshooters at the plant have corrected them and Pilums are now rolling off the assembly lines. Most of these vehicles are scheduled to enter service with AFFC front-line units, but the extent of the Pilum's deployment remains unknown at this time.

VARIANTS

Currently, Valiant designers are working on an artillery-support version of the Pilum, which features an Arrow IV artillery system in place of the LRM racks. Apparently, Valiant intends this new design to be used with the new Pegasus hovercraft.

Type: **Pilum Heavy Tank**
Technology Base: Inner Sphere
Movement Type: Wheeled
Tonnage: 70

Equipment		Mass
Internal Structure:		7
Engine:	260	20.5
Type:	Fusion	
Cruising MP:	4	
Flank MP:	6	
Heat Sinks:	10	0
Control Equipment:		3.5
Lift Equipment:		0
Power Amplifier:		0
Turret:		2
Armor Factor:	179	10

	Armor Value
Front	40
R/L Side	33/33
Rear	33
Turret	40

Weapons and Ammo	Location	Tonnage
LRM 15	Turret	7
Artemis IV FCS	Turret	1
LRM 15	Turret	7
Artemis IV FCS	Turret	1
Ammo (LRM) 24	Body	3
Streak SRM 2	Turret	1.5
Streak SRM 2	Turret	1.5
Ammo (SRM) 50	Body	1
Medium Pulse Laser	Front	2
Medium Pulse Laser	Front	2

PILUM HEAVY TANK

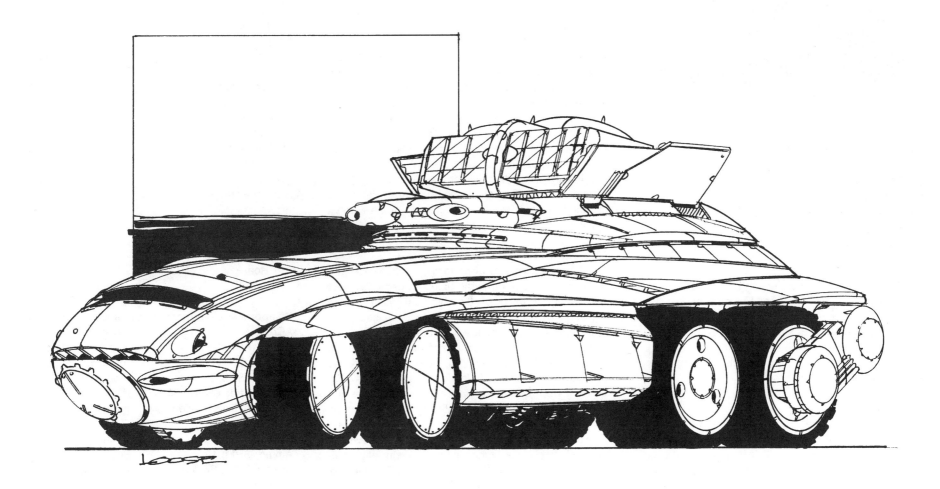

Mass: 70 tons
Movement Type: Wheeled
Power Plant: Breen 190 Fusion
Cruising Speed: 32 kph
Flank Speed: 54 kph
Armor: ArcShield Maxi IV Ferro-Fibrous
Armament:
    1 Luxor Devastator-20 Autocannon
    4 Holly Streak SRM Racks
    1 Harpoon-6 SRM Rack
    2 Sutel Precision Line Medium Pulse Lasers
    1 Sutel Precision Line Small Pulse Laser
Manufacturer: Jalastar Aerospace
    Primary Factory: Panpour
Communications System: Omicron 1500
Targeting and Tracking System: Jalastar TargiTrack
  717 with Beagle Active Probe

OVERVIEW

After the Armed Forces of the Federated Commonwealth lost its Demolisher factory on Sudeten during the Clan invasion, AFFC leaders solicited bids for a new urban combat vehicle. Jalastar, the manufacturer of the Manticore, eventually won the contract with its wheeled Typhoon design. Production of the Typhoon began in early 3057 at Jalastar's factory on Panpour. Almost all Typhoons manufactured have been shipped to the Davion Guards units.

CAPABILITIES

The low-slung Typhoon is well suited for its role as an urban combat vehicle. The main weapon of the design's diverse arsenal is the Luxor Devastator-20 series autocannon, a powerful weapon capable of destroying many vehicles and even BattleMechs with a single hit. The Typhoon also boasts a turret-mounted Harpoon-6 missile system and a pair of turret-mounted Holly Streak launchers. Two additional Streak systems mounted on the front of the Typhoon complete its ballistic armament.

A pair of turret-mounted Sutel Precision Line medium pulse lasers provide the Typhoon with devastating short-range firepower. A rear-firing small pulse laser completes the Typhoon's arsenal.

Finally, a Beagle active probe enables a Typhoon crew to detect enemy units long before they detect the Typhoon, a considerable advantage in urban combat situations.

DEPLOYMENT

Typhoons have proved their effectiveness with numerous Davion and Lyran units. Perhaps the most convincing showing of the Typhoon occurred on Tigress, shortly after Archon Katrina Steiner issued her recall of all Lyran troops following the Marik–Liao invasion of the Sarna March. Apparently, the Davion Assault Guards stationed on Tigress opposed the Fifteenth Lyrans Guards' plans to evacuate the world. When Lyran DropShips landed at the Tigressian spaceport to aid in the evacuation, the Davion troops attempted to seize them, and a bitter clash ensued between the Davion and Lyran units. The Assault Guards' company of Typhoons proved especially effective in the confines of the spaceport. Though the Typhoon units took considerable losses, they destroyed nearly an entire company of Lyran troops.

VARIANTS

Several early prototypes of the Typhoon featured tracked locomotion systems. Though these designs were never mass-produced, several dozen of them remain in service with AFFC units.

Type: **Typhoon Urban Assault Vehicle**
Technology Base: Inner Sphere
Movement Type: Wheeled
Tonnage: 70

Equipment		Mass
Internal Structure:		7
Engine:	190	11.5
Type:	Fusion	
Cruising MP:	3	
Flank MP:	5	
Heat Sinks:	10	0
Control Equipment:		3.5
Lift Equipment:		0
Power Amplifier:		0
Turret:		2.5
Armor Factor:	197	11

	Armor Value
Front	43
R/L Side	40/40
Rear	32
Turret	42

Weapons and Ammo	Location	Tonnage
AC/20	Turret	14
Ammo (AC) 15	Body	3
2 Streak SRM 2	Turret	3
2 Streak SRM 2	Front	3
Ammo (Streak SRM) 50	Body	1
2 Medium Pulse Lasers	Turret	4
Small Pulse Laser	Rear	1
SRM 6	Turret	3
Ammo (SRM) 15	Body	1
Beagle Active Probe	Front	1.5

BRUTUS ASSAULT TANK

Mass: 75 tons
Movement Type: Tracked
Power Plant: Rawlings 225 Fusion
Cruising Speed: 32 kph
Flank Speed: 54 kph
Armor: Kressly Stoneskin 40X
Armament:
    2 Firmir MaxiLase Heavy Lasers
    1 Delta Dart LRM-20 Rack
    2 Hovertec SRM 6
    1 Hovertec SRM 2
Manufacturer: Kressly Warworks
    Primary Factory: Epsilon Eridani
Communications System: Angst Clear Channel 3
Targeting and Tracking System: Dwyerson Mark XII

OVERVIEW

Though the Brutus has never achieved the fame of other, more renowned tank designs, its power and reliability have made it a favorite of forces throughout the Inner Sphere. Despite its highly successful initial test runs in 2998, the Capellan High Command relegated the Brutus to second-line forces, where it remained for decades. The Brutus's fortunes changed, however, when Hanse Davion's armies rolled over the Capellan forces during the Fourth Succession War. The AFFC forces captured large numbers of Brutus tanks and were so impressed with the combat performance of the design that the new AFFC High Command supplied Brutuses to its front-line Regimental Combat Teams (RCTs). The Brutus compared well with other famous tank designs such as the Von Luckner and the Manticore, and the versatile Brutus soon became a common sight among combat, garrison and militia forces. Today, the design is more popular than ever. Brutus tanks are deployed with numerous units in the Chaos March.

CAPABILITIES

The Brutus possesses an impressive combination of long- and short-range weapons. Its two turret-mounted MaxiLase heavy lasers and turret-mounted LRM-20 rack provide a solid long-range punch. For short-range engagements, the Brutus can unload fourteen-missile volleys from the reliable Hovertec SRM racks mounted on the tank's front.

The Brutus has respectable armor protection and speed for its weight class. Though it has less armor than comparable models such as the Manticore, the Brutus's superior firepower amply compensates for this weakness.

DEPLOYMENT

Brutus tanks are deployed with Davion and Lyran RCTs and numerous Davion, Lyran and Capellan border-world garrison units. Recently, several Capellan front-line units have begun to use Brutus tanks. Many of the troops of the Chaos March's minor nobles and powers also possess Brutuses appropriated from retreating Capellan forces.

VARIANTS

Kressly has produced a number of Brutus variants. Most of these variants feature missile launchers in place of the standard configuration's heavy lasers. Others feature particle projection cannons in place of the original design's LRM rack.

Type: Brutus Assault Tank
Technology Base: Inner Sphere
Movement Type: Tracked
Tonnage: 75

Equipment		Mass
Internal Structure:		7.5
Engine:	225	15
Type:	Fusion	
Cruising MP:	3	
Flank MP:	5	
Heat Sinks:	16	6
Control Equipment:		4
Lift Equipment:		0
Power Amplifier:		0
Turret:		2
Armor Factor:	136	8.5

	Armor Value
Front	34
R/L Side	27/27
Rear	21
Turret	27

Weapons and Ammo	Location	Tonnage
Large Laser	Turret	5
Large Laser	Turret	5
LRM 20	Turret	10
Ammo (LRM) 18	Body	3
SRM 6	Front	3
SRM 6	Front	3
Ammo (SRM 6) 15	Body	1
SRM 2	Front	1
Ammo (SRM 2) 50	Body	1

BRUTUS ASSAULT TANK

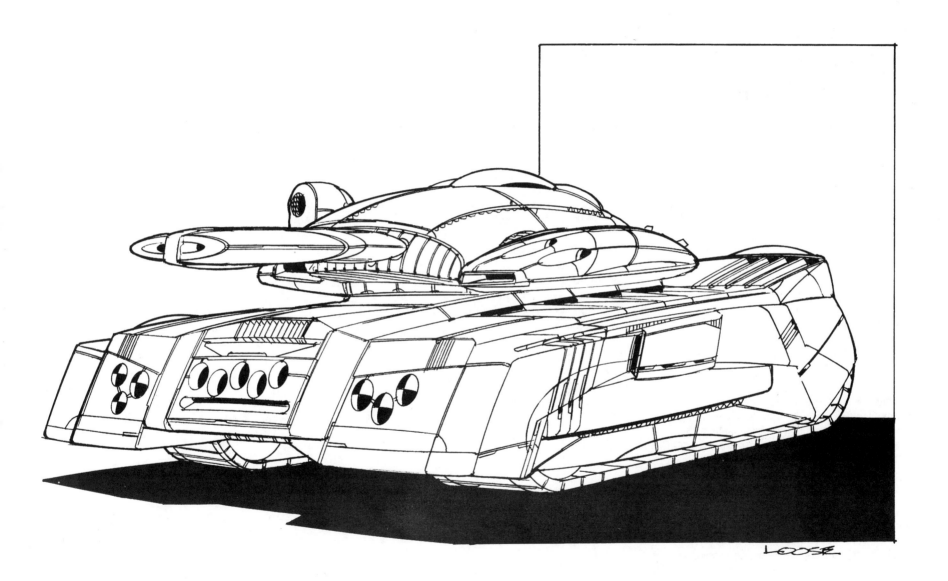

PADILLA HEAVY ARTILLERY TANK

VEHICLES

Mass: 75 tons
Movement Type: Tracked
Power Plant: Ragusson 375 XL
Cruising Speed: 54 kph
Flank Speed: 86 kph
Armor: Star Slab/1
Armament:
    1 Katyusha Arrow IV Missile Launcher
    2 Martell Medium Pulse Lasers
    1 Burow Anti-Missile System
Manufacturer: Leopard Armor
    Primary Factory: Terra
Communications System: Teldon 19
Targeting and Tracking System: Scope 30 RDNST

OVERVIEW

Designed to supplement the Chaparral medium missile tank, the Padilla was introduced into SLDF ground forces in 2620. The first Padillas typically were teamed with light, fast, TAG-equipped BattleMechs that would skirt the enemy's positions and direct missile barrages from Padillas stationed away from the main battle lines. The highly mobile Padilla proved a difficult target for enemy gunners, and the design served well in its capacity as a mobile missile platform. Though Padillas are rare today, this heavy vehicle remains one of the most effective artillery tanks ever designed.

CAPABILITIES

The core of the Padilla's offensive capabilities is the rugged Katyusha Arrow IV missile system, which is mounted in a sleek box launcher set in the front of the vehicle. The Arrow IV system, with its extensive range and damage capability, makes the Padilla devastating in combat. Twin Martell medium pulse lasers provide the Padilla with short-range firepower, and a Burow anti-missile system provides protection against incoming missile attacks. Initially, the Burow system proved susceptible to jamming, and the SLDF quartermaster corps initiated a recall of Padillas to replace the system with the McArthur anti-missile system. However, most Padillas were assigned to front-line combat units and never received the new systems.

Speed and maneuverability remain the lightly armored Padilla's most effective forms of defense, however. The design possesses a top speed of 86 kph, and only the fastest recon BattleMechs or vehicles can hope to hit a moving Padilla.

DEPLOYMENT

Almost all of the SLDF's Padillas were destroyed during Operation Liberation. At the time of the First Succession War, only twenty Padillas were known to exist. House Liao possessed these vehicles but later stripped them of their Arrow IV systems when the supply of Arrow IV missiles dwindled. In recent years, a few Padillas have appeared among Com Guard units. Fifteen Padillas—all in their original weapons configurations—are currently deployed with Com Guard units in the Free Rasalhague Republic.

Type: Padilla Heavy Artillery Tank
Technology Base: Inner Sphere
Movement Type: Tracked
Tonnage: 75

Equipment		Mass
Internal Structure:		7.5
Engine:	375	29.5
Type:	XL Fusion	
Cruising MP:	5	
Flank MP:	8	
Heat Sinks:	10	0
Control Equipment:		4
Lift Equipment:		0
Power Amplifier:		0
Turret:		0
Armor Factor:	88	5.5

	Armor Value
Front	28
R/L Side	24/24
Rear	12

Weapons and Ammo	Location	Tonnage
Arrow IV System	Front	15
Medium Pulse Laser	Front	2
Medium Pulse Laser	Front	2
Anti-Missile System	Front	.5
TAG	Front	1
Ammo (Arrow IV) 30	Body	6
Ammo (Anti-Missile) 24	Body	2

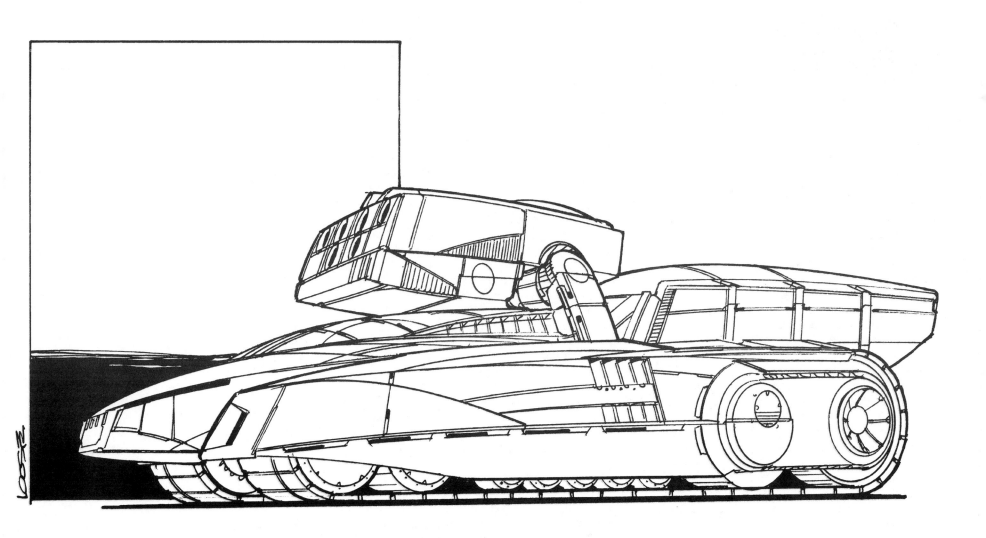

ZHUKOV HEAVY TANK

VEHICLES

Mass: 75 tons
Movement Type: Tracked
Power Plant: 225 Internal Combustion
Cruising Speed: 32 kph
Flank Speed: 54 kph
Armor: ArcShield Max I
Armament:
2 SarLon MaxiCannon AC/10
1 Harvester 20K SRM-6 Launcher
Manufacturer: Aldis Industries
Primary Factory: Betelgeuse
Communications System: Olmstead 30
Targeting and Tracking System: Cirxese
BallistaCheck, Cirxese RockeCheck

OVERVIEW

The Zhukov is Aldis Industries' follow-up to its successful Demolisher design and incorporates several elements from that vehicle. Smaller and less heavily armed than the Demolisher, the Zhukov features better armor and a lower profile, reducing its battlefield vulnerability. Wolf's Dragoons were the first large unit to use the Zhukov, beginning in 3030. Over the course of the past twenty-eight years Aldis has made many design refinements based on suggestions from Dragoon commanders.

CAPABILITIES

The Zhukov is an evolutionary design. Its hull and turret are different from those of the Demolisher, but its running gear, suspension, transmission and automo-tive controls remain the same. The autoloader for the SarLon MaxiCannon is also very similar to the autoloader of the Demolisher's ChemJet 185mm guns.

Though the Demolisher appears to outclass the Zhukov—with similar armor protection and ammunition load, and weapons with almost twice the throw weight of the Zhukov's—the Zhukov is nevertheless a superior machine. Its SarLon autocannons have a significant range advantage over the Demolisher's ChemJets, and a Zhukov commander can aim and fire the weapons from a sight mounted on his cupola. Additionally, the Zhukov's smaller silhouette, lower weight and lower ground pressure give this vehicle significant tactical advantages over its larger cousin. The most extreme example of this advantage was demonstrated during the War of Andurien Succession in 3031 on the planet Watermael. Marik commanders threw a battalion of Zhukovs in the path of a battalion of enemy Demolishers that had broken through the front and were headed for the Marik logistical base. The Demolishers came charging through a vast field of standing sugar cane, bounded on the right and left by marshy fields that had been flooded in preparation for spring planting. The lighter Zhukovs could traverse the marshes more easily than the heavy Demolishers. The tall, dense cane blocked all the vehicles' gunnery sights, but the Zhukov commanders could track the Demolishers' movements by observing the waving cane and firing the guns at the movement. By the time the Demolishers pushed through the cane fields and into effective firing range, twenty-five of the battalion's tanks lay burning in the cane. The Zhukov battalion wiped out the remaining Demolishers within minutes.

DEPLOYMENT

The Zhukov is in service with Wolf's Dragoons, the Free Worlds League and the Capellan Confederation. Other Inner Sphere Houses have bought small numbers for evaluation, but none have made major investments in this vehicle.

Type: Zhukov Heavy Tank
Technology Base: Inner Sphere
Movement Type: Tracked
Tonnage: 75

Equipment		Mass
Internal Structure:		7.5
Engine:	225	20
Type:	ICE	
Cruising MP:	3	
Flank MP:	5	
Heat Sinks:	0	0
Control Equipment:		4
Turret:		2.5
Armor Factor:	176	11

	Armor Value
Front	44
R/L Side	32/32
Back	24
Turret	44

Weapons and Ammo	Location	Tonnage
AC/10	Turret	12
AC/10	Turret	12
Ammo (AC) 20	Body	2
SRM 6	Front	3
Ammo (SRM) 15	Body	1

ZHUKOV HEAVY TANK

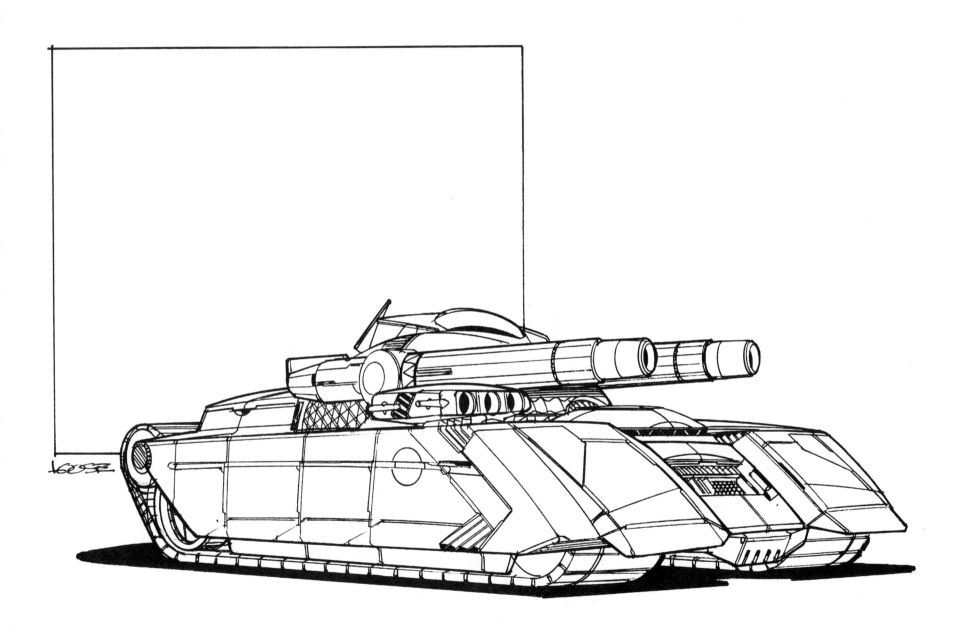

PARTISAN AIR DEFENSE TANK

VEHICLES

Mass: 80 tons
Movement Type: Tracked
Power Plant: GM Super 240 Fusion
Cruising Speed: 32 kph
Flank Speed: 54 kph
Armor: Kallon Unity Weave Ferro-Fibrous
Armament:
    2 Imperator Code Red LB 10-X Autocannons
    2 Imperator Smoothie Light Autocannons
Manufacturer: Kallon Industries
    Primary Factory: Nanking
Communications System: Kallon Secure Net
Targeting and Tracking System: Kallon Sure-Shot C^3

OVERVIEW

Kallon Industries' revamped Partisan provides the Inner Sphere with its first anti-aerospace weapons platform effective against Clan Omnifighters. Using the old, battle-tested Partisan design as a starting point, Kallon upgraded the design's weapons array and added a highly effective C^3 system to augment its targeting systems. The redesigned Partisan has proved a formidable opponent for Clan aerospace assets.

CAPABILITIES

Pairs of turret-mounted Imperator Code Red LB 10-X autocannons and Imperator Smoothie light autocannons provide the main firepower of the redesigned Partisan. The Code Red guns deliver a lethal barrage of flak that can destroy an attacking fighter's control surfaces and cause it to crash. The turret-mounted Smoothie guns provide firepower at extreme ranges.

The design's C^3 system enables a group of Partisans to produce interlocking fields of fire to simultaneously engage enemy aircraft (see **Variants** below for further information). Additionally, the system enables each Partisan in a group to engage a target at the optimum range for the entire group. This means that an enemy fighter will fly into a firestorm that will keep him too busy with evasive maneuvers to aim straight.

The new Partisan also features a compact fusion engine and Kallon Unity Weave ferro-fibrous armor.

DEPLOYMENT

Though few Partisan tanks have reached front-line troops yet, observers believe that at least three Houses have placed orders for the tank. The Kallon factory is located on the planet Nanking in the Sarna March, and recent events in that sector may be delaying delivery of Partisans. In fact, some observers claim that hostilities have broken out on Nanking itself.

VARIANTS

At least two variants of the Partisan are known to exist. The lance-command variant features a C^3 Master system that enables it to coordinate the fire of up to four Partisans. The company-command variant features two C^3 Master systems that enable it to coordinate the fire of up to twelve Partisans (see **Capabilities** for further information).

Both of these C^3 Master systems are larger and heavier than standard C^3 systems. To compensate for this increased weight, the lance-command variant replaces the standard configuration's Code Red LB 10-X autocannons with a pair of Imperator Rapid-Fire medium Ultra autocannons. The company-command vehicle sacrifices both Smoothie light autocannons to make room for its two C^3 Master systems and additional LB 10-X ammunition.

According to unconfirmed reports, Kallon is working on a Partisan prototype fitted with an XL engine, twin LB 10-X autocannons and twin Ultra autocannons. Reportedly, the production costs of these prototypes stand at around 12 million C-bills each, which will undoubtedly limit the number of this new machine sent into the field.

Type: Partisan Air Defense Tank
Technology Base: Inner Sphere
Movement Type: Tracked
Tonnage: 80

Equipment		Mass
Internal Structure:		8
Engine:	240	17.5
Type:	Fusion	
Cruising MP:	3	
Flank MP:	5	
Heat Sinks:	10	0
Control Equipment:		4
Lift Equipment:		0
Power Amplifier:		0
Turret:		3.5
Armor Factor:	143	8

	Armor Value
Front	35
R/L Side	26/26
Rear	21
Turret	35

Weapons and Ammo	Location	Tonnage
LB 10-X AC	Turret	11
LB 10-X AC	Turret	11
Ammo (LB 10-X) 30	Body	3
AC/2	Turret	6
AC/2	Turret	6
Ammo (AC) 45	Body	1
C^3 Slave	Body	1

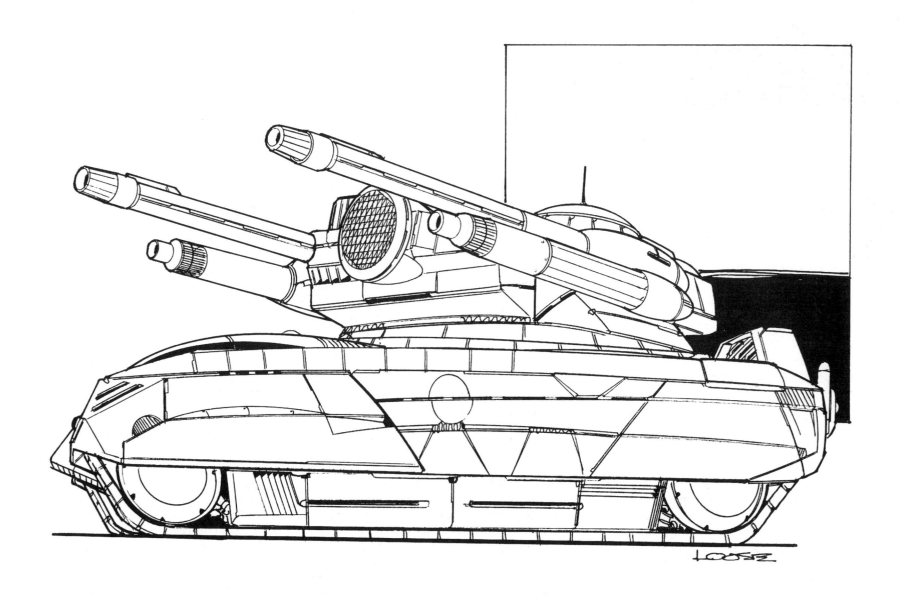

VEHICLES

Mass: 90 tons
Movement Type: Tracked
Power Plant: GM 270 XL Fusion
Cruising Speed: 32 kph
Flank Speed: 54 kph
Armor: Kallon Unity Weave Ferro-Fibrous
Armament:
  1 Poland Main Model A Gauss Rifle
  1 Imperator Code Red LB 10-X Autocannon
  2 Martell Medium Pulse Lasers
  2 Federated Super Streak SRM-2 Racks
  1 Federated 10-Shot LRM Launcher
  1 Exostar Small Pulse Laser
  1 MainFire Point-Defense Anti-Missile System
Manufacturers: Kallon Industries and General Motors
  Primary Factory: Kirklin
Communications System: Wunderland XXV-2 Series
Targeting and Tracking System: Kallon Lock-On with
  Artemis FCS

OVERVIEW

During the Clan invasion of the Inner Sphere, two of the Inner Sphere's largest weapons manufacturers, Kallon Industries and General Motors, made a bold decision. Realizing that the Inner Sphere might not be able to produce enough refitted BattleMechs to stem the Clan thrust, they decided to devote some resources to producing new conventional vehicles. Apparently, they reasoned that the greater ease and lower costs of manufacturing vehicles would enable the Great House armies to flood the battlefields with them and overwhelm the Clan OmniMechs by their

sheer numbers. Many existing vehicles received field refits or minor modifications as part of this effort. However, Kallon and General Motors also decided to design an entirely new super-heavy main battle tank that could go head-to-head with most 'Mechs. The Challenger X Main battle tank is that vehicle.

CAPABILITIES

The Challenger features an impressive mix of speed, firepower and durability. A GM XL engine powers the tank. Though the power plant is quite expensive, it provides the Challenger with enough speed to evade Elemental attacks, a particularly dangerous threat for tank units fighting the Clans.

The Challenger's streamlined, low-profile turret houses an array of powerful guns. A Poland Main Model A Gauss rifle provides tremendous long-range punch, especially when paired with the accurate and efficient Imperator Code Red LB 10-X autocannon. A Federated 10-shot long-range missile rack, slaved to an Artemis fire-control system, provides the Challenger with striking power at extreme ranges. The rest of the vehicle's weapons provide highly effective point defense. These include a pair of forward-mounted Martell medium pulse lasers, side-mounted Federated Super Streak missile racks and a rear-mounted Exostar small pulse laser.

A staggering fourteen tons of Kallon Unity Weave ferro-fibrous armor provide the Challenger with unmatched protection. A turret-mounted MainFire Point-Defense anti-missile system provides additional protection against enemy missile attacks.

DEPLOYMENT

Kallon only recently began full production of the Challenger at its factory on Kirklin. As a result, only a few units, such as the Davion Heavy Guards RCT, possess any Challengers. Curiously, very few of these vehicles have reached troops in the Lyran Alliance and instead appear concentrated among units in Davion sectors. Sources at the Kallon factory claim that a lack of JumpShips available for military traffic in their sector has created this distribution pattern. Regardless of the rea-

son, it appears that the Challenger will see action on the Capellan front long before it appears on the Clan fronts.

Type: **Challenger X Main Battle Tank**
Technology Base: Inner Sphere
Movement Type: Tracked
Tonnage: 90

Equipment		Mass
Internal Structure:		9
Engine:	270	11.5
Type:	XL Fusion	
Cruising MP:	3	
Flank MP:	5	
Heat Sinks:	10	0
Control Equipment:		4.5
Lift Equipment:		0
Power Amplifier:		0
Turret:		3.5
Armor Factor:	251	14

	Armor Value
Front	57
R/L Side	50/50
Rear	37
Turret	57

Weapons and Ammo	Location	Tonnage
Gauss Rifle	Turret	15
Ammo (Gauss) 16	Body	2
LB 10-X AC	Turret	11
Ammo (LB 10-X) 20	Body	2
LRM 10	Turret	5
Artemis IV FCS	Turret	1
Ammo (LRM) 12	Body	1
Medium Pulse Laser	Front	2
Medium Pulse Laser	Front	2
Streak SRM 2	Left	1.5
Streak SRM 2	Right	1.5
Ammo (SRM) 50	Body	1
Small Pulse Laser	Rear	1
Anti-Missile System	Turret	.5
Ammo (Anti-Missile) 12	Body	1

CHALLENGER X MBT

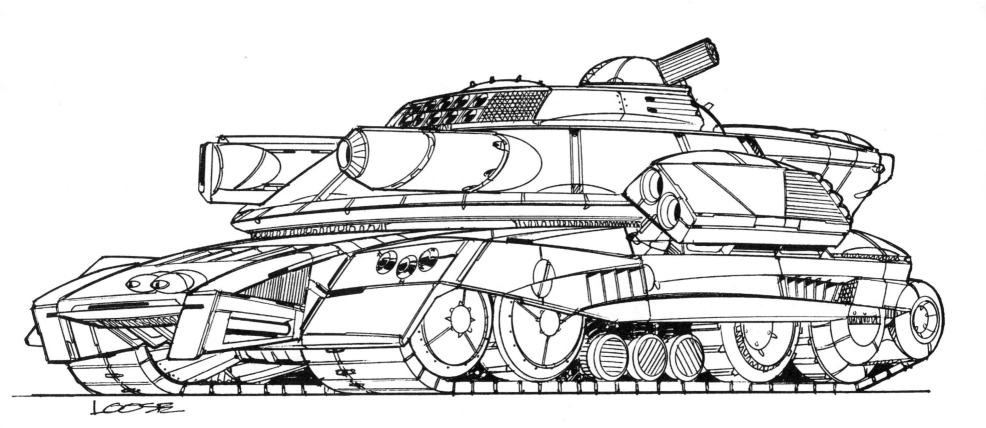

ALACORN MK VI HEAVY TANK

VEHICLES

Mass: 95 tons
Movement Type: Tracked
Power Plant: Pitban 285 XL Fusion Engine
Cruising Speed: 32 kph
Flank Speed: 54 kph
Armor: Star Guard Type VH
Armament:
  3 Norse-Storm Model-7D Gauss Rifles
Manufacturer: New Earth Trading Company
  Primary Factory: New Earth
Communications System: CeresCom Recon Model
  21-Rs
Targeting and Tracking System: TharHes Digital
  Scanlok 347

OVERVIEW

The Alacorn dates back to the Star League—the New Earth Trading Company delivered the first Alacorns to the SLDF in 2587. These machines were deployed with SLDF forces in the Periphery, where the Alacorn earned a reputation as a dependable and effective tank. General Aleksandr Kerensky allegedly took hundreds of Alacorns with him during the Exodus. New Earth Trading Company continued producing Alacorns until the start of the Second Succession War, when a shortage of XL engines and Gauss rifles halted production. Recently New Earth resurrected the design, and the first of these new Alacorns reached Federated Commonwealth units in 3055. New Earth has already received numerous orders for Alacorns from mercenary units and small planets without 'Mech planetary-defense forces.

CAPABILITIES

An XL fusion engine makes the Alacorn fast enough to keep up with most assault 'Mechs, and saves enough weight to mount substantial weapons systems and armor. Three Gauss rifles, mounted on a rotary turret that provides the tank with a full 360-degree firing arc, give the Alacorn devastating firepower. Five tons of Gauss ammunition let the Alacorn stay in combat for a long time. Thirteen tons of armor cover the Alacorn's chassis, providing the tank with excellent armor protection. The front of the Alacorn alone is protected by three tons of armor, making the Alacorn more heavily armored than Rommel and Von Luckner tanks.

Such speed and armor protection do not come without a price, however. The suspension system suffers considerable stress when 95 tons of charging tank makes a 90-degree turn at 54 kph. To keep the vehicle working properly, tank crews must constantly check the track tension. If the track is too loose, the tank will shear its treads off on the first hard turn. If it is too tight, the road wheels and other suspension systems are liable to be damaged or destroyed.

Adjusting track tension is relatively easy. The crew runs a taut string from the idler wheel in the front to the top of the drive sprocket. The tread hangs in a shallow arc under the string. If the lowest point of the arc is between 40 and 65 millimeters under the string, then the track is properly adjusted.

Official gauges and rulers were issued to Alacorn crews to help them make these measurements, but troopers frequently misplaced them in the field. The tank crews then came up with an ingenious expedient, using the popular Pharaoh beer produced by a Federated Suns brewing company. Pharaoh beer is packaged in an unusual container shaped like a truncated pyramid, exactly 40 millimeters wide at the top and 65 millimeters wide at the base. Most Alacorn crews used these widely available cans as gauges to measure that critical distance when checking track tension. Because the internal pressure caused by the beverage inside the container slightly distorted its shape, however, only a freshly emptied Pharaoh could be

used to make the proper adjustments. Not surprisingly, Alacorn tank crews perform track maintenance frequently and thoroughly.

DEPLOYMENT

Alacorns are deployed with Davion and Lyran forces throughout the Inner Sphere.

Type: Alacorn Mk VI Heavy Tank
Technology Base: Star League
Movement Type: Tracked
Tonnage: 95

Equipment		Mass
Internal Structure:		9.5
Engine:	285	13
Type:	XL Fusion	
Cruising MP:	3	
Flank MP:	5	
Heat Sinks:	10	0
Control Equipment:		5
Lift Equipment:		0
Power Amplifier:		0
Turret:		4.5
Armor Factor:	208	13

	Armor Value
Front	50
R/L Side	40/40
Rear	28
Turret	50

Weapons and Ammo	Location	Tonnage
Gauss Rifle	Turret	15
Gauss Rifle	Turret	15
Gauss Rifle	Turret	15
Ammo (Gauss) 40	Body	5

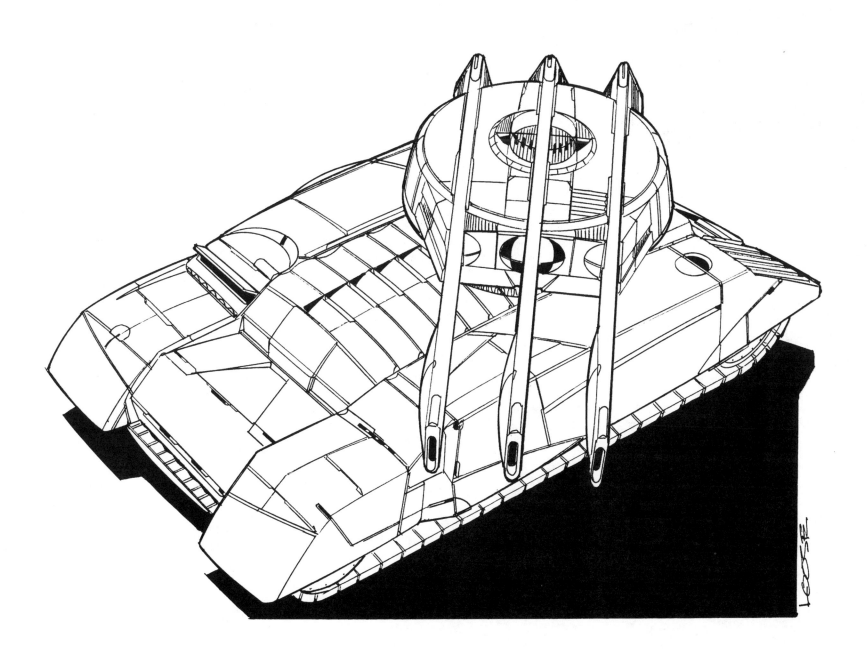

ONTOS HEAVY TANK

Mass: 95 tons
Movement Type: Tracked
Power Plant: GM 285 Cold-Start
Cruising Speed: 32 kph
Flank Speed: 54 kph
Armor: Duralex Lite Ferro-Fibrous with CASE
Armament:
    4 Hellion V Medium Lasers
    3 Intek Medium Pulse Lasers
    1 Delta Dart LRM-15
    1 Hovertec SRM-4
    1 Harpoon-6 SRM-6
Manufacturer: Grumman Amalgamated
    Primary Factory: Shiro III
Communications System: Easy Talk 4
Targeting and Tracking System: GuideRite with
  Laser Coordination Link and Artemis FCS

OVERVIEW

The Ontos heavy tank saw extensive action during the Succession Wars, when its twin LongFire missile launchers and large array of lasers made it a mainstay of House troops throughout the Inner Sphere. However, many commanders considered the Ontos an inferior tank because a lack of sufficient heat sinks limited its battlefield effectiveness. In 3053, Grumman Amalgamated set out to remedy this problem, using recovered technology and improved manufacturing methods to create an updated Ontos.

CAPABILITIES

Grumman's next-generation Ontos features a GM 285 Cold-Start fusion engine in place of the original design's bulky power plant. The use of a compact fusion engine eliminated the need for power amplifiers and freed up tonnage for weapons and armor improvements.

Intek medium pulse lasers replaced half of the Hellion V medium lasers mounted in the original Ontos's turret, providing greater accuracy. A single Delta Dart launcher, slaved to an Artemis fire-control system, replaces the two LongFre launchers. A pair of Artemis-linked SRM launchers, mounted just below the Delta Dart system, round out the Ontos's armament.

Ammunition for the LRM and SRM systems is stored immediately behind the turret in an armored area that features CASE technology to protect the tank in the event of an ammunition explosion. Additionally, the new tank features Duralex Lite ferro-fibrous armor, which provides the upgraded Ontos with effectively 30 percent more armor protection than the original design.

DEPLOYMENT

In production for almost five years now, upgraded Ontoses are deployed with many Marik, Capellan and Federated Commonwealth units. A number of Ontoses are deployed with mercenary troops as well. The tank is a common sight in the Chaos March, where both Marik and Federated Commonwealth units use them.

Type: Ontos Heavy Tank
Technology Base: Inner Sphere
Movement Type: Tracked
Tonnage: 95

Equipment		Mass
Internal Structure:		9.5
Engine:	285	25
Type:	Fusion	
Cruising MP:	3	
Flank MP:	5	
Heat Sinks:	24	14
Control Equipment:		5
Lift Equipment:		0
Power Amplifier:		0
Turret:		2.5
Armor Factor:	170	9.5

	Armor Value
Front	40
R/L Side	32/32
Rear	30
Turret	36

Weapons and Ammo	Location	Tonnage
4 Medium Lasers	Turret	4
3 Medium Pulse Lasers	Turret	6
LRM 15	Turret	7
Artemis IV FCS	Turret	1
Ammo (LRM) 16	Body	2
1 SRM 4	Turret	2
Artemis IV FCS	Turret	1
Ammo (SRM 4) 25	Body	1
1 SRM 6	Turret	3
Artemis IV FCS	Turret	1
Ammo (SRM 6) 15	Body	1
CASE	Body	.5

ONTOS HEAVY TANK

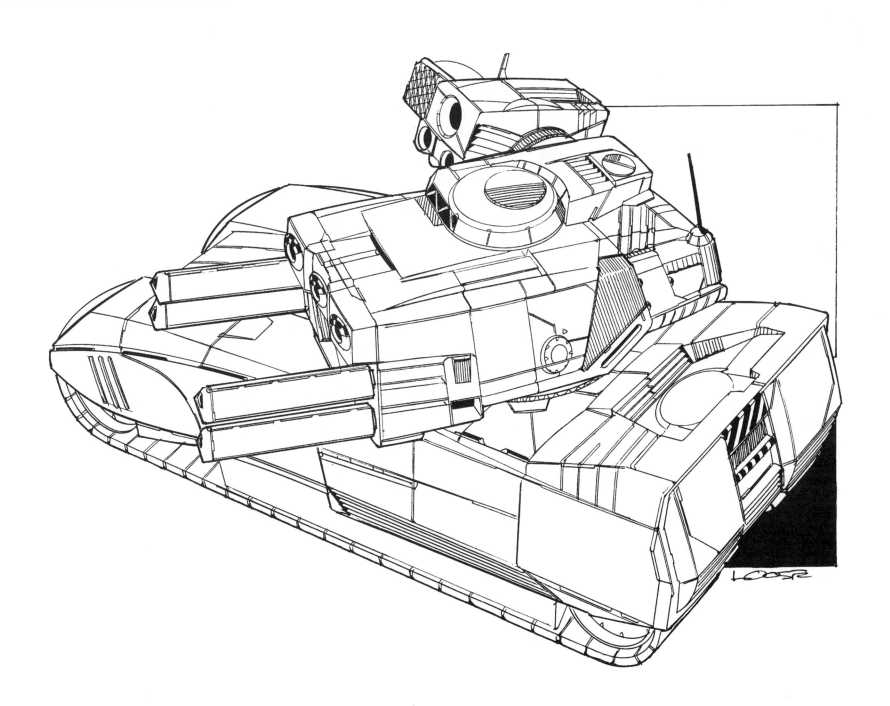

INNER SPHERE MECHS

Spurred by the consciousness of passing time and the increasing shakiness of the Truce of Tukayyid, Inner Sphere political and military establishments have undergone drastic changes that would have been unthinkable a mere decade ago. Once bitter enemies, the militaries of Houses Davion and Kurita now work side by side to defeat the Clans, and BattleMech manufacturers in both realms have begun to follow suit. Setting aside centuries of mutual mistrust, they have begun to pool their resources in the interests of the entire Inner Sphere.

This new atmosphere of cooperation, however, has not eliminated independent development. Like those of all Great Houses, Kurita scientists have been diligently working to decode the secrets of Clan technology. However, the four fully functional OmniMechs gained as part of the victory on Wolcott in 3050 have given them a significant edge. After more than seven years of analysis, the DCMS is fielding the first of its own OmniMechs, all of which are being built in a new high-security facility operated by Luthien Armor Works and heavily subsidized by the Combine government.

The need for ever-increasing numbers of new BattleMechs has led to the development of several new BattleMech manufacturing concerns, as the more established manufacturers have been unable to keep up with the demand. Companies such as Norse-Storm BattleMechs, Inc., Blackstone BattleMechs Ltd., Blue Shot Weapons, Mountain Wolf BattleMechs, J.B. BattleMechs, Inc. and others have taken up the slack and eased some of the pressure on the older companies. Using plans and guidelines drawn from the Gray Death memory core, many of these new companies are producing Star League-era 'Mech designs that the better-known companies lack the production space to make. Many of the new BattleMech manufacturers have sprung up on Lyran Alliance worlds, subsidized by Lyran Archon Katherine Steiner-Davion in an effort to bolster her realm's economy.

This technical briefing contains ComStar's latest intelligence on BattleMech designs now being produced across the Inner Sphere. Some have seen action against the Clans, either during the Battle of Tukayyid or against Clan raiders in the years since; others have yet to see combat outside the testing grounds.

—Frances Pryce
Adept X-Omega
ComStar Archives, Terra
4 January 3058

INNER SPHERE MECHS

Mass: 25 tons
Chassis: Endo Steel
Power Plant: 175 XL
Cruising Speed: 76 kph
Maximum Speed: 119 kph
Jump Jets: None
   Jump Capacity: None
Armor: Standard
Armament:
   11.5 tons of pod space available
Manufacturer: Luthien Armor Works
   Primary Factory: Luthien
Communications System: Unknown
Targeting and Tracking System: Unknown

OVERVIEW

The *Raptor* is one of the first homegrown Inner Sphere OmniMechs. Many in the Draconis Combine Mustered Soldiery consider the *Raptor*, classified as a light 'Mech, a "proof of concept" 'Mech rather than a fully operational design. The Luthien Armor Works engineers began to reverse-engineer Clan OmniMech technology as soon as they received it from the units that conquered Wolcott, but many of the Clan improvements were beyond the technological abilities of the Combine at that point. The modular weapon concept that gives the Clans their incredible tactical flexibility, however, was not beyond their reach. The DCMS commissioned Luthien Armor Works to develop a light 'Mech chassis capable of accepting various weapons modules, with the goal of testing the Combine's manu-

facturing capabilities as well as providing the DCMS with operational experience using OmniMechs. If these tests proved successful, then the Draconis Combine would launch full-scale production of the *Black Hawk-KU*, *Avatar*, *Sunder* and other proposed OmniMech designs.

CAPABILITIES

The *Raptor* is built around a massive weapons bay that is very similar in shape to a Clan *Vulture* missile pod. The weapons bay contains five communications ports that connect to the targeting systems of the weapon modules, simple containers that can be loaded into the bay and connected to the 'Mech and to other ammunition modules if necessary. An extensible rail mounted on the top of the weapons bay helps technicians change modules. Weapon modules can also be fitted to the unit's arms and usually contain small-caliber machine guns or light to medium lasers.

The weapons bay of the *Raptor*'s primary configuration carries three small LRM modules and two machine gun modules, plus the necessary ammunition containers. The arms mount twin small and medium lasers.

The Alpha and Charlie configurations serve as test platforms for various laser and heat sink modules, while the Beta configuration is designed to put short-range missile racks and their affiliated ammo modules through their paces.

The Delta configuration is considered the most successful version of the *Raptor* and is widest deployed. This configuration incorporates a C[3] module and is being used to develop tactics that best fuse together the advantages offered by this new technology.

DEPLOYMENT

The first *Raptor* came off the production line in May of 3052 and was issued to the Dragon's Claws of the DCMS for operational testing. Further units were then sent to various Sword of Light, Genyosha and some Ghost Regiment units. *Raptor*s have also been seen operating in the Federated Commonwealth, presumably on loan from the Combine, but never more than a lance in any unit.

Type: **Raptor**
Technology Base: Inner Sphere OmniMech
Tonnage: 25

Equipment			Mass
Internal Structure:	Endo Steel		1.5
Engine:	175 XL		3.5
Walking MP:	7		
Running MP:	11		
Jumping MP:	0		
Heat Sinks:	10 [20]		0
Gyro:			2
Cockpit:			3
Armor Factor:	56		3.5

	Internal Structure	Armor Value
Head	3	6
Center Torso	8	8
Center Torso (rear)		2
R/L Torso	6	7
R/L Torso (rear)		2
R/L Arm	4	5
R/L Leg	6	6

Weight and Space Allocation

Location	Fixed	Spaces Remaining
Head	Endo Steel	0
Center Torso	None	2
Right Torso	3 Engine	6
	3 Endo Steel	
Left Torso	3 Engine	6
	3 Endo Steel	
Right Arm	3 Endo Steel	2
	Double Heat Sink	
Left Arm	2 Double Heat Sinks	2
Right Leg	2 Endo Steel	0
Left Leg	2 Endo Steel	0

RTX1-0 RAPTOR

Weapons and Ammo	Location	Critical	Tonnage
Primary Weapons Configuration			
LRM 5	CT	1	2
LRM 5	LT	1	2
LRM 5	RT	1	2
Ammo (LRM) 24	CT	1	1
2 Machine Guns	RT	2	1
Ammo (MG) 100	RT	1	.5
Medium Laser	LA	1	1
Small Laser	LA	1	.5
Medium Laser	RA	1	1
Small Laser	RA	1	.5
Alternate Configuration A			
Large Laser	LT	2	5
Large Laser	RT	2	5
Small Laser	RT	1	.5
Small Laser	LA	1	.5
Small Laser	RA	1	.5
Alternate Configuration B			
SRM 6	CT	2	3
SRM 6	LT	2	3
SRM 6	RT	2	3
Ammo (SRM) 30	LT	2	2
Small Laser	RT	1	.5

Weapons and Ammo	Location	Critical	Tonnage
Alternate Configuration C			
2 Medium Lasers	CT	2	2
2 Medium Lasers	RT	2	2
2 Medium Lasers	LT	2	2
Small Pulse Laser	RA	1	1
Double Heat Sink	RA	3	1
Small Pulse Laser	LA	1	1
Double Heat Sink	LA	3	1
Anti-Missile System	RT	1	.5
Ammo (AMS) 12	RT	1	1

Weapons and Ammo	Location	Critical	Tonnage
Alternate Configuration D			
C³ Slave	CT	1	1
Beagle Active Probe	LT	2	1.5
TAG	RT	1	1
Streak SRM 2	CT	1	1.5
Streak SRM 2	LT	1	1.5
Streak SRM 2	RT	1	1.5
Ammo (SRM) 50	LT	1	1
2 Machine Guns	RT	2	1
Ammo (MG) 100	RT	1	.5
Small Laser	LA	1	.5
Small Laser	RA	1	.5

BISKE

OW-1 OWENS

INNER SPHERE MECHS

Mass: 35 tons
Chassis: Standard
Power Plant: 280 XL
Cruising Speed: 86 kph
Maximum Speed: 130 kph
Jump Jets: None
   Jump Capacity: None
Armor: Standard
Armament:
   7 tons of pod space available
Manufacturer: Luthien Armor Works
   Primary Factory: Luthien
Communications System: C³ Network
Targeting and Tracking System: Beagle Active Probe with TAG

OVERVIEW

After analyzing the results of the *Raptor*'s manufacturing and operational tests, the DCMS authorized production of a full line of Inner Sphere OmniMechs. The first Omni off the line was a simple copy of the Clan *Black Hawk*. The second was an improved version of the *Jenner*, which the DCMS christened the *Owens*. Unlike many Kurita 'Mechs, whose names come from their appearance, the *Owens* takes its name from its primary mission: the traditional cavalry role of screening and reconnaissance. The name comes from a Terran drinking song titled *Gray Owens*, a tune traditionally associated with cavalry units. It is interesting to note that the Draconis Combine, whose culture derives from the Oriental societies of Earth, found inspiration for the name of its new light OmniMech in a Western ditty.

CAPABILITIES

The *Owens* represents design modifications and other changes based on reports of the experiences of DCMS troops operating the *Raptor*. The modular weapon containers were standardized and perfected for the *Owens* so that the weapons could operate with all future OmniMech designs. An interesting feature of the *Owens* is the amount of electronics it carries; the 'Mech has internal C³ networks, Beagle active probes, and TAG gear. This array indicates that the DCMS sees the *Owens* primarily as a recon 'Mech capable of finding and fixing the enemy with indirect fire from supporting elements while the main body moves against the enemy's flank.

The primary configuration uses small and medium lasers for self-defense, while LRM racks on the 'Mech's arms offer suppressive fire in indirect support of other units in the lance or company. Most of the other configurations carry assorted short-range weapons of incredible accuracy, though one version also mounts a heavy laser. The *Owens* rarely engages and destroys the enemy directly; instead, it uses its targeting and communications systems to assist heavier units in performing that task.

DEPLOYMENT

The DCMS began deploying the *Owens* in 3056. Most front-line regiments currently have at least a lance of these versatile machines, and many have an entire company of *Owenses*. Some *Owens* are reportedly being tested by the armies of the other Successor States, but none have yet appeared in great numbers.

Type: Owens
Technology Base: Inner Sphere OmniMech
Tonnage: 35

Equipment			Mass
Internal Structure:			3.5
Engine:	280 XL		8
Walking MP:	8		
Running MP:	12		
Jumping MP:	0		
Heat Sinks:	10		0
Gyro:			3
Cockpit:			3
Armor Factor:	112		7

	Internal Structure	Armor Value
Head	3	9
Center Torso	11	16
Center Torso (rear)		5
R/L Torso	8	12
R/L Torso (rear)		4
R/L Arm	6	10
R/L Leg	8	15

Weight and Space Allocation

Location	Fixed	Spaces Remaining
Head	None	1
Center Torso	None	2
Right Torso	3 Engine	7
	TAG	
	C³ Slave	
Left Torso	3 Engine	7
	Beagle Active Probe	
Right Arm	None	8
Left Arm	None	8
Right Leg	None	2
Left Leg	None	2

OW-1 OWENS

Weapons and Ammo	Location	Critical	Tonnage
Primary Weapons Configuration			
Medium Laser	H	1	1
2 Small Lasers	CT	2	1
LRM 5	LA	1	2
LRM 5	RA	1	2
Ammo (LRM) 24	LT	1	1
Alternate Configuration A			
Small Pulse Laser	H	1	1
2 Machine Guns	CT	2	1
Ammo (MG) 200	RT	1	1
Streak SRM 2	LA	1	1.5
Streak SRM 2	RA	1	1.5
Ammo (SRM) 50	LT	1	1
Alternate Configuration B			
Small Laser	H	1	.5
3 Small Lasers	LA	3	1.5
SRM 6	RA	2	3
Artemis IV FCS	RA	1	1
Ammo (SRM) 15	RT	1	1
Alternate Configuration C			
Large Laser	LA	2	5
2 Medium Lasers	RA	2	2
Alternate Configuration D			
Narc Missile Beacon	LA	2	3
Ammo (Narc) 6	LT	1	1
SRM 4	RA	1	2
Ammo (SRM) 25	RT	1	1

SR1-O STRIDER

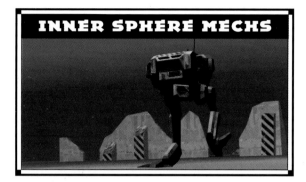

INNER SPHERE MECHS

Mass: 40 tons
Chassis: Endo Steel
Power Plant: 240 Standard
Cruising Speed: 65 kph
Maximum Speed: 97 kph
Jump Jets: None
    Jump Capacity: None
Armor: Standard with CASE
Armament:
    12 tons of pod space available
Manufacturer: Luthien Armor Works
    Primary Factory: Luthien
Communications System: Unknown
Targeting and Tracking System: Unknown

OVERVIEW

The *Strider* is House Kurita's medium-class OmniMech. Based on the *Cicada* manufactured by the Hartford Company, the *Strider* represents a solid, if uninspired, design. Like most medium 'Mechs, the *Strider* is too heavy to run away from trouble and too light to stand up to sustained combat. The *Cicada's* major advantage was its speed, an advantage that the *Strider* sacrifices for dubious gains in armor protection and firepower. The *Strider's* twelve tons of weapon space is a significant increase over the firepower available in the basic *Cicada* design, but not a major advantage when compared to the capabilities of other 40- to 50-ton 'Mechs. The *Strider* is as well-armored as some heavy 'Mechs, which makes it tougher but also slows it down and subjects it to more danger.

CAPABILITIES

The DCMS seems content with the trade-offs made in the *Strider's* design. The primary configuration has two short-range missile racks capable of unleashing a barrage of twelve 110 mm rockets. They are tied to two independent Artemis IV fire-control systems, giving the SRMs devastating accuracy. With its heavy armor protection, a *Strider* in this configuration is well equipped to extract its comrades from a major firefight. The *Strider's* other configurations also allow it to deliver heavy and accurate firepower via weapons systems customized for terrain, mission, and likely enemies. The *Strider's* degree of specialization makes it an excellent complement to the DCMS's other, capable medium OmniMech, the *Blackhawk-KU*.

The alpha configuration's Narc beacon, C³ and TAG systems enable the *Strider* to serve as a heavy reconnaissance 'Mech. Unlike the other configurations, this *Strider* is heavily dependent on other units to provide support if it runs across enemy forces.

DEPLOYMENT

Strider 'Mechs appear primarily in DCMS forces, either as lance command vehicles or partnered with *Owens* OmniMechs. They also form the recon elements of heavy or assault battalions. While some *Striders* have entered service with the Federated Commonwealth and the Lyran Alliance, the Combine has given priority to their own internal needs.

Type: Strider
Technology Base: Inner Sphere OmniMech
Tonnage: 40

Equipment		Mass
Internal Structure:	Endo Steel	2
Engine:	240	11.5
Walking MP:	6	
Running MP:	9	
Jumping MP:	0	
Heat Sinks:	10	0
Gyro:		3
Cockpit:		3
Armor Factor:	120	7.5

	Internal Structure	Armor Value
Head	3	9
Center Torso	12	15
Center Torso (rear)		6
R/L Torso	10	14
R/L Torso (rear)		5
R/L Arm	6	12
R/L Leg	10	14

Weight and Space Allocation

Location	Fixed	Spaces Remaining
Head	None	1
Center Torso	None	2
Right Torso	6 Endo Steel	5
	CASE	
Left Torso	6 Endo Steel	5
	CASE	
Right Arm	None	8
Left Arm	None	8
Right Leg	Endo Steel	1
Left Leg	Endo Steel	0
	Heat Sink	

Weapons and Ammo	Location	Critical	Tonnage
Primary Weapons Configuration			
Beagle Active Probe	CT	2	1.5
SRM 6	LA	2	3
Artemis IV FCS	LA	1	1
Ammo (SRM) 15	LT	1	1
SRM 6	RA	2	3
Artemis IV FCS	RA	1	1
Ammo (SRM) 15	RT	1	1
Small Laser	H	1	.5
Alternate Configuration A			
Narc Missile Beacon	LA	2	3
Ammo (Narc) 6	LT	1	1
Narc Missile Beacon	RA	2	3
Ammo (Narc) 6	RT	1	1
Beagle Active Probe	CT	2	1.5
TAG	LT	1	1
C³ Slave	RT	1	1
Small Laser	H	1	.5

SR1-O STRIDER

Weapons and Ammo	Location	Critical	Tonnage
Alternate Configuration B			
LRM 10	LA	2	5
Ammo (LRM) 12	LT	1	1
LRM 10	RA	2	5
Ammo (LRM) 12	RT	1	1
Alternate Configuration C			
LRM 5	LA	1	2
Ammo (LRM) 24	LT	1	1
LRM 5	RA	1	2
Ammo (LRM) 24	RT	1	1
Large Laser	CT	2	5
C³ Slave	H	1	1
Alternate Configuration D			
Streak SRM 2	LA	1	1.5
Medium Pulse Laser	LA	1	2
Streak SRM 2	RA	1	1.5
Medium Pulse Laser	RA	1	2
Ammo (SRM) 50	RT	1	1
Small Laser	H	1	.5
Beagle Active Probe	CT	2	1.5
TAG	LT	1	1
C³ Slave	LT	1	1

INNER SPHERE MECHS

Mass: 45 tons
Chassis: Endo Steel
Power Plant: 270 XL
Cruising Speed: 65 kph
Maximum Speed: 97 kph
Jump Jets: 6
   Jump Capacity: 180 meters
Armor: Standard
Armament:
   2 Flamers
   13.5 tons of pod space available
Manufacturer: Luthien Armor Works/
   Coventry Metal Works
     Primary Factory: Luthien
Communications System: Unknown
Targeting and Tracking System: Unknown

OVERVIEW

During the Clan War, the Great Houses of the Inner Sphere pledged to support each other with exchanges of technical information as well as with troops and munitions. As part of that agreement, the Federated Commonwealth manufacturer Coventry Metal Works gave its Draconis Combine counterpart, Luthien Armor Works, a license and the manufacturing specifications to produce the *Firestarter*. The fact that Coventry chose such an over-specialized 'Mech to exchange when it could have provided much more viable designs speaks volumes about the depth of the Inner Sphere's grudging alliance.

The executives at Luthien Armor Works thanked Coventry for their support and filed away the next-to-useless *Firestarter* designs. When the Combine's turn came to reciprocate, they sent Coventry the slightly modified FS9-O *Firestarter* rather than specifications for the original-design Combine OmniMechs such as the *Avatar* or the *Sunder*. The rationale for this choice provided by Luthien Armor Works stated that Coventry's production line was already set up to manufacture the *Firestarter*, and modifying that line would require less time than starting up a new production line. The Federated Commonwealth has officially accepted this explanation, though some people believe that the DCMS simply did not want to give their cutting-edge 'Mech technology to their ancient enemies.

CAPABILITIES

This standard BattleMech has been modified to accept modular weapon systems, though it retains fixed forward- and rear-firing flamers. Its primary configuration is equipped with a Beagle active probe, two large lasers, and two additional flamers, raising the number of flamers to four. This configuration closely matches the standard *Firestarter* weapons mix, making the operational transition to the new Omni technology easier for units receiving this 'Mech.

The other known configurations show the standard situation-dependent mix of weapons. It is interesting to note that almost all of these configurations incorporate a C^3 slave unit. It appears that the Draconis Combine is beginning to accept C^3 as a integral part of their tactical doctrine.

DEPLOYMENT

The modular *Firestarter* is currently being manufactured for the Federated Commonwealth, Lyran Alliance, and Free Worlds League. The Federated Commonwealth is replacing older versions of the *Firestarter* with the new design on a one-for-one basis at battalion and regimental headquarters. Other House militaries are beginning to deploy them in lance-sized units.

Type: **Firestarter**
Technology Base: Inner Sphere OmniMech
Tonnage: 45

Equipment			Mass
Internal Structure:	Endo Steel		2.5
Engine:	270 XL		7.5
Walking MP:	6		
Running MP:	9		
Jumping MP:	6		
Heat Sinks:	12 [24]		2
Gyro:			3
Cockpit:			3
Armor Factor:	136		8.5

	Internal Structure	Armor Value
Head	3	9
Center Torso	14	20
Center Torso (rear)		7
R/L Torso	11	16
R/L Torso (rear)		6
R/L Arm	7	12
R/L Leg	11	16

Weight and Space Allocation

Location	Fixed	Spaces Remaining
Head	None	1
Center Torso	Flamer	0
	Flamer (rear)	
Right Torso	3 Engine	3
	3 Jump Jets	
	Double Heat Sink	
Left Torso	3 Engine	1
	3 Jump Jets	
	2 Endo Steel	
	Double Heat Sink	
Right Arm	3 Endo Steel	5
Left Arm	5 Endo Steel	3
Right Leg	2 Endo Steel	0
Left Leg	2 Endo Steel	0

FS9-0 FIRESTARTER

Weapons and Ammo	Location	Critical	Tonnage
Primary Weapons Configuration			
Large Laser	LA	2	5
Large Laser	RA	2	5
2 Flamers	RA	2	2
Beagle Active Probe	RT	2	1.5
Alternate Configuration A			
LB 10-X AC	RA	6	11
Ammo (LB 10-X) 20	RT	2	2
Small Laser	LA	1	.5
Alternate Configuration B			
Large Pulse Laser	RA	2	7
Small Laser	RA	1	.5
2 Medium Pulse Lasers	LA	2	4
C^3 Slave	LT	1	1
TAG	RT	1	1
Alternate Configuration C			
LRM 10	LA	2	5
Ammo (LRM) 12	LA	1	1
LRM 10	RA	2	5
Ammo (LRM) 12	RA	1	1
C^3 Slave	LT	1	1
Small Laser	RT	1	.5
Alternate Configuration D			
ER PPC	LA	3	7
LRM 5	RA	1	2
Ammo (LRM) 24	RA	1	1
Medium Laser	RA	1	1
C^3 Slave	LT	1	1
Guardian ECM Suite	RT	2	1.5

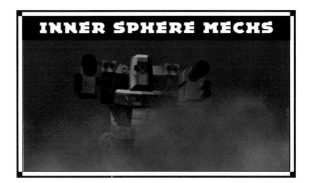

INNER SPHERE MECHS

Mass: 50 tons
Chassis: Endo Steel
Power Plant: 200 XL
Cruising Speed: 43 kph
Maximum Speed: 65 kph
Jump Jets: 4
Jump Capacity: 120 meters
Armor: Standard
Armament:
    26.5 tons of pod space available
Manufacturer: Luthien Armor Works/
  Irian Battlemechs Unlimited
    Primary Factory: Luthien
Communications System: Unknown
Targeting and Tracking System: Unknown

OVERVIEW

Luthien Armor Works received a license to manufacture the *Blackjack* from Ceres Metal Works in the St. Ives Compact, as part of the Combine's newly implemented technology exchange program. The Draconis Combine manufacturer began producing the design it received for the BJ-2 version, but only a few examples of this 'Mech rolled off the assembly line before plant executives ended production and retooled the line to manufacture an OmniMech version.

The BJ2-O *Blackjack* was the first OmniMech design exported for manufacturing, in this case to Irian BattleMechs Unlimited. Though this level of technological exchange seems remarkably enlightened, many claimed at the time that the DCMS was only allowing

"monkey" versions of their OmniMech technology to be exported. This claim is supported by the fact that the exported plans called for weapons bays that could only accept DCMS standard connections, while the OmniMechs actually being fielded by the DCMS had connectors that allowed them to use captured Clan weapons and ammunition. The DCMS claimed that the *Blackjack* was rushed into production before the manufacturers had perfected the necessary, complex software interfaces. Without such interfaces, Inner Sphere targeting and fire-control systems could not interact with Clan weapons—therefore, fitting the exported *Blackjacks* with extra connections would have been a waste of time and money. This problem has been resolved in current production models, and all earlier versions of the *Blackjack* are routinely upgraded during their first major overhaul. Nevertheless, this incident placed great strain on the relationship between the Combine and the other Great Houses.

CAPABILITIES

The *Blackjack* can carry an impressive 26.5 tons of weapons and sensors, as much or more than many heavy 'Mechs. Its jump jets also make the *Blackjack* a maneuverable and dangerous opponent. In its primary configuration, this 'Mech is a deadly infighter: four medium lasers and two Ultra autocannons can throw out a barrage of energy beams and hypervelocity slugs that few enemy 'Mechs can withstand.

As with other OmniMech designs, the *Blackjack's* alternate configurations reflect the needs of specific missions. Because the *Blackjack* is being deployed primarily with Free Worlds League and Capellan Confederation units, the alternative configurations do not include any enhanced targeting, electronics or command-and-control systems. Specifically, the Free Worlds League armed forces appear to have decided that the additional space taken up by these devices can be put to better use increasing the 'Mech's raw firepower.

DEPLOYMENT

The Free Worlds League and Capellan Confederation field the majority of the existing BJ2-O

units. Ceres Metal Works is reported to have converted a standard *Blackjack* production line to produce the OmniMech version, and has begun manufacturing modular *Blackjacks* for the St. Ives Compact and the Federated Commonwealth.

Type: **Blackjack**
Technology Base: Inner Sphere OmniMech
Tonnage: 50

Equipment			Mass
Internal Structure:	Endo Steel		2.5
Engine:	200 XL		4.5
Walking MP:	4		
Running MP:	6		
Jumping MP:	4		
Heat Sinks:	10 [20]		0
Gyro:			2
Cockpit:			3
Armor Factor:	152		9.5

	Internal Structure	Armor Value
Head	3	9
Center Torso	16	22
Center Torso (rear)		9
R/L Torso	12	18
R/L Torso (rear)		6
R/L Arm	8	14
R/L Leg	12	18

Weight and Space Allocation

Location	Fixed	Spaces Remaining
Head	Endo Steel	0
Center Torso	Endo Steel	1
Right Torso	3 Engine	3
	6 Endo Steel	
Left Torso	3 Engine	3
	6 Endo Steel	
Right Arm	Double Heat Sink	5
Left Arm	Double Heat Sink	5
Right Leg	2 Jump Jets	0
Left Leg	2 Jump Jets	0

BJ2-0 BLACKJACK

Weapons and Ammo	Location	Critical	Tonnage
Primary Weapons Configuration			
Ultra AC/5	LA	5	9
2 Medium Lasers	LA	2	2
Ultra AC/5	RA	5	9
2 Medium Lasers	RA	2	2
2 Machine Guns	LT	2	1
Ammo (AC) 20	LT	1	1
2 Machine Guns	RT	2	1
Ammo (AC) 20	RT	1	1
Ammo (MG) 100	CT	1	.5
Alternate Configuration A			
LRM 20	LA	5	10
Ammo (LRM) 12	LA	2	2
LRM 20	RA	5	10
Ammo (LRM) 12	RA	2	2
Medium Laser	LT	1	1
Medium Laser	RT	1	1
Small Laser	CT	1	.5
Alternate Configuration B			
Gauss Rifle	LA	7	15
Ammo (Gauss) 16	LT	2	2
LRM 10	RA	2	5
Artemis IV FCS	RA	1	1
Ammo (LRM) 24	RA	2	2
Small Laser	RT	1	.5
C³ Slave	CT	1	1
Alternate Configuration C			
LB 10-X AC	LA	6	11
LB 10-X AC	RA	6	11
Ammo (LB 10-X) 10	LT	1	1
Medium Laser	LT	1	1
Ammo (LB 10-X) 10	RT	1	1
Medium Laser	RT	1	1
Small Laser	CT	1	.5
Alternate Configuration D			
PPC	LA	3	7
Medium Pulse Laser	LA	1	2
Double Heat Sink	LA	3	1
2 Large Lasers	RA	4	10

Weapons and Ammo	Location	Critical	Tonnage
Double Heat Sink	RA	3	1
2 Medium Lasers	LT	2	2
Medium Pulse Laser	LT	1	2
Double Heat Sink	RT	3	1
Small Laser	CT	1	.5

INNER SPHERE MECHS

Mass: 60 tons
Chassis: Standard
Power Plant: 300 XL
Cruising Speed: 54 kph
Maximum Speed: 86 kph
Jump Jets: 5
   Jump Capacity: 150 meters
Armor: Standard
Armament:
   17 tons of pod space available
Manufacturer: Luthien Armor Works
   Primary Factory: Luthien
Communications System: Unknown
Targeting and Tracking System: Unknown

OVERVIEW

In the aftermath of the battle for Luthien, Draconis Combine troops salvaged several damaged Clan OmniMechs. Prominent Kurita scientists and manufacturers had already begun a crash OmniMech-development program using the spoils of their victory over Clan Smoke Jaguar on Wolcott, but had been unable to replicate any of the captured 'Mechs because the OmniMechs' ferro-fibrous armor and endo-steel skeletons were beyond their technological grasp. The spoils of Luthien, however, provided numerous examples of the *Black Hawk*, a Clan OmniMech that used standard materials for its internal structure and armor. Engineers at Luthien Armor Works swiftly realized that they could copy this OmniMech, and immediately began converting their primary factory to produce the *Black Hawk-KU*. The new 'Mech matched the Clan *Black Hawk* in

maneuverability, weapons load, and protection. Because Inner Sphere weapons are heavier than their Clan counterparts, the designers had to upgrade the engine and internal skeleton, adding 20 percent to the 'Mech's overall weight.

CAPABILITIES

Like most heavy 'Mechs, the *Black Hawk-KU* is slower than lighter machines and has less impressive firepower than assault 'Mechs. However, the use of OmniMech technology and a solid understanding of its advantages make this 'Mech a flexible and deadly machine.

Currently, DCMS troops are testing weapon configurations like those of the Clan *Black Hawk*. In its primary configuration, the *Black Hawk-KU* mounts a total of four pulse lasers and six standard lasers in arm pods, plus two smaller lasers in armored blisters on either side of the cockpit. Unlike the Clan configuration, however, the DCMS version can fire all its lasers at once without risking an immediate heat shutdown.

The alpha variant is equipped with dual ER PPCs and twin anti-missile systems. The AMS systems allow the 'Mech to survive massed long-range missile fire long enough to silence the missile launcher with accurate PPC fire. While heat build-up can pose problems, the 'Mech can sustain fire for more than a minute before excessive heat shuts it down. The beta variant also carries long-range weapons, a large pulse laser and an Ultra autocannon. Weight considerations make it impossible to match the Clan *Black Hawk*, whose beta variant adds two machine guns and an improved small laser, but these short-range weapons do not add appreciably to the 'Mech's offensive firepower. The only variant to suffer from the weight restrictions is the charlie variant. This 'Mech carries a Gauss rifle as lethal as its Clan cousin's; however, its medium laser does not make up for the loss of the Clan version's SRM-4 and improved small pulse laser. The remaining version, the delta variant, carries an improved long-range laser and massive LRM rack whose destructive power matches the Clan version's LB-X autocannon and LRM array.

DEPLOYMENT

The *Black Hawk-KU* has recently been deployed to the Legion of Vega for operational testing. Additional reports indicate that Luthien Armor Works is cross-licensing the design to Coventry Metal Works in the Lyran Alliance as part of a technology exchange agreement.

Type: Black Hawk-KU
Technology Base: Inner Sphere OmniMech
Tonnage: 60

Equipment		Mass
Internal Structure:		6
Engine:	300 XL	9.5
Walking MP:	5	
Running MP:	8	
Jumping MP:	5	
Heat Sinks:	14 [28]	4
Gyro:		3
Cockpit:		3
Armor Factor:	200	12.5

	Internal Structure	Armor Value
Head	3	9
Center Torso	20	30
Center Torso (rear)		9
R/L Torso	14	20
R/L Torso (rear)		8
R/L Arm	10	20
R/L Leg	14	28

Weight and Space Allocation

Location	Fixed	Spaces Remaining
Head	None	1
Center Torso	Jump Jet	1
Right Torso	3 Engine	6
	Double Heat Sink	
Left Torso	3 Engine	6
	Double Heat Sink	
Right Arm	None	8
Left Arm	None	8
Right Leg	2 Jump Jets	0
Left Leg	2 Jump Jets	0

BHKU-O BLACK HAWK-KU

Weapons and Ammo	Location	Critical	Tonnage
Primary Weapons Configuration			
2 Medium Pulse Lasers	LA	2	4
3 Medium Lasers	LA	3	3
2 Medium Pulse Lasers	RA	2	4
3 Medium Lasers	RA	3	3
Small Laser	LT	1	.5
Double Heat Sink	LT	3	1
Small Laser	RT	1	.5
Double Heat Sink	RT	3	1
Alternate Configuration A			
ER PPC	LA	3	7
ER PPC	RA	3	7
Anti-Missile System	LT	1	.5
Ammo (AMS) 12	LT	1	1
Anti-Missile System	RT	1	.5
Ammo (AMS) 12	RT	1	1
Alternate Configuration B			
Large Pulse Laser	LA	2	7
Ultra AC/5	RA	5	9
Ammo (AC) 20	RA	1	1
Alternate Configuration C			
Gauss Rifle	LA	7	15
Ammo (Gauss) 8	LT	1	1
Medium Laser	RA	1	1
Alternate Configuration D			
LRM 20	LA	5	10
Ammo (LRM) 12	LT	2	2
ER Large Laser	RA	2	5

AV1-O AVATAR

INNER SPHERE MECHS

Mass: 70 tons
Chassis: Standard
Power Plant: 280 XL
Cruising Speed: 43 kph
Maximum Speed: 65 kph
Jump Jets: None
    Jump Capacity: None
Armor: Standard with CASE
Armament:
    2 Medium Lasers
    34 tons of pod space available
Manufacturer: Luthien Armor Works
    Primary Factory: Luthien
Communications System: Unknown
Targeting and Tracking System: Unknown

OVERVIEW

The Combine victory on Luthien in December of 3051 also won the DCMS numerous damaged Clan OmniMechs, many of which ended up at Luthien Armor Works for technical evaluation. The DCMS also elected to field some of the captured Clan 'Mechs, but soon discovered that units composed of Clan OmniMechs were excessively prone to problems and breakdowns because the DCMS lacked the technological expertise to maintain the complex Clan machines. Within two or three months, most DCMS units equipped with captured OmniMechs reported at least 50 percent of their 'Mechs unavailable for combat because of equipment failures.

The DCMS turned to Luthien Armor Works for a solution. The engineering team chose to rebuild the captured Clan 'Mechs using only those components that the DCMS could maintain and selected several captured *Vultures* for the first attempt. The engineers kept the *Vulture*'s leg design, but replaced the engine. That change required them to redesign the 'Mech's upper torso to fit the bulkier Inner Sphere engine. The designers also reworked other components, and eventually christened their new 'Mech the *Avatar*.

CAPABILITIES

The *Avatar* fills the traditional role played by heavy 'Mechs in the Combine's new OmniMech force. Though slightly slower than its likely Clan opponents, it is better armored and its weapons bays are 25 percent bigger. Though the Inner Sphere weapons it carries are less capable than their Clan counterparts, the *Avatar* still has a slight firepower advantage over most Clan heavy 'Mechs.

The *Avatar* has two fixed medium lasers, an unusual configuration. The fire-control systems of the weapons pod in the first prototypes was prone to short out at inopportune times, and so the designers elected to give the 'Mech a set of hardwired lasers that the pilot could use in self-defense if the weapons pod shorted out in combat. The fire-control glitch was resolved in the production models, but the fixed lasers were never removed.

DEPLOYMENT

The *Avatar* is currently being deployed in DCMS heavy 'Mech lances along the Clan border, and has also appeared in limited numbers with Com Star and Lyran Alliance forces.

Type: **Avatar**
Technology Base: Inner Sphere OmniMech
Tonnage: 70

Equipment			Mass
Internal Structure:			7
Engine:	280 XL		8
Walking MP:	4		
Running MP:	6		
Jumping MP:	0		
Heat Sinks:	10 [20]		0
Gyro:			3
Cockpit:			3
Armor Factor:	192		12

	Internal Structure	Armor Value
Head	3	9
Center Torso	22	30
Center Torso (rear)		9
R/L Torso	15	22
R/L Torso (rear)		8
R/L Arm	11	16
R/L Leg	15	26

Weight and Space Allocation

Location	Fixed	Spaces Remaining
Head	None	1
Center Torso	2 Medium Lasers	0
Right Torso	3 Engine	8
	CASE	
Left Torso	3 Engine	8
	CASE	
Right Arm	None	8
Left Arm	None	8
Right Leg	None	2
Left Leg	None	2

AV1-O AVATAR

Weapons and Ammo	Location	Critical	Tonnage
Primary Weapons Configuration			
2 Medium Pulse Lasers	LA	2	4
LB 10-X AC	RA	6	11
Ammo (LB 10-X) 20	RT	2	2
LRM 10	LT	2	5
Artemis IV FCS	LT	1	1
Ammo (LRM) 36	LT	3	3
Machine Gun	LT	1	.5
Machine Gun	RT	1	.5
Ammo (MG) 200	RT	1	1
LRM 10	RT	2	5
Artemis IV FCS	RT	1	1
Alternate Configuration A			
ER Large Laser	LA	2	5
AC/20	RA	10	14
Ammo (AC) 15	RT	3	3
SRM 6	RT	2	3
SRM 6	LT	2	3
Ammo (SRM) 30	LT	2	2
2 Jump Jets	RL	2	2
2 Jump Jets	LL	2	2
Alternate Configuration B			
LRM 15	RA	3	7
Artemis IV FCS	RA	1	1
LRM 15	LA	3	7
Artemis IV FCS	LA	1	1
LRM 10	LT	2	5
Artemis IV FCS	LT	1	1
Ammo (LRM 10) 12	LT	1	1
Ammo (LRM 15) 16	LT	2	2
LRM 10	RT	2	5
Artemis IV FCS	RT	1	1
Ammo (LRM 10) 12	RT	1	1
Ammo (LRM 15) 16	RT	2	2

Weapons and Ammo	Location	Critical	Tonnage
Alternate Configuration C			
PPC	LA	3	7
Ultra AC/5	RA	5	9
Ammo (AC) 20	RA	1	1
C3 Computer	LT	5	5
LRM 10	LT	2	5
LRM 10	RT	2	5
Ammo (LRM) 24	RT	2	2

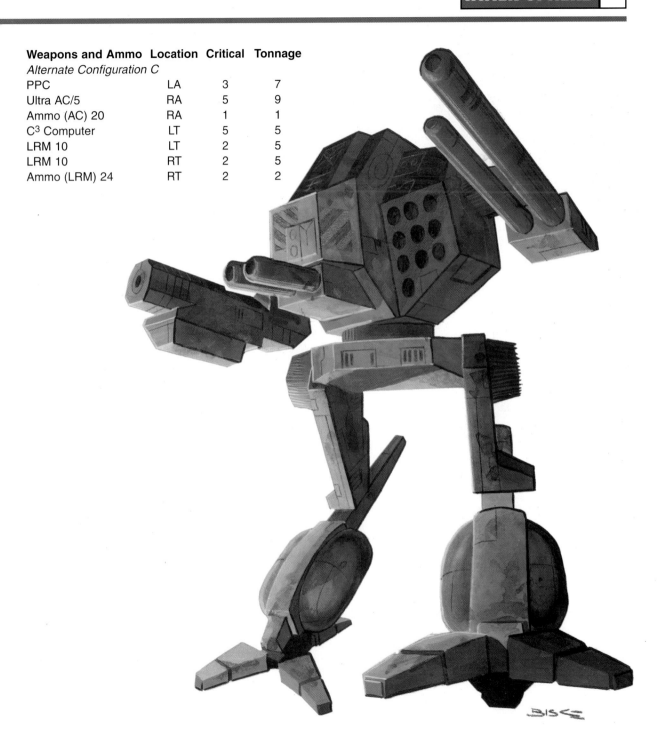

SD1-O SUNDER

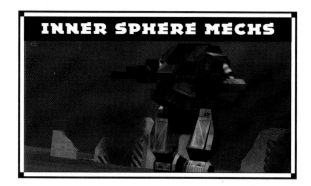

INNER SPHERE MECHS

Mass: 90 tons
Chassis: Standard
Power Plant: 360 XL
Cruising Speed: 43 kph
Maximum Speed: 65 kph
Jump Jets: None
Jump Capacity: None
Armor: Standard
Armament:
36 tons of pod space available
Manufacturer: Luthien Armor Works
Primary Factory: Luthien
Communications System: Unknown
Targeting and Tracking System: Unknown

OVERVIEW

Like the *Avatar*, the *Sunder* was an attempt to re-engineer captured Clan equipment to make it compatible with Inner Sphere technology. The *Sunder* used captured *Loki* and *Thor* chassis as its basis. Unfortunately, this 'Mech's development process was plagued with false starts and technological failures. The first problem to crop up involved the chassis design and weight allocation—the *Sunder* was intended to carry twenty more tons of equipment than the Clan *Loki* and *Thor* OmniMechs on which it was based. The engineers at Luthien Armor Works believed they could easily add this extra weight, and it is true that the additional stress did not cause catastrophic failures in the skeleton. However, the *Sunder*'s actuators wore out at an alarming rate and had to be replaced with larger and more robust versions.

The upper torso was redesigned to accept a bulkier Inner Sphere engine. This change meant rearranging the 'Mech's internal spaces, and so the designers moved the torso weapons bay above the cockpit. This reconfiguration posed no problems when the weapon pods were loaded with energy weapons, but firing missiles sprayed caustic gasses all over the cockpit canopy and sensor arrays. The engineers eventually fixed the problem, but the delays made the *Sunder* one of the last DCMS OmniMechs to be authorized for full-scale production.

CAPABILITIES

When compared to other Inner Sphere assault 'Mechs, the *Sunder* is an extremely capable machine. However, the inferior quality of its Inner Sphere weapons technology makes it no real match for the Clan *Masakari* and *Gladiator* assault 'Mechs. The *Sunder*'s bay can accept an equivalent weapon load, but Inner Sphere weapons tend to be bulkier and less efficient than their Clan equivalents.

One configuration of the *Sunder*, intended to serve as a company command vehicle in a C3 network, is equipped with two C3 master units—one for the company commander's lance and the other to coordinate the activities of the remaining two lances. The prevalence of C3 systems in other DCMS OmniMechs offers a real hope that the Draconis Combine's technological innovation may turn the balance of power back to the Inner Sphere when the conflict with the Clans resumes.

DEPLOYMENT

The *Sunder* is being deployed with DCMS assault lances along the border with the Clan occupied zones.

Type: **Sunder**
Technology Base: Inner Sphere OmniMech
Tonnage: 90

Equipment			Mass
Internal Structure:			9
Engine:	360 XL		16.5
Walking MP:	4		
Running MP:	6		
Jumping MP:	0		
Heat Sinks:	15 [30]		5
Gyro:			4
Cockpit:			3
Armor Factor:	264		16.5

	Internal Structure	Armor Value
Head	3	9
Center Torso	29	41
Center Torso (rear)		12
R/L Torso	19	28
R/L Torso (rear)		10
R/L Arm	15	30
R/L Leg	19	33

Weight and Space Allocation

Location	Fixed	Spaces Remaining
Head	None	1
Center Torso	None	2
Right Torso	3 Engine	9
Left Torso	3 Engine	9
Right Arm	Double Heat Sink	5
Left Arm	None	8
Right Leg	None	2
Left Leg	None	2

Weapons and Ammo Location Critical Tonnage

Primary Weapons Configuration

Weapons and Ammo	Location	Critical	Tonnage
AC/20	LA	10	14
2 Large Lasers	RA	4	10
SRM 4	H	1	2
2 SRM 4	CT	2	4
Medium Laser	LT	1	1
Ammo (AC) 5	LT	1	1
Ammo (SRM) 25	LT	1	1
Medium Laser	RT	1	1
Ammo (AC) 5	RT	1	1
Ammo (SRM) 25	RT	1	1

SD1-O SUNDER

Weapons and Ammo	Location	Critical	Tonnage
Alternate Configuration A			
Gauss Rifle	LA	7	15
Ammo (Gauss) 16	LT	2	2
ER PPC	RA	3	7
LRM 5	H	1	2
2 LRM 5	CT	2	4
Ammo (LRM) 48	RT	2	2
Medium Pulse Laser	LT	1	2
Medium Pulse Laser	RT	1	2
Alternate Configuration B			
LRM 20	LA	5	10
Ammo (LRM) 18	LA	3	3
2 Medium Pulse Lasers	RA	2	4
C³ Computer	RT	5	5
Medium Laser	RT	1	1
C³ Computer	LT	5	5
Medium Laser	LT	1	1
LRM 10	CT	2	5
Ammo (LRM) 12	LT	1	1
Ammo (LRM) 12	RT	1	1

NXS1-A NEXUS

INNER SPHERE MECHS

Mass: 25 tons
Chassis: Skobel 100-ROB Endo Steel
Power Plant: 175 Nissan
Cruising Speed: 76 kph
Maximum Speed: 119 kph
Jump Jets: Rawlings 55
   Jump Capacity: 120 meters
Armor: Krupp 200 Ferro-Fibrous
Armament:
   1 McArthur Anti-Missile System
   2 Blankenburg Technologies Medium Pulse
      Lasers
   1 Blankenburg Technologies Medium Lasers
   2 Intek Small Lasers
Manufacturer: Skobel MechWorks
   Primary Factory: Russia, Terra
Communications System: Exeter Longscan 200
Targeting and Tracking System: Garret T15AJ

OVERVIEW

The *Nexus* has a checkered past. It began as the *Jackrabbit*, a light 'Mech developed by the SLDF at Skobel MechWorks just two years before the Amaris Civil War. Mere weeks after Skobel finished the *Jackrabbit*'s preliminary testing, Stefan Amaris's armies seized the factory. Amaris the Usurper ordered the *Jackrabbit* mass-produced for his Republican army—ultimately, the would-be dictator deployed more than five hundred *Jackrabbit*s against the Star League soldiers for whose use they had originally been intended.

General Kerensky recaptured the Skobel MechWorks plant relatively intact during the Liberation of Terra, but refused to use the 'Mech that Amaris had sent against its developers. He shut down the factory, and ComStar kept it closed for several centuries. Kerensky's army took no *Jackrabbit*s on the Exodus. Outside ComStar, few records of the 'Mech's existence remained.

In 3054, ComStar's Precentor Martial Focht modified the *Jackrabbit*'s design, replacing the engine with the faster Nissan 175, removing the ballistic and missile weapons, and installing jump jets and an array of energy weapons. The BattleMech, newly refitted and renamed *Nexus,* soon began production.

CAPABILITIES

The *Nexus* is a fast mover that can reach a target, deliver a solid punch and get out quickly. Its speed and its highly effective McArthur anti-missile system makes it difficult to hit, and its Rawlings 55 jump jets make it difficult to pursue.

An impressive combination of medium- and short-range energy weapons allows for devastating volleys in most combat situations. Blankenburg Technologies' shoulder-mounted medium laser provides the punches at a distance, and Intek's efficient shoulder-mounted small lasers give the *Nexus* excellent firepower in tight situations. The 'Mech's main slugging power, however, comes from Blankenburg Technologies' excellent medium pulse lasers that have replaced the *Jackrabbit*'s hand actuators.

DEPLOYMENT

Since mid-3055 the *Nexus* has been deployed in the ComStar Fourth Army's 366th Division (Wolf Bait). The 366th Division, decimated by Clan Wolf hit-and-run raids on Tukayyid, used large numbers of *Nexus*es to replace their losses. The *Nexus* is expected to live up to every word of the 366th Division's promising initial reports.

Type: **Nexus**
Technology Base: Inner Sphere
Tonnage: 25

Equipment			Mass
Internal Structure:		Endo Steel	1.5
Engine:		175	7
Walking MP:		7	
Running MP:		11	
Jumping MP:		4	
Heat Sinks:		10 [20]	0
Gyro:			2
Cockpit:			3
Armor Factor:		36	2
	Internal Structure	Armor Value	
Head	3	4	
Center Torso	8	6	
Center Torso (rear)		2	
R/L Torso	6	3	
R/L Torso (rear)		2	
R/L Arm	4	3	
R/L Leg	6	4	

Weapons and Ammo	Location	Critical	Tonnage
Anti-Missile System	LT	1	.5
Ammo (Anti-Missile) 12	LT	1	1
Medium Laser	LA	1	1
Medium Pulse Laser	RA	1	2
Medium Pulse Laser	LA	1	2
Small Laser	LA	1	.5
Small Laser	RA	1	.5
Jump Jets	LT	2	1
Jump Jets	RT	2	1

NXS1-A NEXUS

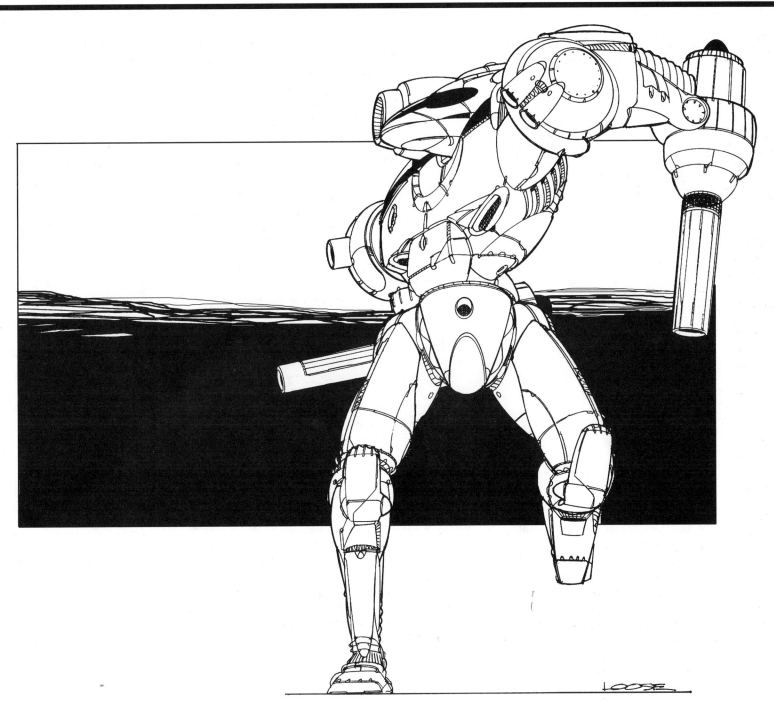

INNER SPHERE MECHS

Mass: 35 tons
Chassis: Kallon Light Type 2AXQ
Power Plant: Omni 175 XL
Cruising Speed: 54 kph
Maximum Speed: 86.4 kph
Jump Jets: None
   Jump Capacity: None
Armor: Kallon Light Ferro-Fibrous
Armament:
   1 Fusigon Longtooth PPC
   2 Tronel XII Medium Pulse Lasers
   1 Diverse Optics Small Pulse Laser
   1 Martell Medium Laser
Manufacturer: Kallon Industries
   Primary Factory: Asuncion
Communications System: Irian TelStar
Targeting and Tracking System: GuideRite with Laser Coordination Link

OVERVIEW

In 2768, the SLDF High Command released a report that set forth new design, weapon and armor guidelines for all future light 'Mechs. Kallon Industries, in the Free Worlds League, was one of the many BattleMech manufacturers to receive the report and one of the first to build a new light prototype 'Mech—the Falcon Hawk—under the new guidelines.

Intended as the SLDF's new light raider and recon 'Mech, the Falcon Hawk never went beyond the prototype stage. The upheaval of the Amaris Civil War cut short the 'Mech's development, and Kallon's light

BattleMech plant was destroyed by House Steiner forces in May of 2794 at the start of the First Succession War. It was not until the decoding of the Gray Death memory core led to the rediscovery of Star League-era technologies that Kallon was able to restart the development and production of the Falcon Hawk.

CAPABILITIES

Built to serve as a raider and a deep scout/recon 'Mech, the Falcon Hawk is one of a new series of light 'Mechs being produced by the Inner Sphere for defense against the Clans. The Falcon Hawk utilizes the highly efficient Omni 175 XL engine, which gives the Falcon Hawk respectable speed, while allowing for the installation of heavier weapons and three additional double heat sinks.

The Falcon Hawk's weapons are well suited for its missions. The primary weapon is the Fusigon Longtooth extended-range PPC, which gives the Falcon Hawk approximately the same firing range as its Clan counterparts. Secondary weapons include two medium pulse lasers, a small pulse laser, and a rear-firing medium laser mounted in the center torso. Light ferro-fibrous armor, spread across the 'Mech's frame for maximum effect, gives the Falcon Hawk excellent protection for its weight class.

DEPLOYMENT

Though the Falcon Hawk never had an opportunity to demonstrate its merits to the SLDF, the High Command of the Free Worlds League has great hopes for the 'Mech, and has stationed two lances of Falcon Hawks near its Lyran Alliance–Periphery border. The Lyran Alliance has stationed three lances of Falcon Hawks on its border with the Clans, while the Federated Commonwealth has stationed its eight Falcon Hawks with the Davion Light Guards. All three militaries anticipate that their new 'Mechs will obtain valuable combat experience in the near future.

VARIANTS

Currently Kallon Industries is offering only one variant of the Falcon Hawk. Designated the 9K1A, this variant replaces the ER PPC and medium pulse lasers with an extended-range large laser, a standard large laser, and a medium laser. This model is exported to the Federated Commonwealth, the Lyran Alliance and the Draconis Combine, as well as being sold to mercenary units throughout the Inner Sphere.

Type: **Falcon Hawk**
Technology Base: Inner Sphere
Tonnage: 35

Equipment			Mass
Internal Structure:			3.5
Engine:		175 XL	3.5
Walking MP:		5	
Running MP:		8	
Jumping MP:		0	
Heat Sinks:		13 [26]	3
Gyro:			2
Cockpit:			3
Armor Factor:		119	7

	Internal Structure	Armor Value
Head	3	9
Center Torso	11	16
Center Torso (rear)		6
R/L Torso	8	12
R/L Torso (rear)		4
R/L Arm	6	12
R/L Leg	8	16

Weapons and Ammo	Location	Critical	Tonnage
ER PPC	RA	3	7
Medium Pulse Laser	LA	1	2
Medium Pulse Laser	LA	1	2
Small Pulse Laser	H	1	1
Medium Laser	CT (R)	1	1

FNHK-9K FALCON HAWK

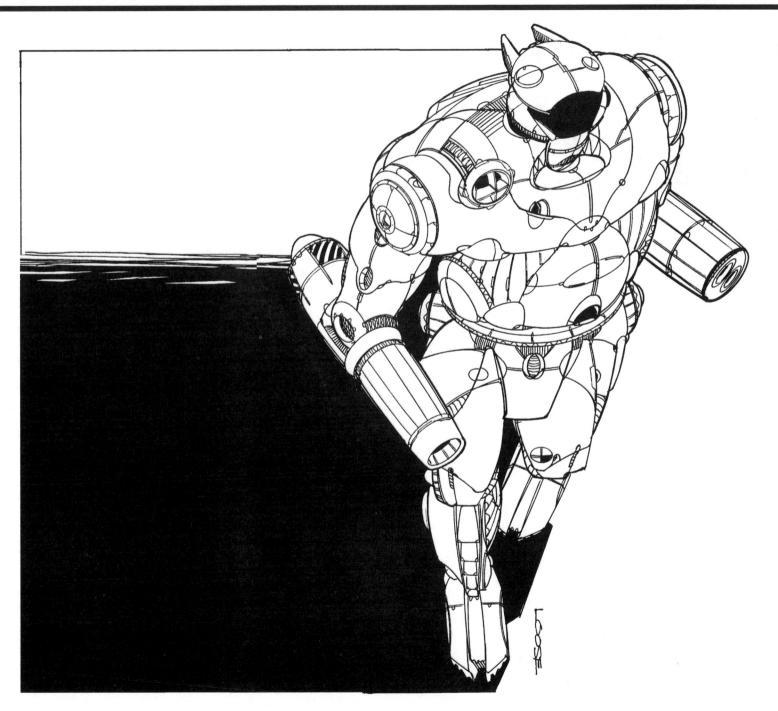

NTK-2Q NIGHT HAWK

INNER SPHERE MECHS

Mass: 35 tons
Chassis: Telestar Model 6LQ
Power Plant: GM 210 XL
Cruising Speed: 65 kph
Maximum Speed: 97 kph
Jump Jets: None
    Jump Capacity: None
Armor: ProtecTech Light
Armament:
    1 Maxell Extended Range Large Laser
    1 Defiance B3L Large Laser
    1 Defiance P5M Medium Pulse Laser
Manufacturer: Mountain Wolf BattleMechs
    Primary Factory: Vendrell
Communications System: TharHes Kr-A P/comm
Targeting and Tracking System: RCA Instatrac Mk X

OVERVIEW

The SLDF High Command developed the *Night Hawk* during the Reunification War to hunt down Periphery 'Mech units raiding behind SLDF lines. The High Command needed a light 'Mech weighing no more than 35 tons, as fast or faster than the *Stinger* or the *Wasp* and well-armed. In particular, the High Command wanted the new 'Mech to have energy-based weapons for maximum field endurance.

In May of 2565 Defiance Industries and Mountain Wolf BattleMechs, a newcomer in the field of BattleMech production, submitted designs to the SLDF High Command for the new 'Mech. The High Command had both companies build prototype 'Mechs, which the High Command then put through six

months of grueling combat trials. In January of 2566, the High Command chose the Mountain Wolf design and placed an order for 700 units.

Mountain Wolf delivered the first of the new 'Mechs, christened the *Night Hawk*, in October 2566. The *Night Hawk* received its baptism by fire in December of the same year and served with the SLDF for more than two centuries. After the fall of the Star League, the 'Mech saw action with various House militaries until August 2945, when Marik BattleMech forces destroyed Mountain Wolf's *Night Hawk* factory. The *Night Hawk* vanished from Inner Sphere armies until Brandon O'Leary, great-grandson of Mountain Wolf's last president and CEO Eli O'Leary, reopened Mountain Wolf BattleMechs on the planet Vendrell in April of 3055. In November of that year, Mountain Wolf delivered the first new *Night Hawk*s to the Federated Commonwealth.

CAPABILITIES

Built for fast-response and raiding duties, the *Night Hawk* accomplishes both these missions well. It is as fast as the *Stinger* and the *Wasp*, but better armed and armored than its lighter cousins. The *Night Hawk* uses tested and reliable components, making it easy to maintain. To help the *Night Hawk* survive extended combat, the design team at Mountain Wolf gave the 'Mech maximum armor protection with ProtecTech Light BattleMech armor, a proven and respected product.

The 'Mech's primary weapons are the Maxell extended-range large laser and the Defiance large laser. These weapons give the *Night Hawk* great striking power, as well as the ability to deliver devastating damage that most light 'Mechs cannot withstand. Completing the *Night Hawk's* weapons is a Defiance medium pulse laser.

DEPLOYMENT

The *Night Hawk* is deployed along the Jade Falcon–Lyran Alliance front, as well as the Alliance's border with the Periphery. However, the *Night Hawk* has yet to see combat. Mountain Wolf recently announced plans to sell a limited number of *Night Hawk*s to select mercenary units in the next few months.

Type: Night Hawk
Technology Base: Inner Sphere
Tonnage: 35

Equipment			Mass
Internal Structure:			3.5
Engine:		210 XL	4.5
Walking MP:		6	
Running MP:		9	
Jumping MP:		0	
Heat Sinks:		12 [24]	2
Gyro:			3
Cockpit:			3
Armor Factor:		112	7

	Internal Structure	Armor Value
Head	3	9
Center Torso	11	17
Center Torso (rear)		4
R/L Torso	8	13
R/L Torso (rear)		3
R/L Arm	6	10
R/L Leg	8	15

Weapons and Ammo	Location	Critical	Tonnage
Large Laser	CT	2	5
ER Large Laser	RA	2	5
Medium Pulse Laser	LA	1	2

NTK-2Q NIGHT HAWK

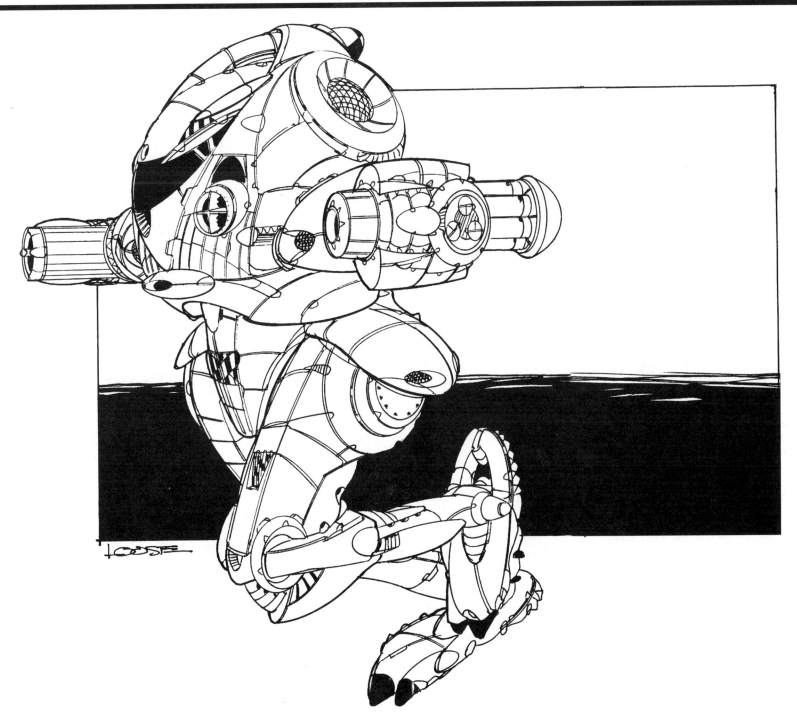

SPR-5F SPECTOR

INNER SPHERE MECHS

Mass: 35 tons
Chassis: Norse XT-Light Type AE (Endo)
Power Plant: Magna 245 XL
Cruising Speed: 75.6 kph
Maximum Speed: 118.8 kph
Jump Jets: HildCo Model 11c
  Jump Capacity: 210 meters
Armor: Starshield Light
Armament:
  1 Nightwind Large Laser
  2 Defiance B3M Medium Laser
  1 Defiance B4S Small Laser
Manufacturer: Norse-Storm Technologies Inc.
  Primary Factory: Loxley
Communications System: AR-12 Sheathed
  Directional Beacon
Targeting and Tracking System: DLK Type Phased
  Array Sensor System with Norse Guardian ECM Suite

OVERVIEW

Modeled on the *Exterminator* BattleMech, the *Spector* was developed to target command 'Mechs and HQ units attached to light 'Mech companies. As its secondary role, the *Spector* was intended to act as a deep scout and raider. In June of 2639, the first *Spector* rolled off the assembly line at Norse Technologies and began six months of intensive testing. By April of 2640, Norse Technologies delivered the first combat-ready *Spector*s to the SLDF.

CAPABILITIES

One of the fastest 'Mechs ever produced, the *Spector* fulfilled all of its missions with great success.

The engineering team at Norse Technologies used the Magna 245 XL engine to give the *Spector* a maximum speed of more than 118 kph and added jump jets that allowed the 'Mech to jump a maximum distance of 210 meters. To help the *Spector* perform its deep recon and raiding missions, the Norse Technologies design team gave it the same advanced stealth systems as the *Exterminator* and added one other. The *Spector*'s design included a Chameleon Light Polarization Shield and special heat baffles in the 'Mech's feet, making it nearly impossible to detect. For added protection, the design team added a Guardian ECM suite that enables the *Spector* to jam the sensor systems of any enemy 'Mech.

The *Spector*'s armament is as impressive as its stealth systems. The Northwind large laser is the 'Mech's primary weapon, backed up by two medium lasers and a small laser. Though some critics of the *Spector* argued that the weapons mix was too light to be effective, simulated combat tests consistently showed that the *Spector*'s laser array was more than adequate to do the job for which the 'Mech had been designed. To compensate for the intense heat of multiple laser weapons, eleven double heat sinks keep the *Spector* cool on the battlefield.

Once the *Spector* joined the arsenal of the SLDF, the covert nature of its missions denied it the usual press coverage afforded many other SLDF 'Mechs. All records of the *Spector* were believed lost with the fall of the Star League until September of 3048, when rumors started spreading throughout the Inner Sphere that the mercenary unit McCarron's Armored Cavalry had found a Star League base and several lostech 'Mechs on its home planet of Menke. At about the same time, the mercenary unit Storm's Metal Thunder began raiding Marik border worlds in 'Mechs that a few experts recognized from Star League-era books. Neither McCarron's Armored Cavalry nor Storm's Metal Thunder have admitted to deploying vintage Star League 'Mechs, including the deadly *Spector*.

DEPLOYMENT

Norse-Storm Technologies has completed four production runs of the *Spector*, three of which have been sent to the Armed Forces of the Federated Commonwealth. The fourth run has been sold to various mercenary units throughout the Inner Sphere.

Type: SPR-5F Spector
Technology Base: Inner Sphere
Tonnage: 35

Equipment		Mass
Internal Structure:	Endo Steel	2
Engine:	245 XL	6
Walking MP:	7	
Running MP:	11	
Jumping MP:	7	
Heat Sinks:	11 [22]	1
Gyro:		3
Cockpit:		3
Armor Factor:	119	7.5

	Internal Structure	Armor Value
Head:	3	9
Center Torso	11	17
Center Torso (rear)		5
R/L Torso	8	12
R/L Torso (rear)		4
R/L Arm	6	12
R/L Leg	8	16

Weapons and Ammo	Location	Critical	Tonnage
Large Laser	RA	2	5
Medium Laser	LA	1	1
Medium Laser	LA	1	1
Small Laser	H	1	.5
Guardian ECM	RT	2	1.5
Jump Jet	CT	1	.5
Jump Jets	RT	2	1
Jump Jets	LT	2	1
Jump Jet	RL	1	.5
Jump Jet	LL	1	.5

SPR-5F SPECTOR

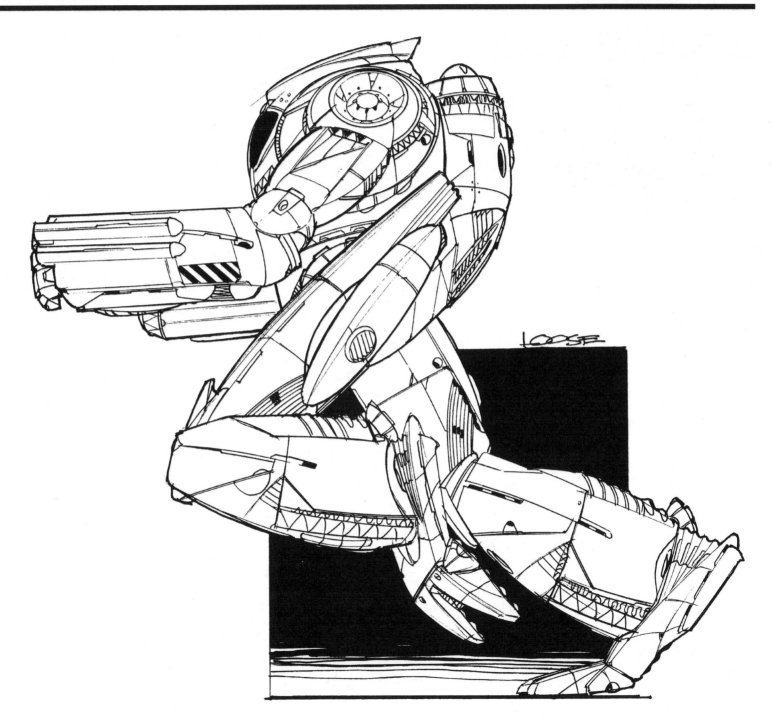

TLN-5W TALON

INNER SPHERE MECHS

Mass: 35 tons
Chassis: Blackstone QTS Light
Power Plant: Edasich Motors 280 XL
Cruising Speed: 86 kph
Maximum Speed: 130 kph
Jump Jets: None
Jump Capacity: None
Armor: Kallon Light Shield A
Armament:
  1 Lord's Light-2 ER PPC
  2 ChisComp 39 Medium Lasers
Manufacturer: Blackstone BattleMechs, Ltd.
  Primary Factory: Inarcs
Communications System: Lockheed/CBM Comset 100
Targeting and Tracking System: Sturmfeur Highlight with BlindFire Radar

OVERVIEW

Fast, well-armed, and heavily armored, the *Talon* was designed to complement the SLDF's *Mongoose* light command 'Mech. Though the *Talon* weighs ten tons more than the *Mongoose*, it is just as fast as the smaller 'Mech. After witnessing the *Talon*'s impressive combat trials in the fall of 2669, the Star League High Command ordered the 'Mech into full-scale production. In May of 2670, the *Talon* reached the first front-line light 'Mech companies.

During the First Succession War many of the Houses formed raiding companies of combined *Mongoose*/*Talon* lances consisting of one *Mongoose* and three *Talon*s. The *Talon*s provided long-range fire support with their PPCs while the *Mongoose* advanced, sweeping the surrounding areas with its Beagle probe in search of camouflaged enemy positions. The *Mongoose* had the firepower to deal with lightly equipped infantry and the speed to get away from more heavily armed opponents—if the *Mongoose* ran into something it could not handle, it would speed away under the covering fire of the *Talon*.

Unfortunately, missions like this were extremely dangerous even when everything went according to plan. Once things fell apart, the lance commander's 'Mech was invariably the first to fall, depriving the unit of its leader at the time it needed him most. As the meat grinder of the Succession Wars progressed, more and more *Talon*/*Mongoose* raiding companies were lost. In 2815 the last *Talon* production facility vanished in a thermonuclear fireball, and by 2830 the last known *Talon* had been cannibalized for parts.

In 3056 Blackstone opened a new *Talon* production line, though the company has yet to begin full-scale production.

CAPABILITIES

With a top speed of more than 130 kph, the *Talon* is one of the fastest of the Star League-era 'Mechs, surpassed only by the *Hussar* and the *Hermes*. To achieve this speed, the design team used a Vox 280 XL engine, one of the most efficient fusion plants produced during the Star League era. To help the *Talon* withstand combat, the design team gave it the maximum armor protection feasible for its weight class. In addition, the *Talon* carries three impressive weapons. The BattleMech's primary weapon is an extended-range PPC, which gives the *Talon* excellent striking power at all ranges. Rounding out the *Talon*'s weapons are two ChisComp 39 medium lasers. Because all its weapons are energy-based, the *Talon* can remain in the field for extended periods of time without needing ammunition reloads. This capability makes the *Talon* a valuable asset of any light 'Mech company.

DEPLOYMENT

Eighteen *Talons* currently help patrol the Jade Falcon–Lyran Alliance border. The 'Mechs have yet to see combat, but that could change soon. Blackstone recently announced plans to produce at least two more runs of the *Talon*.

Type: **Talon**
Technology Base: Inner Sphere
Tonnage: 35

Equipment			Mass
Internal Structure:			3.5
Engine:		280 XL	8
Walking MP:		8	
Running MP:		12	
Jumping MP:		0	
Heat Sinks:		11 [22]	1
Gyro:			3
Cockpit:			3
Armor Factor:		119	7.5

	Internal Structure	Armor Value
Head	3	9
Center Torso	11	17
Center Torso (rear)		5
R/L Torso	8	12
R/L Torso (rear)		4
R/L Arm	6	12
R/L Leg	8	16

Weapons and Ammo	Location	Critical	Tonnage
ER PPC	RA	3	7
Medium Laser	LA	1	1
Medium Laser	LA	1	1

TLN-5W TALON

LN-7V Chameleon

INNER SPHERE MECHS

Mass: 50 tons
Chassis: Enran TXS2A
Power Plant: Vlar 300
Cruising Speed: 67.3 kph
Maximum Speed: 95.9 kph
Jump Jets: McCloud Specials
Jump Capacity: 180 meters
Armor: SimplePlate Manufacturers Type M
Armament:
1 Cyclops Eye Large Laser
2 Intek Medium Lasers
3 Defiance B3S Small Lasers
2 ScatterGun Light Machine Guns
Manufacturer: J.B. BattleMechs Inc.
Primary Factory: Storfors
Communications System: JoLex Systems
Targeting and Tracking System: Optisight-12

OVERVIEW

Manufactured since the early 2500's, the Chameleon is best known as the premier training 'Mech for hundreds of thousands of Inner Sphere MechWarriors. Though the Clan invasion has prompted many manufacturers to step up production of front-line 'Mechs, the Chameleon is still being produced in record numbers. These new Chameleons are being manufactured for the military academies, many of which have expanded their training programs to accommodate the flood of applicants interested in becoming MechWarriors.

In 3052, Defiance Industries announced plans to sell all plans and molds for the Chameleon to free up more production lines for new front-line 'Mechs. In June of 3053, Defiance sold its rights to the Chameleon to Jillianne Suliben, the daughter of a wealthy Tamar businessman killed during the Clan invasion. Using her father's government connections, Ms. Suliben purchased the remains of an old manufacturing plant on the planet Storfors and officially incorporated J.B. BattleMechs. In February of 3056, the first new Chameleons rolled off the production line.

CAPABILITIES

The Chameleon and its heavier counterpart, the Crockett, served as the SLDF's training 'Mechs for more than a hundred years. The Chameleon was the training vehicle for would-be pilots of fast, jump-capable medium and light 'Mechs. Its weapons, though average by battlefield standards, are well suited to the abilities of a relatively green pilot. A large laser and two medium lasers comprise the 'Mech's heavy firepower, while three small lasers and two machine guns help the new recruit fend off infantry attacks. To teach pilots-in-training about the dangers of excess heat, the Chameleon's battle computer can be set to lock out all weapons and jump jets if the heat rises above a certain level. New recruits quickly learn the value of monitoring the heat scale indicator.

DEPLOYMENT

The standard Chameleon 7V serves in MechWarrior academies throughout the Inner Sphere and the Periphery. The combat variants of the Chameleon have yet to see action.

VARIANTS

J.B. BattleMechs has several combat variants of the Chameleon in the works. The 7W variant drops all the small lasers and both machine guns and adds two tons of armor and double heat sinks. An extended-range large laser replaces the standard large laser, and the left arm-mounted medium laser is upgraded to a medium pulse laser. The 7Z variant replaces the standard 300 Vlar engine with an XL engine and adds three and a half extra tons of armor for maximum protection. In addition, a second large laser and an ER large laser replace the small and medium lasers and machine guns. To help dissipate the extra heat generated by the new weapons, the design includes double heat sinks.

Type: Chameleon
Technology Base: Inner Sphere
Tonnage: 50

Equipment		Mass
Internal Structure:		5
Engine:	300	19
Walking MP:	6	
Running MP:	9	
Jumping MP:	6	
Heat Sinks:	10	
Gyro:		3
Cockpit:		3
Armor Factor:	112	7

	Internal Structure	Armor Value
Head	3	9
Center Torso	16	18
Center Torso (rear)		5
R/L Torso	12	12
R/L Torso (rear)		4
R/L Arm	8	12
R/L Leg	12	12

Weapons and Ammo	Location	Critical	Tonnage
Large Laser	RA	2	5
Medium Laser	RA	1	1
Medium Laser	LA	1	1
Small Laser	RT	1	.5
Small Laser	RT	1	.5
Small Laser	LT	1	.5
Ammo (MG) 100	LT	1	.5
Machine Gun	CT	1	.5
Machine Gun	CT	1	.5
Jump Jet	RT	1	.5
Jump Jet	LT	1	.5
Jump Jets	RL	2	1
Jump Jets	LL	2	1

CLN-7V CHAMELEON

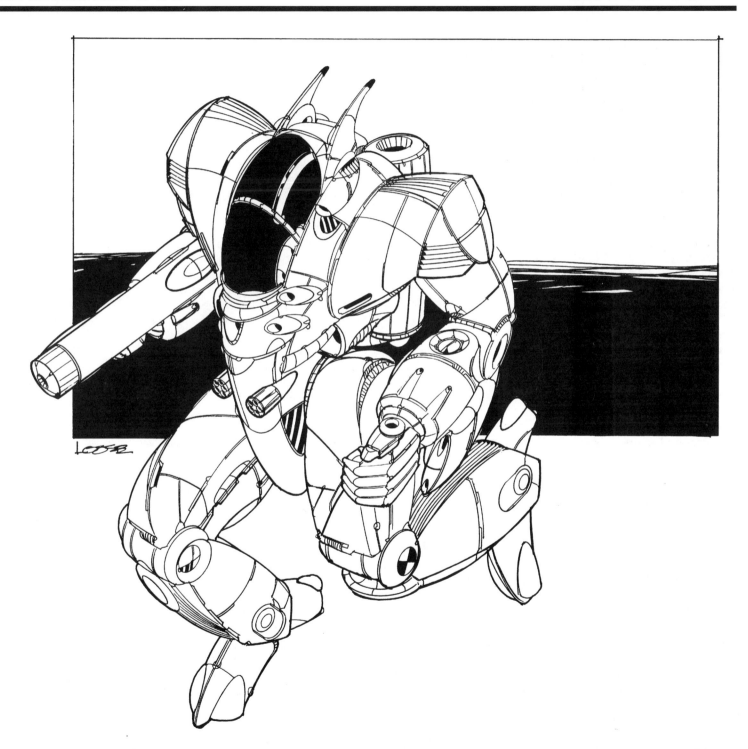

END-6Q ENFIELD

INNER SPHERE MECHS

Mass: 50 tons
Chassis: Blackstone MD2E Endo Steel
Power Plant: Magna 250 XL
Cruising Speed: 54 kph
Maximum Speed: 86 kph
Jump Jets: None
   Jump Capacity: None
Armor: StarGuard III with CASE
Armament:
   1 Defiance Disintegrator LB 10-X Autocannon
   1 Thunderbolt-12 Large Pulse Laser
   2 Defiance B3M Medium Lasers
   1 ChisComp 32 Small Laser
Manufacturer: Blackstone BattleMechs, Ltd.
   Primary Factory: Inarcs
Communications System: CommuTech Multi
   Channel 10
Targeting and Tracking System: Tek Tru-Trak

OVERVIEW

House Davion's armed forces discovered the plans for the *Enfield* in the rubble of an engineering library on the planet Achernar in 2870. Unfortunately, the warring Great Houses had by that time lost the ability to build the advanced LB 10-X autocannon, the endo steel chassis, and the XL engine. Not until almost two centuries later did the Inner Sphere regain the knowledge necessary to build this Star League-era 'Mech design. Just a few years ago the Federated Commonwealth licensed Blackstone BattleMechs to produce the *Enfield,* and by July of 3055 Blackstone BattleMechs had delivered the first of the new 'Mechs

to units stationed along what is now the border between the Lyran Alliance and Clan-held space. The 'Mech is named for the famous rifle of ancient Terra.

CAPABILITIES

Designed to supplement the *Enforcer* as a medium fire-support 'Mech, the *Enfield* performs its intended mission excellently. The *Enfield's* Magna 250 XL engine gives the 'Mech enough speed to keep up with most medium 'Mechs, and the lighter endo steel frame allowed Blackstone's designers to install an impressive weapons array: an LB 10-X autocannon, a Thunderbolt-12 large pulse laser, two medium lasers and a small laser. Though the pulse laser is somewhat handicapped by its short range, in close combat its extra punch makes up for that drawback.

To protect the pilot from ammo explosions, Blackstone installed CASE in the 'Mech's right torso along with the potentially dangerous autocannon shells. To help the *Enfield* lay down devastatingly accurate fire, the *Enfield* uses the well respected Tek Tru-Track targeting and tracking system. Currently, only the Lyran Alliance and the Federated Commonwealth are able to build the Tek Tru-Track.

DEPLOYMENT

Since its introduction, the *Enfield* has garnered popular support among all those MechWarriors who have piloted it, and even further support by word of mouth. All the *Enfields* built so far have been stationed on planets in what is now Lyran Alliance territory, at the Alliance–Clan border.

VARIANTS

Reportedly, Blackstone is hard at work on a jump-capable version of the *Enfield*. The most probable design changes will replace the large pulse laser with a standard large laser and remove the small laser altogether. Blackstone's designers are said to be leaning toward HildCo model 13 jump jets, which would give the jump-capable *Enfield* a maximum jump of 150 meters. This variant, however, has yet to make it off the drawing board.

Type: Enfield
Technology Base: Inner Sphere
Tonnage: 50

Equipment			Mass
Internal Structure:		Endo Steel	2.5
Engine:		250 XL	6.5
Walking MP:		5	
Running MP:		8	
Jumping MP:		0	
Heat Sinks:		11 [22]	1
Gyro:			3
Cockpit:			3
Armor Factor:		169	11
	Internal Structure	Armor Value	
Head	3	9	
Center Torso	16	26	
Center Torso (rear)		6	
R/L Torso	12	20	
R/L Torso (rear)		4	
R/L Arm	8	16	
R/L Leg	12	24	

Weapons and Ammo	Location	Critical	Tonnage
LB 10-X AC	RA	6	11
CASE	RT	1	.5
Large Pulse Laser	LA	2	7
Medium Laser	LA	1	1
Medium Laser	CT	1	1
Small Laser	CT	1	.5
Ammo (LB 10-X) 20	RT	2	2

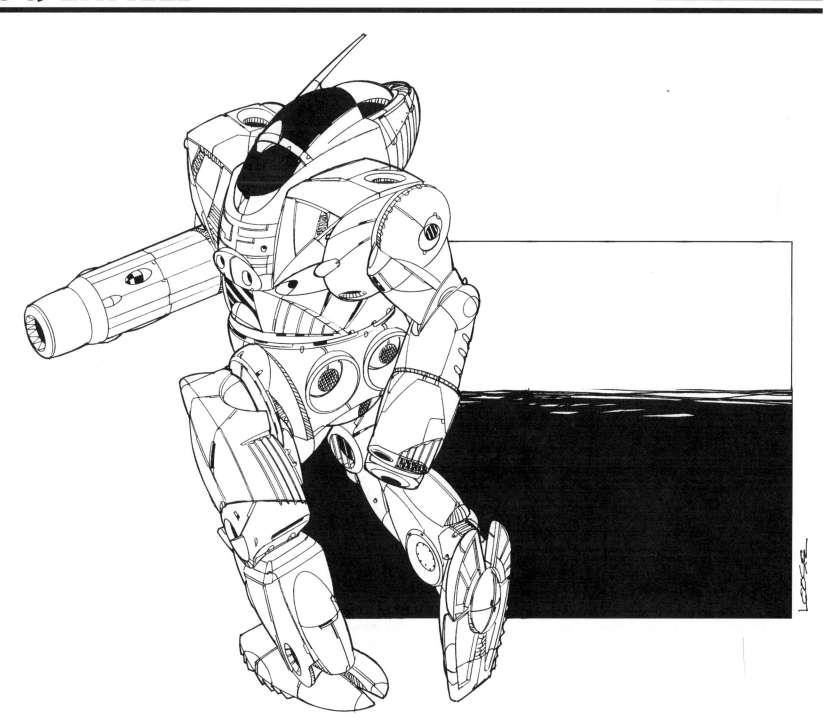

RJN101-A RAIJIN

INNER SPHERE MECHS

Mass: 50 tons
Chassis: Krupp 200
Power Plant: Vlar 300 XL
Cruising Speed: 65 kph
Maximum Speed: 97 kph
Jump Jets: Rawlings 60
    Jump Capacity: 180 meters
Armor: Krupp 200 Ferro-Fibrous
Armament:
    1 Blankenburg Technologies 200 ER PPC
    3 Blankenburg Technologies Medium Pulse
      Lasers
    1 Holly SRM-6
    1 Holly Streak SRM-2 Pack
Manufacturer: Krupp Armaments Works
    Primary Factory: Germany, Terra
Communications System: Exeter Longscan 200
Targeting and Tracking System: Garret T12A

OVERVIEW

ComStar designed the *Raijin* to refit depleted Com Guard units in the aftermath of Tukayyid. Not content to rely on the Com Guard's stockpile of Star League-era BattleMechs on Terra, Precentor Martial Focht wanted a new 'Mech whose technology would be unfamiliar to both the Inner Sphere and the Clans.

One of the first 'Mechs to be built at Krupp Armaments Works in Germany since Amaris occupation forces razed the factory after the coup three centuries earlier, the *Raijin* rolled off the line in six months. Jerome Blake had ordered the Krupps facility rebuilt after Stefan Amaris's defeat—he then mothballed the factory and several other large 'Mech plants, confident that these facilities could be quickly reactivated should ComStar need them. The speed with which the Krupp plant produced the *Raijin* testifies to the wisdom of Blake's planning.

CAPABILITIES

An all-purpose 'Mech, the *Raijin* moves fast, has excellent jump capability and carries impressive firepower centered around an extended-range PPC. Mounted on the external housing of the *Raijin*'s right torso, the PPC gives the *Raijin* high-energy firepower with an extended reach. As a potential edge against the Clans, the designers outfitted the *Raijin* with several Rawlings 60 jump jets. According to Precentor Martial Focht's analysis of Clan OmniMechs, the Clans rarely deploy jump-capable machines.

The *Raijin* originally mounted a one-shot Holly SRM pack opposite the PPC. Concealed on the torso, this SRM rack was heavily insulated to prevent detection by IR scanning. MechWarriors used this hidden weapon at close ranges to devastating effect against an unprepared enemy. Recent models of the *Raijin* come equipped with a standard SRM-6 rack for more staying power.

The bulk of the *Raijin*'s medium- to short-range firepower rests in three medium pulse lasers mounted in the 'Mech's left arm. Though these weapons and the ER PPC generate excessive heat, their reliability gives this 'Mech a deadly short-range punch.

The Holly SRM Streak pack mounted in the *Raijin*'s right torso has proven to be the 'Mech's only design problem; the angle of the launcher tends to jam the loading mechanism. Techs have made field modifications to *Raijin*s already deployed, however, and the Krupp plant has corrected the problem on new machines.

Thin armor is the *Raijin*'s only weak point; a few well-placed shots can easily cripple it. However, the *Raijin* is less vulnerable than opponents might expect. Though its designers clearly intended the mobile *Raijin* to keep opposition at a distance, the 'Mech has enough firepower to destroy any enemy that gets too close.

DEPLOYMENT

Most of the *Raijin*s built thus far have been shipped to ComStar's Eighth Army and deployed in the 85th and 167th Divisions.

Type: Raijin
Technology Base: Inner Sphere
Tonnage: 50

Equipment			Mass
Internal Structure:			5
Engine:		300 XL	9.5
Walking MP:		6	
Running MP:		9	
Jumping MP:		6	
Heat Sinks:		10 [20]	0
Gyro:			3
Cockpit:			3
Armor Factor:		125	7

	Internal Structure	Armor Value
Head	3	9
Center Torso	16	18
Center Torso (rear)		8
R/L Torso	12	13
R/L Torso (rear)		6
R/L Arm	8	13
R/L Leg	12	13

Weapons and Ammo	Location	Critical	Tonnage
ER PPC	RT	3	7
Medium Pulse Laser	LA	1	2
Medium Pulse Laser	LA	1	2
Medium Pulse Laser	LA	1	2
SRM 6	LT	2	3
Ammo (SRM) 15	LT	1	1
Streak SRM 2	RT	1	1.5
Ammo (Streak SRM) 50	RT	1	1
Jump Jets	CT	2	1
Jump Jets	RL	2	1
Jump Jets	LL	2	1

RJN101-A RAIJIN

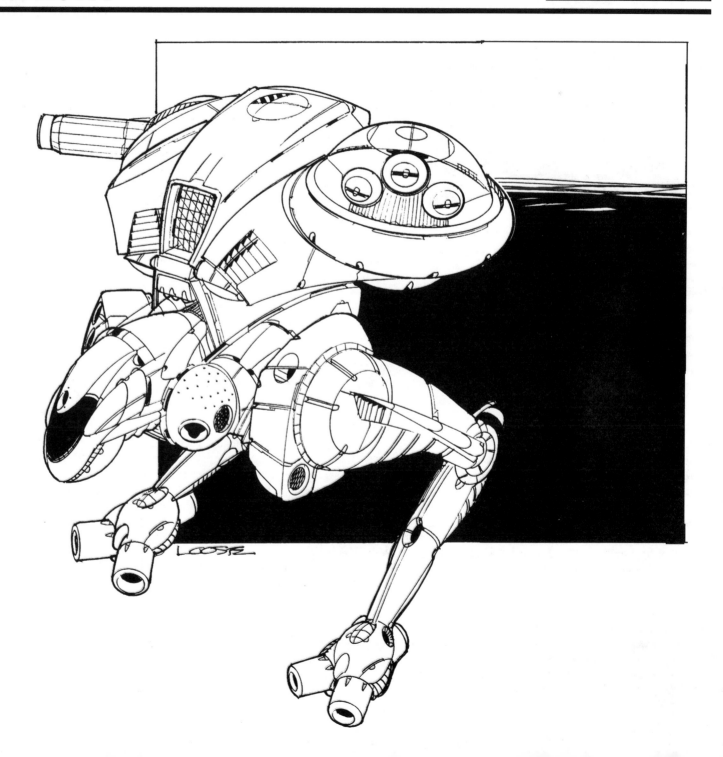

INNER SPHERE MECHS

Mass: 50 tons
Chassis: Thor-4 Endo Steel
Power Plant: Magna 250
Cruising Speed: 54 kph
Maximum Speed: 86 kph
Jump Jets: Odin's Own Model 34z
  Jump Capacity: 150 meters
Armor: Norse-34 Ferro-Fibrous with CASE
Armament:
  2 BlazeFire Systems Large Lasers
  2 Defiance B3M Medium Lasers
  1 TharHes 4 pack Short-Range Missile
  1 Defiance B4M Small Laser
Manufacturer: Blue Shot Weapons
  Primary Factory: Loxley
Communications System: Tek BattleCom
Targeting and Tracking System: FireScan with
  IndirecTrack

OVERVIEW

In response to orders from General Aleksandr Kerensky for the production of a new medium 'Mech, Blue Shot Weaponry was awarded a contract in 2765 to build the *Starslayer* for the SLDF. However, the numerous delays that plagued Blue Shot throughout the 'Mech's production run prevented it from being built in great numbers. By the time the bugs had been worked out, the SLDF was embroiled in the Amaris Civil War, and more *Starslayers* ended up in storage than on the front lines. These hidden *Starslayers* later became a boon to House and mercenary units that

stumbled on them. Recent versions of the *Starslayer* replace the standard chassis with endo steel, making the 'Mech both lighter and sturdier.

CAPABILITIES

Built to be rugged and dependable, the *Starslayer* was intended for garrison, mop-up and recon duties. The designers at Blue Shot used well-established technologies in an effort to make the *Starslayer* easy to maintain and to allow the 'Mech to remain in the field for long periods. A Magna 250 engine makes the *Starslayer* as fast as most of the SLDF's medium 'Mechs, and jump jets give the *Starslayer* greater mobility. Ferro-fibrous armor provides the *Starslayer* with maximum protection at a reduced weight which, when coupled with an endo steel frame, allows the 'Mech to carry heavy weapons. Two large lasers give the *Starslayer* its heavy firepower, backed up by two medium lasers and a small laser. To discourage enemy 'Mechs from attacking the rear of the *Starslayer*, the small laser fires in the 'Mech's rear arc. An SRM-4 missile pack enables the *Starslayer* to engage in close fighting, and CASE protects the pilot from ammo explosions.

DEPLOYMENT

Blue Shot has already completed three production runs of the new *Starslayer* 3C, and most of these 'Mechs have been deployed with various militia units in the Lyran Alliance. Some have also been sold to the Magistracy of Canopus and several mercenary units stationed in Lyran space.

VARIANTS

Blue Shot Weapons offers a variant of the *Starslayer* known as the 3D model. The 3D drops the torso-mounted large laser, the SRM-4 with its ammo, and CASE in favor of an extended-range PPC. The 3D also adds an extra double heat sink and replaces the rear-firing small laser with a medium laser.

Type: STY-3C Starslayer
Technology Base: Inner Sphere
Tonnage: 50

Equipment		Mass
Internal Structure:	Endo Steel	2.5
Engine:	250	12.5
Walking MP:	5	
Running MP:	8	
Jumping MP:	5	
Heat Sinks:	11 [22]	1
Gyro:		3
Cockpit:		3
Armor Factor:	169	9.5

	Internal Structure	Armor Value
Head	3	9
Center Torso	16	26
Center Torso (rear)		6
R/L Torso	12	19
R/L Torso (rear)		5
R/L Arm	8	16
R/L Leg	12	24

Weapons and Ammo	Location	Critical	Tonnage
Large Laser	RA	2	5
Large Laser	RT	2	5
SRM 4	LT	1	2
Medium Laser	LT	1	1
Medium Laser	LT	1	1
Ammo (SRM) 25	LT	1	1
CASE	LT	1	.5
Small Laser	H (R)	1	.5
Jump Jet	CT	1	.5
2 Jump Jets	RT	2	1
2 Jump Jets	LT	2	1

STY-3C STARSLAYER

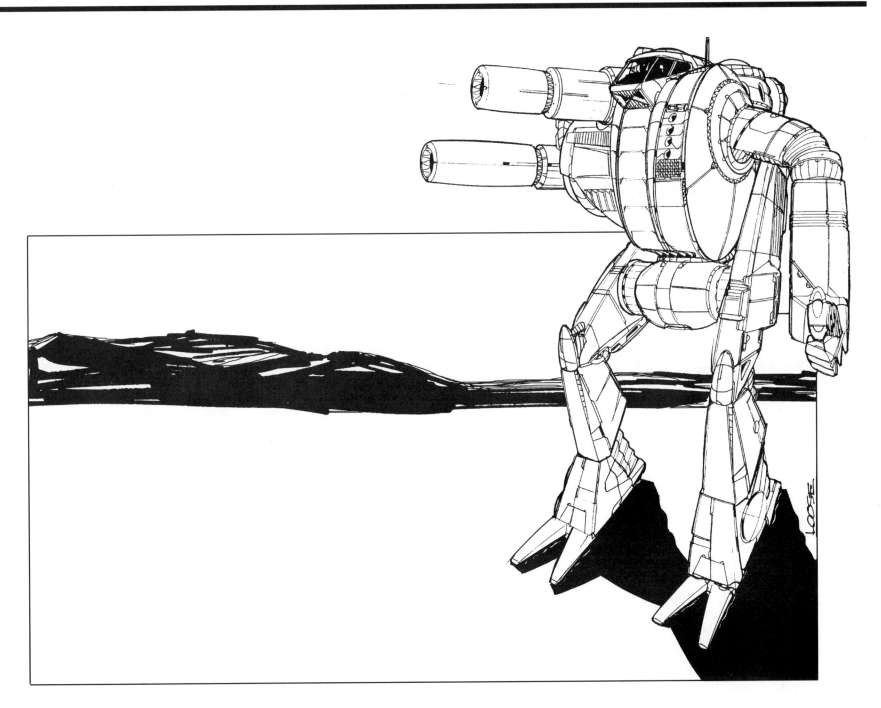

BSW-X1 BUSHWACKER

INNER SPHERE MECHS

Mass: 55 tons
Chassis: Earthwerk GRF
Power Plant: Hermes 275 XL
Cruising Speed: 54 kph
Maximum Speed: 86 kph
Jump Jets: None
  Jump Capacity: None
Armor: Kallon Unity Weave Ferro-Fibrous with CASE
Armament:
  2 Federated 5-Shot LRM Missile Systems
  1 BlazeFire Sweetshot Extended-Range Large
  Laser
  1 Mydron Model B Autocannon
  2 Johnston MiniGuns
Manufacturer: TharHes Industries
  Primary Factory: Tharkad
Communications System: TharHes Euterpe HM-14
Tracking and Tracking System: TharHes Ares-8a

OVERVIEW

The prototype *Bushwacker* was under construction at the start of the Clan invasion. An ambitious, unorthodox design, the *Bushwacker* featured a long, narrow upper torso designed to present a minimal target profile to enemy units. This unconventional configuration resulted in an extremely complex interior layout, with the 'Mech's fusion engine, sensors and communications suites crowded together. Unfortunately, the engine shielding proved insufficient to insulate the sensors and communications suites from the engine's radiation, and the *Bushwacker* experienced frequent

targeting and sensor system failures. Attempts to increase the engine shielding made the 'Mech too heavy and cumbersome for battle use. Though the *Bushwacker* program seemed destined for cancellation, many observers praised the innovative design as a daring work of BattleMech engineering.

It was the Clan invasion that saved the *Bushwacker* from the scrap pile. A raid on a Jade Falcon base on Twycross yielded a vast haul of technical specifications and schematics for various Clan BattleMechs. The *Bushwacker* design team were given the specs for the Clan *Vulture*. Using these documents as a guide, the *Bushwacker* team was able to reconfigure the 'Mech's interior spaces and eliminate the electronic interference.

CAPABILITIES

The *Bushwacker* is built with long-range combat in mind. Its two LRM launchers, along with its improved large laser and Mydron autocannon, give this 'Mech the ability to really reach out and touch someone. While against Inner Sphere opponents this weapons mix is quite lethal, Clan opponents are a different matter: the Clan weapon systems out-range their Inner Sphere counterparts by up to 50 percent. Engaging in a long-range slugging duel with Clan troops is suicide for any Inner Sphere 'Mech, even as one as well armed as the *Bushwacker*.

To compensate for this disadvantage, *Bushwacker* units attempt to use the terrain and natural obstacles to engage Clan units at relatively close range. In a lance of *Bushwacker*s, one member will serve the remaining three units as a spotter for indirect LRM fire.

DEPLOYMENT

The *Bushwacker* was put into full scale production in 3053, though many Federated Commonwealth units received pre-production models during the Clan invasion. The *Bushwacker* commonly replaced units lost from medium 'Mech lances on the Clan border. As a result, most of the *Bushwacker*s in service belong to units of the Lyran Alliance, with only a handful serving in the remainder of the Federated Commonwealth.

Type: **Bushwacker**
Technology Base: Inner Sphere
Tonnage: 55

Equipment		Mass
Internal Structure:		5.5
Engine:	275 XL	8
Walking MP:	5	
Running MP:	8	
Jumping MP:	0	
Heat Sinks:	11 [22]	1
Gyro:		3
Cockpit:		3
Armor Factor:	161	9

	Internal Structure	Armor Value
Head	3	9
Center Torso	18	26
Center Torso (rear)		8
R/L Torso	13	22
R/L Torso (rear)		4
R/L Arm	9	11
R/L Leg	13	22

Weapons and Ammo	Location	Critical	Tonnage
AC/10	RA	7	12
Ammo (AC) 10	RT	1	1
LRM 5	LA	1	2
ER Large Laser	CT	2	5
Machine Gun	RT	1	.5
Machine Gun	LT	1	.5
Ammo (MG) 100	RT	1	.5
CASE	RT	1	.5
LRM 5	LT	1	2
Ammo (LRM) 24	LT	1	1
CASE	LT	1	.5

KW1-LH2 LINEHOLDER

INNER SPHERE MECHS

Mass: 55 tons
Chassis: Kressly GRF1A-MDX
Power Plant: CoreTek 275 Fusion
Cruising Speed: 54 kph
Maximum Speed: 83 kph
Jump Jets: None
    Jump Capacity: None
Armor: Kressly Stoneskin 30M
Armament:
    2 LongFire V LRM Racks
    4 Intek Medium Lasers
    1 BlazeFire Systems Large Laser
Manufacturer: Kressly Warworks
    Primary Factory: Epsilon Eridani
Communications System: Angst Clear Channel 3
Targeting and Tracking System: RCA Instatrac Mk XII

OVERVIEW

The *Lineholder* is Kressly Warworks' first BattleMech design. Though it breaks no new technological ground, the *Lineholder* meets all of its original specifications and in less than a year has broken sales records for 'Mechs in the 55-ton weight class. Its low price is quickly making the *Lineholder* the standard 'Mech of choice for smaller powers and minor nobles throughout the Inner Sphere.

CAPABILITIES

The *Lineholder* was designed as a mobile weapons platform with the ability to withstand considerable punishment. For a medium 'Mech, the *Lineholder* fulfills these goals extremely well. Armed with a pair of LongFire missile racks above its right shoulder and a BlazeFire large laser in its left arm, the *Lineholder* can shell out consistent and deadly long-range fire. For close combat the 'Mech carries four torso-mounted Intek medium lasers, reliable and effective weapons that provide continuous fire support. The *Lineholder* has more than enough heat sinks to deal with potential overheating caused by any of its weapons—problems arise only when the lasers and missile racks are fired simultaneously for extended periods.

DEPLOYMENT

Kressly Warworks originally planned to sell the *Lineholder* to minor noble families throughout the Inner Sphere, but the breakdown of authority in the former Sarna March caused Kressly to change its marketing strategy. The firm now sells the *Lineholder* to the myriad factions in the so-called Chaos March, and new orders for the inexpensive 'Mech are coming in daily.

Though most *Lineholder*s are deployed on various worlds in the Chaos March, a few have appeared in the armies of minor nobles on interior and border worlds in the Inner Sphere.

VARIANTS

Prompted by the brisk sales of the *Lineholder*, Kressly plans to introduce an upscale variant of the design for wealthier customers. The KW1-LH3 replaces the original *Lineholder*'s medium lasers with pulse weapons and upgrades the large laser with an extended-range model. Kressly hopes that the LH3 will become competitive with other contemporary front-line 'Mechs, but only time will tell if the design can achieve such popularity.

Type: Lineholder
Technology Base: Inner Sphere
Tonnage: 55

Equipment			Mass
Internal Structure:			5.5
Engine:	275		15.5
Walking MP:	5		
Running MP:	8		
Jumping MP:	0		
Heat Sinks:	14		4
Gyro:			3
Cockpit:			3
Armor Factor:	160		10

	Internal Structure	Armor Value
Head	3	9
Center Torso	18	25
Center Torso (rear)		6
R/L Torso	13	18
R/L Torso (rear)		5
R/L Arm	9	18
R/L Leg	13	19

Weapons and Ammo	Location	Critical	Tonnage
LRM 5	RA	1	2
LRM 5	RA	1	2
Medium Laser	RT	1	1
Medium Laser	RT	1	1
Medium Laser	LT	1	1
Medium Laser	LT	1	1
Large Laser	LA	2	5
Ammo (LRM) 24	RT	1	1

KW1-LH2 LINEHOLDER

LNX-9Q LYNX

Mass: 55 tons
Chassis: RAMTech QWT
Power Plant: Nissan 275 XL
Cruising Speed: 54 kph
Maximum Speed: 86 kph
Jump Jets: Luxor Load Lifters
Jump Capacity: 150 meters
Armor: Kallon Unity Weave
Armament:
    1 Defiance 1001 ER PPC
    4 Defiance B3M Medium Laser
    1 Defiance B3L Large Laser
Manufacturer: Blue Shot Weapons, Telfar
    BattleMechs (under license)
    Primary Factory: Solaris VII, Midway
Communications System: Lynx-shur
Targeting and Tracking System: Cyclops Multi-
    Tasker 10

OVERVIEW

The Blue Shot Weapons factory on Solaris VII pro-duced the *Lynx* BattleMech during the height of the Star League era, and met its full production capacity right up until the facility was destroyed by Marik raiders in 2928. The Lyran Commonwealth lost its Solaris 'Mech repair facility in the same raid. House Steiner spent five years rebuilding the repair facilities, but Blue Shot could not find the financing needed to rebuild their plant from the ground up. The Inner Sphere would wait for more than a century before the next *Lynx* rolled off the assembly line from Blue Shot's rebuilt Solaris factory in 3056.

CAPABILITIES

Originally designed as a medium fire-support 'Mech for the SLDF, the *Lynx*'s weapons and engine offer a desirable combination of good speed and hitting power. The Nissan 275 XL engine allows the *Lynx* to easily keep pace with other medium 'Mechs used by the House militaries. The impressive array of energy weapons the *Lynx* carries, including the Defiance ER PPC, gives the 'Mech an unlimited supply of devastat-ing firepower. The weapons configuration also pro-duces a tremendous amount of heat, which the *Lynx* compensates for with double heat sinks. Twelve tons of Kallon Unity Weave BattleMech armor give the *Lynx* maximum protection for its weight class and so allows the 'Mech to stay in combat longer. Blue Shot installed the Luxor Load Lifters, which give the 'Mech a jump length of 150 meters, to give the *Lynx* better mobility and allow the pilot to perform the well-known death-from-above maneuver.

DEPLOYMENT

Only three units currently field the *Lynx:* the First Lyran Guards, the Davion Heavy Guards, and Storm's Metal Thunder, a mercenary unit working for the Lyran Alliance in the so-called Chaos March. Blue Shot Weapons recently signed a licensing agreement with Telfar BattleMechs that allows that firm to produce the *Lynx* at their new factory on the planet Midway in the Draconis Combine and has announced that the 'Mech will soon be available to all interested parties.

VARIANTS

Blue Shot Weapons and Telfar BattleMechs cur-rently offer two variants of the *Lynx*. Blue Shot's variant, designated 9R, replaces the large laser with a RAMTech 1200X ER large laser in the left arm. The variant from Telfar, known as the 9C, replaces the large laser with two Guided Technologies second-generation Streak SRM-2 racks, placing one in the head and the other in the right torso. The 9C also carries two tons of ammo for these SRMs. Both variants of the *Lynx* are expected to reach front-line units within six months.

Type: **Lynx**
Technology Base: Inner Sphere
Tonnage: 55

Equipment		Mass
Internal Structure:		5.5
Engine:	Nissan 275 XL	8
Walking MP:	5	
Running MP:	8	
Jumping MP:	5	
Heat Sinks:	15 [30]	5
Gyro:		3
Cockpit:		3
Armor Factor:	185	12

	Internal Structure	Armor Value
Head	3	9
Center Torso	18	28
Center Torso (rear)		8
R/L Torso	13	20
R/L Torso (rear)		6
R/L Arm	9	18
R/L Leg	13	26

Weapons and Ammo	Location	Critical	Tonnage
ER PPC	RA	3	7
Medium Laser	LA	1	1
Medium Laser	LA	1	1
Medium Laser	LT	1	1
Medium Laser	CT	1	1
Large Laser	RT	2	5
Jump Jet	CT	1	.5
2 Jump Jets	RL	2	1
2 Jump Jets	LL	2	1

LNX-9Q LYNX

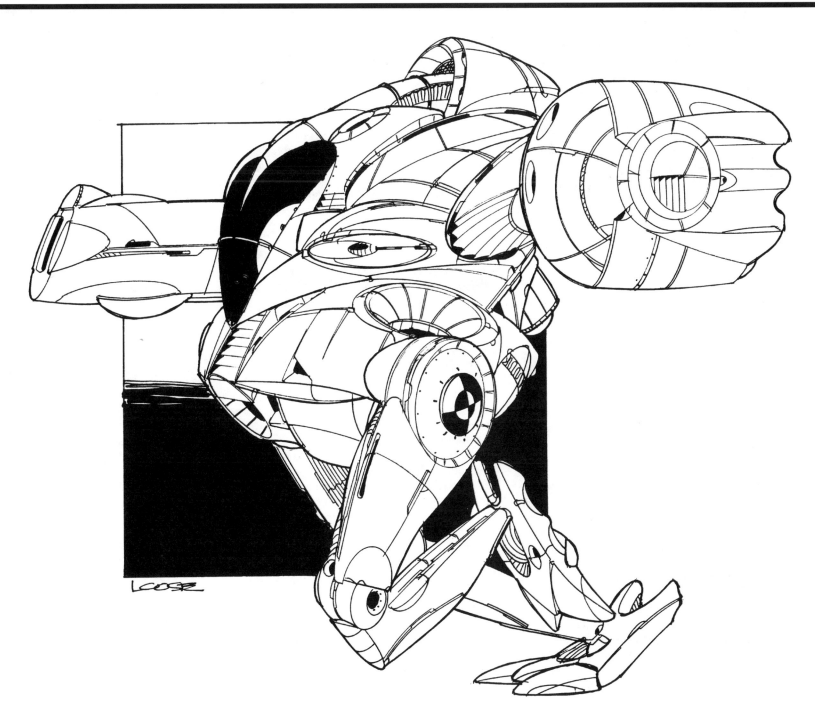

MLN-1A MERLIN

INNER SPHERE MECHS

Mass: 60 tons
Chassis: Heavy Star QAT-4
Power Plant: Pitban 240
Cruising Speed: 43 kph
Maximum Speed: 65 kph
Jump Jets: Pitban LFT 50
    Jump Capacity: 120 meters
Armor: Longanecker PlastiSteel
Armament:
    1 Magna Hellstar PPC
    2 Martell Model 5 Medium Laser
    1 Holly LRM-5 Rack
    1 Zippo Flamer
    1 SperryBrowning Machine Gun
Manufacturer: Mountain Wolf BattleMechs
    Primary Factory: Alpheratz
Communications System: Magestrix Alpha
Targeting and Tracking System: Magestrix Gamma

OVERVIEW

MechWarriors hailed the *Merlin* as a breakthrough when it was introduced in 3010—not because it offered advanced features, but because the *Merlin* was one of the first new 'Mech designs to be produced in the Inner Sphere in several centuries. Rugged and reliable, the *Merlin* is suitable for a variety of assignments. Its versatility makes it a popular choice in the Periphery and with mercenary units throughout the Inner Sphere.

CAPABILITIES

In designing the *Merlin,* its engineers sought to create a BattleMech that would stand up to hard use, serve multiple roles, and that could be easily repaired using commonly available parts. They succeeded on all counts. The Pitban 240 gives the *Merlin* speed comparable to most heavy 'Mechs used in the Inner Sphere and the ten-plus tons of armor offers protection adequate for most situations. A balanced mix of long and short-range weapons makes the *Merlin* versatile enough to handle 'Mechs and infantry with equal ease, and its jump jets provide satisfactory mobility.

DEPLOYMENT

The largest concentration of *Merlin*s in active service belongs to the mercenary unit known as the Wolverton Highlanders, who have spent the last ten years hunting pirates along the border where Steiner and Marik space and the Periphery meet. Though the *Merlin* does appear in House units, those militaries usually can afford more specialized units specifically tailored to the type of tactics those troops favor. Because mercenary troops must be prepared to accept any number of assignment types, they tend to purchase 'Mechs that can handle many tactical styles.

VARIANTS

In 3052, Alliance Defenders Limited of the Outworlds Alliance signed a licensing agreement with Mountain Wolf to build the *Merlin* for the Outworlds military. In 3053, Alliance Defenders introduced the *Merlin* 1B. This model removes the machine gun and MG ammo, adds another heat sink, and moves the LRM ammo from the center torso to the left torso.

Type: **Merlin**
Technology Base: Inner Sphere
Tonnage: 60

Equipment			Mass
Internal Structure:			6
Engine:		240	11.5
Walking MP:		4	
Running MP:		6	
Jumping MP:		4	
Heat Sinks:		18	8
Gyro:			3
Cockpit:			3
Armor Factor:		168	10.5
	Internal Structure	Armor Value	
Head	3	9	
Center Torso	20	26	
Center Torso (rear)		11	
R/L Torso	14	18	
R/L Torso (rear)		8	
R/L Arm	10	16	
R/L Leg	14	19	

Weapons and Ammo	Location	Critical	Tonnage
PPC	RT	3	7
Medium Laser	RA	1	1
Medium Laser	LA	1	1
LRM 5	RT	1	2
Machine Gun	LT	1	.5
Flamer	LT	1	1
Ammo (LRM) 24	CT	1	1
Ammo (MG) 100	CT	1	.5
2 Jump Jets	RL	2	2
2 Jump Jets	LL	2	2

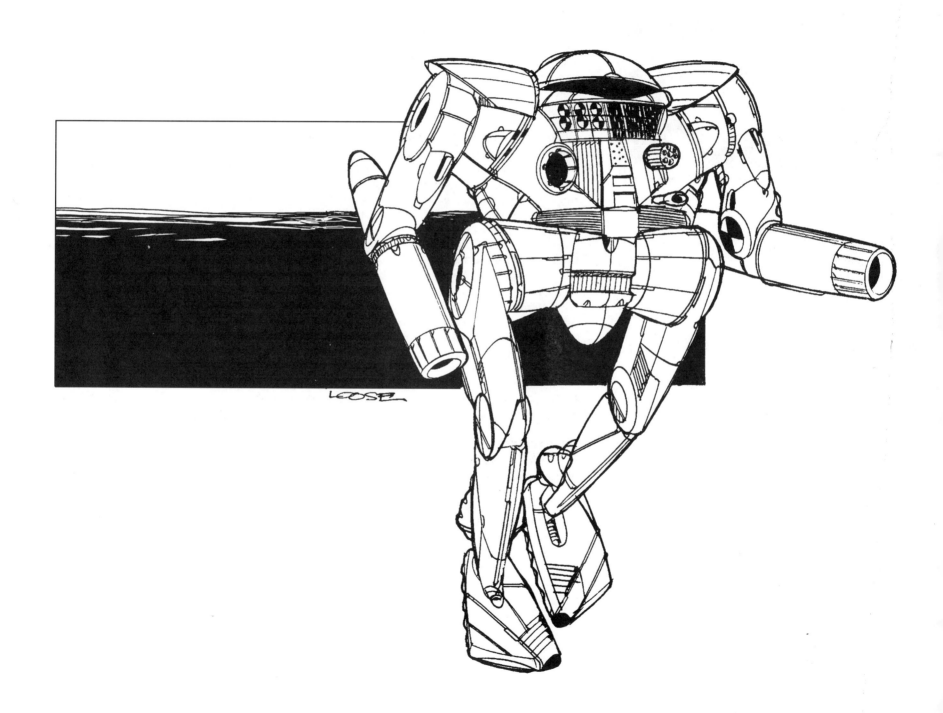

CTS-6Y CESTUS

INNER SPHERE MECHS

Mass: 65 tons
Chassis: GM Heavy CVA
Power Plant: GM 260 XL
Cruising Speed: 43 kph
Maximum Speed: 65 kph
Jump Jets: None
   Jump Capacity: None
Armor: Durallex Special Heavy
Armament:
   2 Defiance B3L Large Lasers
   2 ChisComp 39 Medium Lasers
   1 Poland Main Model A Gauss Rifle
Manufacturer: General Motors, Blue Shot Weapons
   (under license)
   Primary Factory: Kathil, Solaris VII
Communications System: TharHes Thalia HM-22
Targeting and Tracking System: Salamander
   Systems CommPhase Unit

OVERVIEW

Built for the SLDF, the *Cestus* was designed as a medium fire-support 'Mech. It went into production just before the start of the Amaris Civil War and continued to be produced until Kurita forces destroyed GM's *Cestus* production facilities on Kathil at the start of the Second Succession War.

The original design for the *Cestus* called for two PPCs and medium pulse lasers, but problems with overheating prompted the design team to use a gauss rifle as the centerpiece of the *Cestus*'s weapons array. Accordingly, the designers dropped both PPCs and installed standard medium lasers instead of pulse versions.

CAPABILITIES

The excellent GM 260 XL engine gives the *Cestus* a top speed of 65 kph, as fast as most Star League-era heavy 'Mechs. To help dissipate the of heat generated by the 'Mech's weapons, the designers installed twelve double heat sinks. The *Cestus*'s heavy armor and ample ammunition give it impressive longevity on the battlefield.

This 'Mech's weapons are hard-hitting and deadly. A massive Poland Main Model A Gauss Rifle gives the *Cestus* splendid range and striking power. Backing up the rifle are a medium lasers and a large laser in each arm. Although it has twin weapons in the arms like the heavier *Marauder*, the Cestus retains its hand actuators for use in close combat.

DEPLOYMENT

The *Cestus* 'Mechs built by Blue Shot Weapons have recently begun to reach front-line units along the Lyran Alliance–Jade Falcon border. Those produced by General Motors are deployed along the Federated Commonwealth's border with the Capellan Confederation and with the Periphery. Last month, Blue Shot Weapons announced its intention to sell the *Cestus* to mercenary units stationed in the Lyran Alliance. It is not known at this time if GM plans to sell the *Cestus* to mercenary units.

VARIANTS

Currently, General Motors and Blue Shot Weapons both plan to introduce a variant of the *Cestus* based on the 'Mech's original weapons configuration. This model, known as the 6Z, will drop the gauss rifle and ammunition in favor of two PPCs, to be placed in the 'Mech's arms. To deal with the increased heat generated by these weapons, the 6Z variant also adds four more double heat sinks.

Type: Cestus
Technology Base: Inner Sphere
Tonnage: 65

Equipment			Mass
Internal Structure:			6.5
Engine:		260 XL	7
Walking MP:		4	
Running MP:		6	
Jumping MP:		0	
Heat Sinks:		12 [24]	2
Gyro:			3
Cockpit:			3
Armor Factor:		211	13.5
	Internal Structure	Armor Value	
Head	3	9	
Center Torso	21	32	
Center Torso (rear)		10	
R/L Torso	15	22	
R/L Torso (rear)		8	
R/L Arm	10	20	
R/L Leg	15	30	

Weapons and Ammo	Location	Critical	Tonnage
Gauss Rifle	RT	7	15
Ammo (Gauss) 16	RT	2	2
Ammo (Gauss) 8	CT	1	1
Medium Laser	RA	1	1
Medium Laser	LA	1	1
Large Laser	RA	2	5
Large Laser	LA	2	5

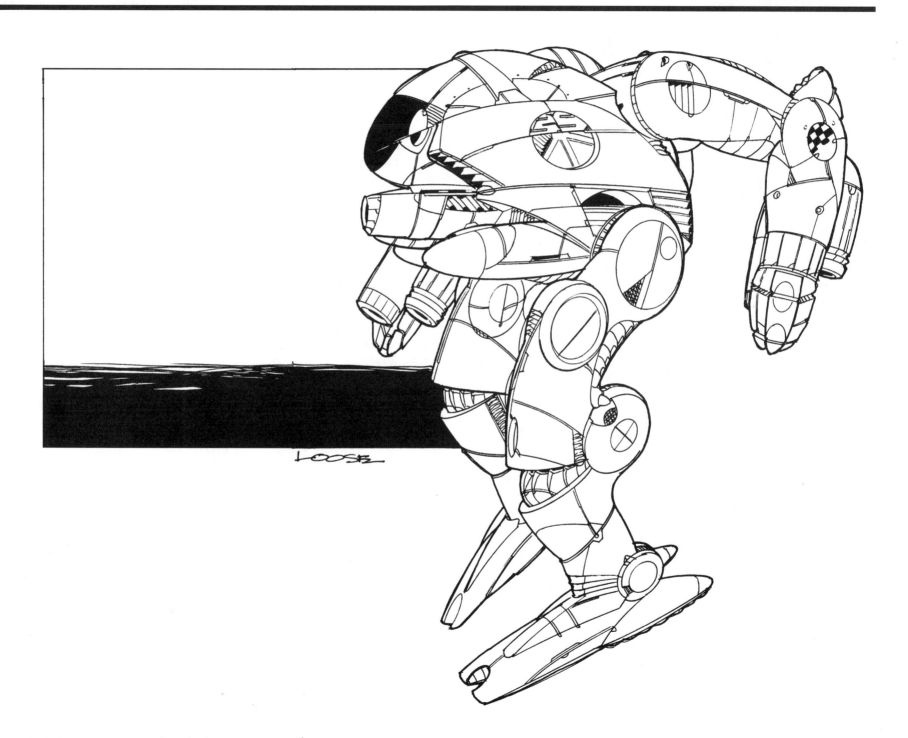

INNER SPHERE MECHS

Mass: 70 tons
Chassis: Corbine 1
Power Plant: Ford 350 XL
Cruising Speed: 54 kph
Maximum Speed: 86 kph
Jump Jets: None
Jump Capacity: None
Armor: Pribak 9000 with CASE
Armament:
    1 Grizzard Model 200 Gauss Rifle
    1 Ingrid Systems LRM-20 Missile Rack
    1 McArthur Anti-Missile System
Manufacturer: Yankee Weapons Systems
    Primary Factory: Terra, New Earth
Communications System: Faulk 203 Comset
Targeting and Tracking System: KBC Starsight
    Model QTA1

OVERVIEW

Yankee Weapons introduced the *Excalibur* in a limited production run and delivered the first models to Star League Defense Force units in 2520. Designed to deliver long-range firepower, the *Excalibur* features a large Grizzard Gauss rifle that extends through a dummy hand on the 'Mech's right arm. The long rifle barrel makes the 'Mech resemble a sword-wielding medieval knight, hence the name *Excalibur*.

CAPABILITIES

The *Excalibur* is one of the fastest 'Mechs in its weight class, thanks to its powerful Ford 350 XL engine. A Grizzard Gauss rifle, known for its accuracy and endurance, an LRM-20 rack, and an Artemis IV fire-control system constitute the 'Mech's long-range armament.

Like many other 'Mechs intended for long-range combat, the *Excalibur* carries a relatively small amount of armor—only seven and a half tons. This relatively light protection keeps *Excalibur*s out of close combat and forces them to withdraw from combat after taking a few hits. Some observers maintain the *Excalibur*'s light armor is a serious design flaw, but Yankee Weapons counters such criticism by pointing out that the *Excalibur* was never intended for close combat. They further contend that the 'Mech's McArthur anti-missile system provides ample protection against incoming missiles.

The *Excalibur* distinguished itself in Operation Smother during the Reunification War, though many of these units were then destroyed in the close-fighting conditions common in the Amaris Civil War. Records show that units equipped with the *Excalibur*, when used in conjunction with other 'Mechs, had a higher kill ratio than other SLDF heavy 'Mech units.

DEPLOYMENT

Currently, only the Com Guard and the mercenary unit known as Rhonda's Irregulars field operational *Excalibur*s. In a welcome move, however, Yankee Weapons Systems has reopened their plant on New Earth and should have the first new *Excalibur*s rolling off the assembly line by March of 3058.

VARIANTS

Currently the Yankee Weapons design team is working on a new variant of the *Excalibur*, the model C1. This variant replaces the original design's twelve standard heat sinks with ten double sinks and adds two tons of armor, primarily to the front torso and arms and legs. The C1 also replaces the anti-missile system with a Defiance B3M medium laser, added to the left arm.

Type: **Excalibur**
Technology Base: Inner Sphere
Tonnage: 70

Equipment		Mass
Internal Structure:		7
Engine:	350 XL	15
Walking MP:	5	
Running MP:	8	
Jumping MP:	0	
Heat Sinks:	12	2
Gyro:		4
Cockpit:		3
Armor Factor:	120	7.5

	Internal Structure	Armor Value
Head	3	9
Center Torso	22	16
Center Torso (rear)		5
R/L Torso	15	14
R/L Torso (rear)		5
R/L Arm	11	13
R/L Leg	15	13

Weapons and Ammo	Location	Critical	Tonnage
Gauss Rifle	RA	7	15
Ammo (Gauss) 16	RT	2	2
LRM 20	LT	5	10
Ammo (LRM) 12	LT	2	2
Anti-Missile System	CT	1	.5
Ammo (Anti-Missile) 12	CT	1	1
Artemis IV FCS	LT	1	1
CASE	LT	1	.5
CASE	RT	1	.5

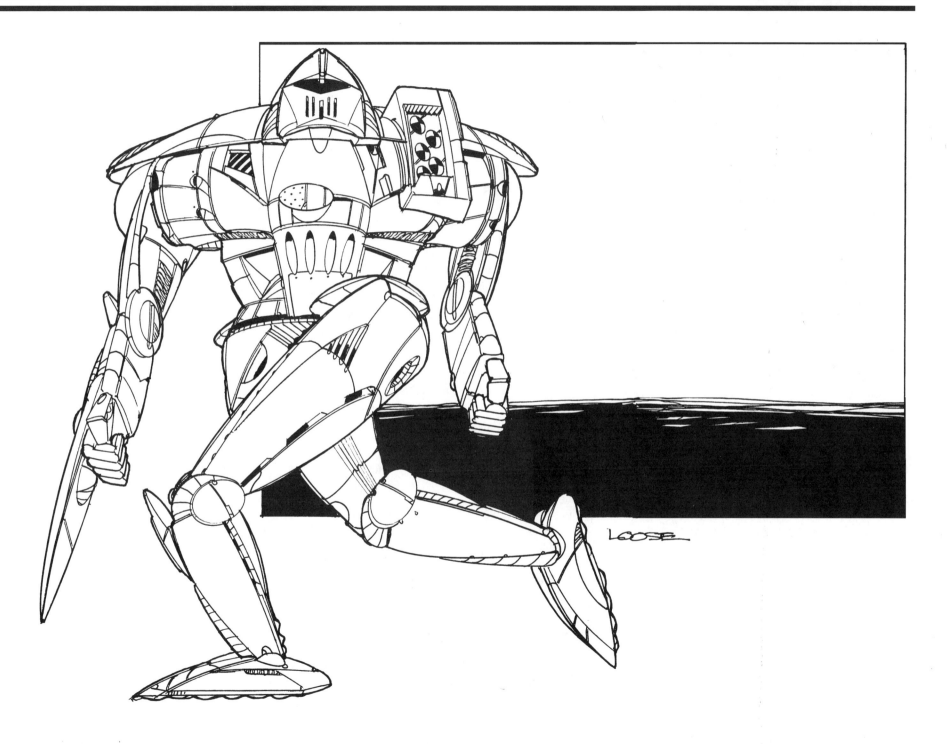

ST-8A SHOOTIST

INNER SPHERE MECHS

Mass: 70 tons
Chassis: Dennenbach-Mitchell Mark IV
Power Plant: VOX 280
Cruising Speed: 43 kph
Maximum Speed: 65 kph
Jump Jets: None
Jump Capacity: None
Armor: Ferro-Fibrous
Armament:
1 Deathgiver Autocannon/20
1 Blankenburg ER Large Laser
2 Blankenburg Medium Pulse Lasers
1 Dinatech Mark III Small Laser
Manufacturer: Mitchell Vehicles
Primary Factory: Terra
Communications System: Dornman Echo II
Targeting and Tracking System: Wayne Marksman

OVERVIEW

Although the *Shootist* was initially tagged as a command 'Mech by its Star League creators, its electronic equipment soon gave way to a new generation of more sophisticated active probes and electronic countermeasures. However, the 'Mech's reliable delivery systems made it a valuable all-around machine, and the Star League Army continued to order *Shootists*. With good speed for its size and an ample weapons bay, the *Shootist* became the perfect 'Mech to provide maximum firepower for heavy lances engaged in close combat. Modern-day *Shootist* pilots among the Com Guards routinely seek the largest opponent on the battlefield and engage it as quickly as possible.

Though it has existed for centuries, the *Shootist* never appeared in great numbers. Even during the height of production, construction of this 'Mech barely kept up with combat losses, and few intact *Shootists* survived anywhere in the Inner Sphere save in ComStar's storage bays. ComStar's use of the *Shootist* in the battle for Tukayyid introduced the 'Mech to most Inner Sphere armies for the first time since the earliest Succession Wars.

CAPABILITIES

Unlike most other 'Mechs, the *Shootist* is designed to provide maximum armor protection rather than firepower. This difference stems from the design's initial role as a battlefield command platform. The 'Mech carries twelve tons of ferro-fibrous armor around a standard frame. Every location is well armored, though a single concentrated salvo can breach the rear torso. When more sophisticated designs replaced the *Shootist* as the favored SLDF command 'Mech, the designers at Mitchell partially modified the *Shootist* but kept the heavy armor to protect *Shootists* against heavier foes.

Although firepower was not the top priority of the *Shootist's* designers, the 'Mech carries a respectable array of weapons. The *Shootist's* primary weapon is a Deathgiver autocannon, a devastating weapon at close range. Those familiar with the *Shootist,* however, see its extended-range large laser as its true claim to fame. Accurate at all ranges, the weapon can savage an opponent as the *Shootist* closes the distance. Two medium pulse lasers and a head-mounted small laser round out this deadly 'Mech's arsenal. Pulse technology had only recently been perfected when the *Shootist* went into production, and the 'Mech's designers took full advantage of it. After a long absence, pulse weapons have begun to re-emerge on Inner Sphere battlefields.

DEPLOYMENT

The *Shootist* is almost exclusively deployed with heavy and command lances. Particularly paranoid commanders occasionally attach a *Shootist* to their personal battlefield bodyguard. *Shootists* work well together, but their limited availability makes the presence of more than one in a lance unlikely. Just as they did in the days of the Star League, these 'Mechs lead the charge of heavy lances and acted as the Com Guards' vanguard when engaging the Clans.

Type: Shootist
Technology Base: Inner Sphere
Tonnage: 70

Equipment			Mass
Internal Structure:			7
Engine:		280	16
Walking MP:		4	
Running MP:		6	
Jumping MP:		0	
Heat Sinks:		13 [26]	3
Gyro:			3
Cockpit:			3
Armor Factor:		215	12

	Internal Structure	Armor Value
Head	3	9
Center Torso	22	34
Center Torso (rear)		10
R/L Torso	15	24
R/L Torso (rear)		5
R/L Arm	11	22
R/L Leg	15	30

Weapons and Ammo	Location	Critical	Tonnage
AC/20	LT	10	14
Ammo (AC) 10	RT	2	2
CASE	RT	1	.5
ER Large Laser	RA	2	5
Medium Pulse Laser	LA	1	2
Medium Pulse Laser	CT	1	2
Small Laser	H	1	.5

DGR-3F DRAGON FIRE

INNER SPHERE MECHS

Mass: 75 tons
Chassis: Royalstar ATE with Endo Steel
Power Plant: Pitban 300 XL
Cruising Speed: 43 kph
Maximum Speed: 65 kph
Jump Jets: None
Jump Capacity: None
Armor: ArcShield Maxi II
Armament:
1 Zeus Slingshot Gauss Rifle
1 Mydron Excel LB 10-X Autocannon
1 Exostar Large Laser
2 Defiance B4M Medium Pulse Laser
Manufacturer: J.B. BattleMechs Inc.
Primary Factory: Storfors
Communications System: CeresCom Model 21-Rs
Targeting and Tracking System: FireScan with IndirecTrack

OVERVIEW

When the fearsome MAD-3R *Marauder* was introduced to the Inner Sphere, House militaries and mercenary units alike hailed it as the first in a new generation of 'Mechs. Unfortunately, the Amaris Civil War prevented three other revolutionary 'Mech designs, including the *Dragon Fire,* from reaching full-scale production. The technical information contained in the Gray Death memory core, recovered in 3028, allowed manufacturers to resume work on these designs.

The DGR-3F *Dragon Fire* is the first of these three new designs to be put into production. GM, the original owner of the design, sold it to J.B. BattleMechs Inc., manufacturer of the *Chameleon* training 'Mech. The *Dragon Fire* will be J.B.'s first front-line BattleMech.

CAPABILITIES

Working from the original blueprints, the *Dragon Fire* design team chose to design a 'Mech specifically to counter the advantages Clan 'Mechs gave their pilots. This meant building a BattleMech that could handle versatile fighting styles and control heat buildup. They used an endo steel chassis and XL engine, which freed up significant tonnage that was allocated to heavier weapons. A Gauss rifle, autocannon, and several lasers constitute the *Dragon Fire's* awesome firepower. Two hand actuators give the 'Mech an edge in hand-to-hand combat and also allow it to retrieve salvage from the battlefield. Ten double heat sinks dissipate heat so efficiently that the *Dragon Fire* can fire all its weapons and move at maximum speed without overheating.

DEPLOYMENT

The *Dragon Fire* has yet to be tested in combat. Despite this lack of a track record, J.B. BattleMechs has already completed two production runs of the *Dragon Fire* and is gearing up for at least three more. Both the Draconis Combine and the Lyran Alliance have placed standing orders for this new 'Mech, as have those mercenary units that can afford it.

VARIANTS

J.B. BattleMechs has no plans to create variants of the *Dragon Fire*, though some units equipped with the 'Mech suggest replacing the large laser with an ER version. This alteration would further increase the 'Mech's weapons range, but at the cost of creating higher heat. J.B. engineers have taken this suggestion under review.

Type: **Dragon Fire**
Technology Base: Inner Sphere
Tonnage: 75

Equipment		Mass
Internal Structure:	Endo Steel	4
Engine:	300 XL	9.5
Walking MP:	4	
Running MP:	6	
Jumping MP:	0	
Heat Sinks:	10 [20]	
Gyro:		3
Cockpit:		3
Armor Factor:	231	14.5

	Internal Structure	Armor Value
Head	3	9
Center Torso	23	38
Center Torso (rear)		8
R/L Torso	16	26
R/L Torso (rear)		6
R/L Arm	12	24
R/L Leg	16	32

Weapons and Ammo	Location	Critical	Tonnage
LB 10-X	RA	6	11
Ammo (LB 10-X) 20	RT	2	2
CASE	RT	1	.5
Gauss Rifle	LA	7	15
Ammo (Gauss) 16	LT	2	2
Large Laser	CT	2	5
Medium Pulse Laser	H	1	2
Medium Pulse Laser	LT	1	2
Guardian ECM	LT	2	1.5

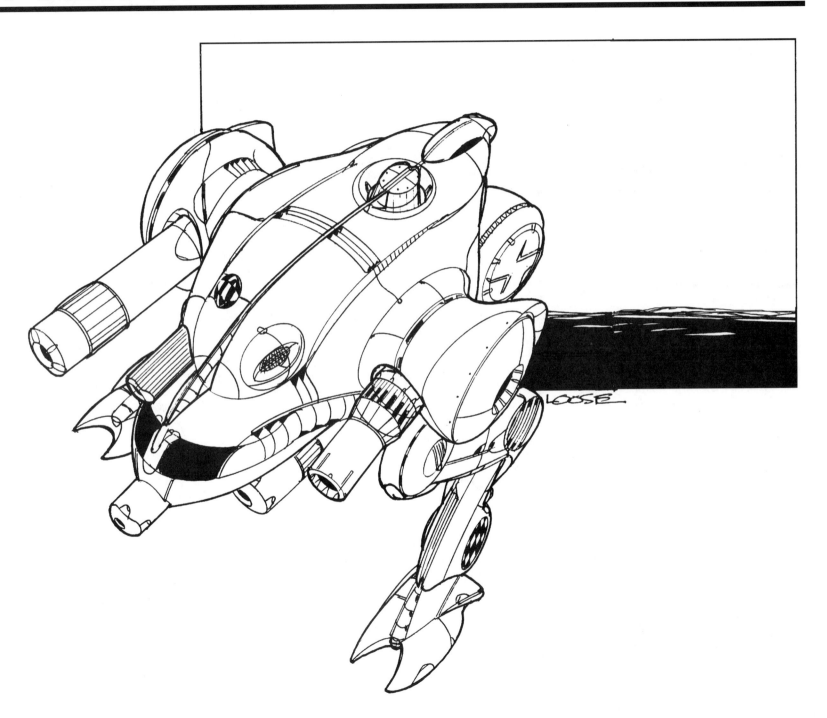

MT-5K MAELSTROM

INNER SPHERE MECHS

Mass: 75 tons
Chassis: Norse TRA34 Heavy
Power Plant: Ford 375 XL
Cruising Speed: 54 kph
Maximum Speed: 86 kph
Jump Jets: None
    Jump Capacity: None
Armor: Kellon Royalstar Heavy
Armament:
    1 Defiance 1001 ER PPC
    1 Cyclops XII Extended Range Large Laser
    2 Defiance P5M Medium Pulse Lasers
    1 Jackson Model 12 Small Laser
Manufacturer: General Motors, Norse-Storm
  BattleMechs, Telfar BattleMechs
    Primary Factory: Kathil, Solaris VII, Midway
Communications System: Sony MSF-21
Targeting and Tracking System: Cirxese
  BallistaCheck, Cirxese RockeCheck

OVERVIEW

The third 'Mech in the *Marauder* series, the *Maelstrom* did not make it off the drawing board and into production before the fall of the Star League. During the past twenty-nine years, as more of the Gray Death memory core has been decoded, manufacturers across the Inner Sphere have gradually re-learned the Star League's technological secrets. Armed with this new technology, GM has gone ahead with plans to produce the three remaining 'Mechs in the *Marauder* series.

Having little room left at its Kathil plant to manufacture the *Maelstrom*, GM sold licensing rights to Norse-Storm BattleMechs. Norse-Storm plans to produce the *Maelstrom* at its new factory on Solaris VII. In the spirit of goodwill between the Federated Commonwealth and the Draconis Combine, GM has also licensed the *Maelstrom* to the Combine manufacturer Telfar BattleMechs.

CAPABILITIES

The *Maelstrom* is similar to the *Marauder* and improves on it in some ways. The *Maelstrom* uses the new Ford 375 XL engine, which gives the 'Mech a top speed of 86 kph. To help the pilot stay in combat longer, the designers used double heat sinks to help dissipate the excess heat generated by the 'Mech's weapons.

The *Maelstrom*'s state-of-the-art weapons are impressive. The main weapon is the Defiance 1001 extended-range PPC, which gives the *Maelstrom* excellent range and striking power. Coupled with the ER PPC is a Cyclops XII extended-range large laser. Two Defiance P5M medium pulse lasers and a Jackson Model 12 small laser round out the *Maelstrom*'s arsenal. The BattleMech also has excellent armor protection—fourteen and half tons of Kellon Royalstar Heavy BattleMech armor are spread across the *Maelstrom*'s frame. Finally, the *Maelstrom*'s TAG system enables it to act as an artillery spotter.

DEPLOYMENT

Maelstrom are currently deployed with Combine units along the Draconis Combine's border with the Clan Smoke Jaguar occupied zone, and several have reportedly been sent to Wolcott. The Lyran Alliance has stationed its *Maelstrom*s along its borders with Clan Jade Falcon and the so-called Chaos March.

Type: Maelstrom
Technology Base: Inner Sphere
Tonnage: 75

Equipment		Mass
Internal Structure:		7.5
Engine:	375 XL	19.5
Walking MP:	5	
Running MP:	8	
Jumping MP:	0	
Heat Sinks:	19 [38]	9
Gyro:		4
Cockpit:		3
Armor Factor:	231	14.5

	Internal Structure	Armor Value
Head	3	9
Center Torso	23	38
Center Torso (rear)		8
R/L Torso	16	26
R/L Torso (rear)		6
R/L Arm	12	24
R/L Leg	16	32

Weapons and Ammo	Location	Critical	Tonnage
ER PPC	RA	3	7
ER Large Laser	LA	2	5
TAG	RT	1	1
Medium Pulse Laser	H	1	2
Medium Pulse Laser	CT	1	2
Small Laser	CT	1	.5

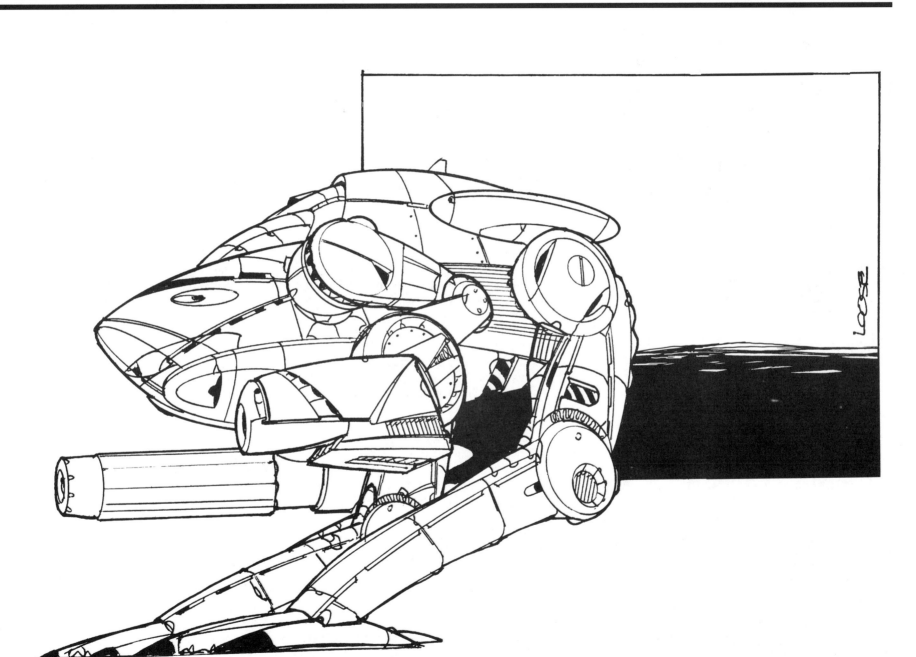

GRN-D-01 GRAND CRUSADER

Mass: 80 tons
Chassis: Crucis-ES Endo Steel
Power Plant: Hermes 240 XL
Cruising Speed: 32 kph
Maximum Speed: 54 kph
Jump Jets: None
   Jump Capacity: None
Armor: Maximillian 45
Armament:
   1 Lindblad Shotgun Anti-Missile System
   2 Tronel PPI-20 Large Pulse Lasers
   2 Holly LRM-20 Packs
   2 Intek Medium Pulse Lasers
Manufacturer: Gibson Federated BattleMechs
   Primary Factory: Gibson
Communications System: O/P COMNET 210A
Targeting and Tracking System: Garret A99 with
   Artemis IV Interface

OVERVIEW

When Precentor Martial Arian assumed command of the Word of Blake Militia in 3052, his forces were in sorry shape. Initially, ComStar had not protested when dissident Com Guard MechWarriors took their equipment when they left their ranks. Later, stricter guidelines enforced by the Com Guards virtually cut off the flow of defecting BattleMechs from the Guards to the Word of Blake. A few Level II units left as a group, but the battered condition of their 'Mechs and other equipment after the fighting on Tukayyid meant that the Word of Blake inherited more problems than solutions.

Precentor Martial Arian commissioned several 'Mech designs to replenish his militia's ranks. He negotiated a contract with Gibson Federated BattleMech Works to construct the new 'Mechs, promising that the Word of Blake would underwrite production costs and allow the designs to be sold on the open market. Gibson Federated agreed.

CAPABILITIES

Though called *Grand Crusader*, this BattleMech bears little resemblance to the traditional *Crusader* 'Mech. Precentor Blane christened the 'Mech from a passage of Jerome Blake's works that states, " … those who fight to preserve technology and knowledge are the grandest crusaders of all."

The *Grand Crusader*'s massive, barrel-chested profile harkens back to old designs such as the Awesome and the Mackie. This image is enhanced by the large smokestack-like pylons rising from the 'Mech's back. Although these devices contribute to the Grand Crusader's steam-age appearance, they are actually sophisticated sensor arrays that are tied into the Artemis IV fire control system.

Mounting two Tronel large pulse lasers, twin Holly LRM-20 packs and a sophisticated Artemis IV fire-control system, the *Grand Crusader* can cripple its opposition at long range. However, the 'Mech's double heat sinks cannot cope with the heat generated by firing all these weapons.

For defense, the *Grand Crusader* mounts a Lindblad anti-missile defense system on a pivot point on top of the cockpit. Blind spots on the sides of the 'Mech's lower legs and its rear pose a problem in using the Lindblad to repel Elemental attacks; however, the Word of Blake has no intention of sending its *Grand Crusader*s against the Clans for many years, allowing plenty of time to correct this oversight.

DEPLOYMENT

The *Grand Crusader* arrived in the Word of Blake's First Division in the late fall of 3053. In subsequent years, the Word of Blake Militia has continued to bolster its divisions with this exceptional new assault 'Mech.

VARIANTS

The only known variation of the *Grand Crusader*, the GRN-D-02, provides only long-range fire support. This variant lacks the anti-missile system and carries two LRM-5 missile packs in place of the original design's medium pulse lasers.

Type: Grand Crusader
Technology Base: Inner Sphere
Tonnage: 80

Equipment			Mass
Internal Structure:		Endo Steel	4
Engine:		240 XL	6
Walking MP:		3	
Running MP:		5	
Jumping MP:		0	
Heat Sinks:		10 [20]	0
Gyro:			3
Cockpit:			3
Armor Factor:		247	15.5

	Internal Structure	Armor Value
Head	3	9
Center Torso	25	35
Center Torso (rear)		15
R/L Torso	17	24
R/L Torso (rear)		10
R/L Arm	13	26
R/L Leg	17	34

Weapons and Ammo	Location	Critical	Tonnage
Anti-Missile System	H	1	.5
Ammo (Anti-Missile) 24	CT	2	2
Large Pulse Laser	RA	2	7
Large Pulse Laser	LA	2	7
LRM 20	RT	5	10
Ammo (LRM) 18	RT	3	3
LRM 20	LT	5	10
Ammo (LRM) 18	LT	3	3
Medium Pulse Laser	RA	1	2
Medium Pulse Laser	LA	1	2
Artemis IV FCS	RT	1	1
Artemis IV FCS	LT	1	1

GRN-D-01 GRAND CRUSADER

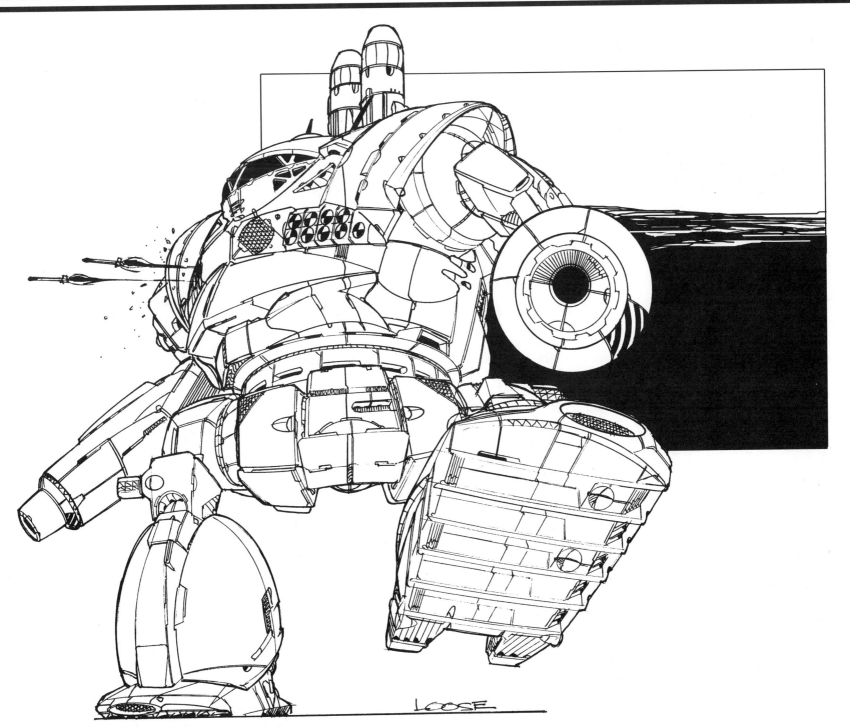

OBK-M10 O-BAKEMONO

INNER SPHERE MECHS

Mass: 80 tons
Chassis: Alshain Class 92b
Power Plant: Hermes 320 XL
Cruising Speed: 43 kph
Maximum Speed: 65 kph
Jump Jets: None
   Jump Capacity: None
Armor: Star Slab/3
Armament:
   1 ChisComp 32 Small Laser
   2 Diverse Optics Type 20 Medium Lasers
   2 Shigunga Arrow IV Missile Systems
Manufacturer: Luthien Armor Works
   Primary Factory: Luthien
Communications System: Sipher Security Plus
Targeting and Tracking System: Matabushi Sentinel

OVERVIEW

The *O-Bakemono*, or "Great Goblin," is an early result of Luthien Armor Works' program to reverse-engineer captured Clan OmniMechs. Though it has yet to go beyond the prototype stage, this 'Mech appears to have a promising future ahead of it.

CAPABILITIES

The *O-Bakemono*'s design is based on the *Naga* OmniMech used by Clan forces, and shares many of that 'Mech's characteristics. Its relatively lightweight XL engine allows the *O-Bakemono*, like its parent OmniMech, to carry heavy weapons and considerable armor. However, the *O-Bakemono*'s engine is less

powerful than the *Naga*'s, and so the *O-Bakemono* has a somewhat slower top speed. With this new design, the designers at Luthien Armor Works have largely overcome the *Naga*'s lack of intermediate-range firepower by replacing two of the *Naga*'s three small lasers with medium lasers. The *O-Bakemono* still carries two Arrow IV missile systems and 30 rounds of ammunition, giving it the same devastating long-range firepower as the *Naga*.

Though the *O-Bakemono*'s weapons are not truly modular, this 'Mech's equipment is much easier to repair or replace in the field than the standard Inner Sphere BattleMech. The Arrow IV systems can be disengaged from the main body of the 'Mech by activating five quick release levers, and the lasers can be removed and replaced in a similar manner. Engine repairs can be made in an hour rather than the standard five hours for a conventional Inner Sphere 'Mech.

The missiles come in pre-loaded canisters that double as shipping containers, which are simply slipped into the 'Mech like a rifle magazine rather than loaded one by one into an internal ammo bay. The *O-Bakemono* represents an important breakthrough in the Inner Sphere's ongoing attempts to develop OmniMech technology.

DEPLOYMENT

The *O-Bakemono* has yet to be officially deployed. According to rumors, however, the prototype received its first trial by fire with the mercenary unit Camacho's Caballeros, in the employ of Coordinator Theodore Kurita's cousin Chandrasekhar Kurita. Reportedly, the prototype distinguished itself in successful actions directed against rebellious Confederation units on the planet Towne in the so-called Chaos March. These reports remain unconfirmed, however.

Type: **O-Bakemono**
Technology Base: Inner Sphere
Tonnage: 80

Equipment		Mass
Internal Structure:		8
Engine:	320 XL	11.5
Walking MP:	4	
Running MP:	6	
Jumping MP:	0	
Heat Sinks:	10 [20]	0
Gyro:		4
Cockpit:		3
Armor Factor:	224	14

	Internal Structure	Armor Value
Head	3	9
Center Torso	25	37
Center Torso (rear)		10
R/L Torso	17	25
R/L Torso (rear)		9
R/L Arm	13	26
R/L Leg	17	24

Weapons and Ammo	Location	Critical	Tonnage
Arrow IV System	LT/LA	15	15
Arrow IV System	RT/RA	15	15
Ammo (Arrow IV) 15	LT	3	3
Ammo (Arrow IV) 15	RT	3	3
Small Laser	H	1	.5
Medium Laser	CT	1	1
Medium Laser	CT	1	1
CASE	LT	1	.5
CASE	RT	1	.5

OBK-M10 O-BAKEMONO

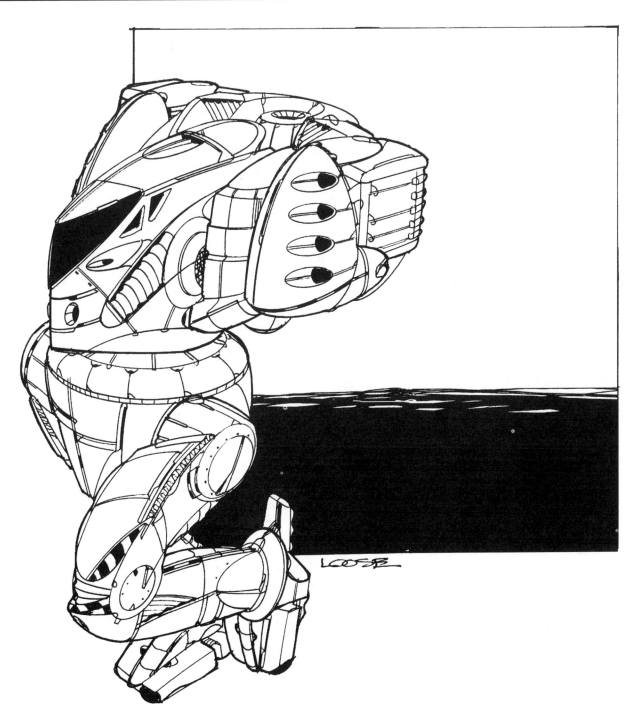

INNER SPHERE MECHS

Mass: 80 tons
Chassis: Geometric 500 Hard Core
Power Plant: Dantrus 400 XL
Cruising Speed: 54 kph
Maximum Speed: 86 kph
Jump Jets: None
   Jump Capacity: None
Armor: Strasbourg Armaments 206 Diamond Weave
Armament:
   1 Kinslaughter H-Class ER PPC
   3 Blankenburg Medium Pulse Lasers
   2 Holly SRM Streak Missile Racks
   1 McArthur Anti-Missile System
Manufacturer: Martinson Armaments
   Primary Factory: None
Communications System: Blow 300 SNA Net
Targeting and Tracking System: Scope 40 RNDST

OVERVIEW

Just before the start of the Amaris Civil War, the Star League begun full production of the *Spartan* class BattleMech at Martinson Armaments on Terra. Martinson delivered 600 *Spartans* to the SLDF before Amaris's troops took Terra and destroyed the production facility. According to ComStar records, General Kerensky took fifty of the two hundred *Spartans* that had survived the Amaris Civil War with him during the Exodus. The last known operational *Spartan*, aside from those among the Com Guard, was believed destroyed during the Third Succession War.

CAPABILITIES

Built as a general-service BattleMech, the *Spartan* is fast, mobile, and able to deliver deadly firepower at all ranges. It has a top speed of more than 86 kph, making it faster than other 'Mechs in its weight class. The core of the *Spartan*'s firepower is a Kinslaughter extended-range PPC, backed by three medium pulse lasers and two SRM-2 Streak missile racks. Because of the Kinslaughter's superior workmanship and special insulating cones installed in the H-Class ER PPC, this model produces less heat than other ER PPCs. Currently, only ComStar and the Word of Blake are building the Kinslaughter H-Class ER PPC. To help the *Spartan* dissipate the tremendous heat built up by its weapons, the N2 model is equipped with thirteen double heat sinks.

The *Spartan* is also equipped with a McArthur anti-missile system and two tons of ammunition. During the Com Guard's battles on Tukayyid, *Spartan* pilots found that the placement of the anti-missile system low in the 'Mech's waist made it prone to jamming when the 'Mech ran or twisted its torso. Fortunately, technicians easily solved the problem by moving the system higher up in the right torso.

The *Spartan*'s armor protection is above average, with fourteen tons of armor covering its frame. The *Spartan* also mounts a TAG system in its left torso to help direct friendly artillery fire.

DEPLOYMENT

Nineteen of the known operational *Spartans* are deployed in ComStar's Com Guard, and a few others belong to three mercenary units. Rhonda's Irregulars has four *Spartans*; two merc units operating in the Periphery, the Black Heart Roses and the Blackstone Highlanders, have two *Spartans* each. All are priceless, as no new *Spartans* have been built in more than two hundred years.

VARIANTS

The only currently existing variant of the *Spartan*, the SPT-NF, features CASE in the left and right torsos but lacks the original design's TAG system.

Type: Spartan
Technology Base: Inner Sphere
Tonnage: 80

Equipment			Mass
Internal Structure:			8
Engine:		400 XL	26.5
Walking MP:		5	
Running MP:		8	
Jumping MP:		0	
Heat Sinks:		13 [26]	3
Gyro:			4
Cockpit:			3
Armor Factor:		224	14

	Internal Structure	Armor Value
Head	3	9
Center Torso	25	31
Center Torso (rear)		12
R/L Torso	17	26
R/L Torso (rear)		8
R/L Arm	13	26
R/L Leg	17	26

Weapons and Ammo	Location	Critical	Tonnage
ER PPC	LT	3	7
Medium Pulse Laser	RA	1	2
Medium Pulse Laser	RA	1	2
Medium Pulse Laser	RA	1	2
Streak SRM 2	CT	1	1.5
Streak SRM 2	CT	1	1.5
Ammo (SRM) 100	LT	2	2
Anti-Missile System	RT	1	.5
Ammo (Anti-Missile) 24	RT	2	2
TAG	LT	1	1

SPT-N2 SPARTAN

STC-2C STRIKER

INNER SPHERE MECHS

Mass: 80 tons
Chassis: Ford CVX 21
Power Plant: Pitban 320
Cruising Speed: 43 kph
Maximum Speed: 65 kph
Jump Jets: None
   Jump Capacity: None
Armor: Leviathan Plus
Armament:
   1 HellStar Particle Projection Cannon
   1 Defiance B3L Large Laser
   1 Pontiac Light Class 5 Autocannon
   3 Hellion-b II Medium Lasers
Manufacturer: Stormvanger Assemblies Unlimited
   Primary Factory: None
Communications System: Basix 200
Targeting and Tracking System: Rander Crosshairs

OVERVIEW

First built in 2550 as one of the SLDF's earliest assault 'Mechs, the *Striker* has proved its worth many times over. As technological advancements enabled the Star League to build heavier assault 'Mechs, the *Striker* was relegated to second-line and garrison units. Over the long centuries of the Succession Wars the number of *Strikers* left in the Inner Sphere steadily decreased, and at present less than 300 *Strikers* remain operational. The primary production facility for the *Striker* was destroyed during a Kurita raid in 2867, and no new *Strikers* have been produced in recent years.

CAPABILITIES

Built with the largest fusion engine available at the time of its initial design, the *Striker* was the fastest and heaviest 'Mech in the Star League inventory until advances in technology displaced it. The massive weight of the *Striker's* engine limited the weapons the design team could install, but they gave the 'Mech the heaviest arsenal it could carry. The primary weapon is a HellStar PPC, supplemented by a large laser to give the *Striker* a knockout one-two punch. Secondary weapons are an AC-5 with one ton of ammunition and three medium lasers. The *Striker* also has fifteen heat sinks and thirteen and a half tons of armor.

DEPLOYMENT

The armed forces of House Steiner and House Liao possess most of the Star League-era *Strikers*, and all of the Steiner machines remain in military forces stationed in the Lyran Alliance. House Liao has recently deployed its *Strikers* in its front-line 'Mech units, whereas most Lyran *Strikers* are in militia units along the Steiner–Periphery border near Marik space. The rest of the known *Strikers* are spread throughout the Inner Sphere and the Periphery, reportedly in the possession of several mercenary units.

VARIANTS

The only known variant of the *Striker*, the 2D model used by the Capellan Confederation, replaces the original fifteen heat sinks with twelve double heat sinks and adds two tons of armor. In addition, the HellStar PPC is replaced with a Magna Firestar extended-range PPC, and the three medium lasers are replaced with two medium pulse lasers.

Type: Striker
Technology Base: Inner Sphere
Tonnage: 80

Equipment			Mass
Internal Structure:			8
Engine:		320	22.5
Walking MP:		4	
Running MP:		6	
Jumping MP:		0	
Heat Sinks:		15	5
Gyro:			4
Cockpit:			3
Armor Factor:		216	13.5

	Internal Structure	Armor Value
Head	3	9
Center Torso	25	35
Center Torso (rear)		10
R/L Torso	17	25
R/L Torso (rear)		8
R/L Arm	13	22
R/L Leg	17	26

Weapons and Ammo	Location	Critical	Tonnage
PPC	RT	3	7
Large Laser	LT	2	5
AC/5	LA	4	8
Medium Laser	CT	1	1
Medium Laser	CT	1	1
Medium Laser	H	1	1
Ammo (AC/5) 20	LT	1	1

STC-2C STRIKER

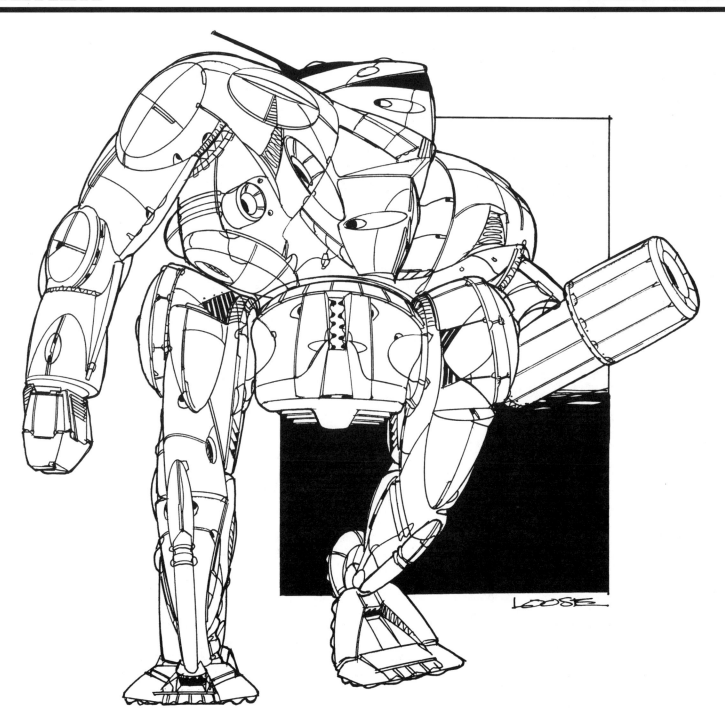

LGB-7Q LONGBOW

INNER SPHERE MECHS

Mass: 85 tons
Chassis: StarCorp 100
Power Plant: Strand 255
Cruising Speed: 34 kph
Maximum Speed: 54 kph
Jump Jets: None
Jump Capacity: None
Armor: StarSlab/9.5 MK II
Armament:
  2 Holly LRM-20 Missile Racks
  2 Delta Dart LRM-5 Missile Racks
  2 Ceres Arms Medium Lasers
Manufacturer: StarCorps Industries
  Primary Factory: Crofton, Loburg, Emirs IV
Communications System: O/P 3000 COMSET, Irian
  TelStar
Targeting and Tracking System: AntiAir Flak
  Systems-1, Octagon Tartrac System C

OVERVIEW

Introduced in 2610, the 7Q *Longbow* was designed to cure some of the problems in the original 0W *Longbow*, such as the lack of sufficient heat sinks, the lack of short-range weapons, and insufficient armor protection. The 7Q is still produced along with a few 0W models at StarCorps' three remaining BattleMech factories in the Free Worlds League.

CAPABILITIES

The 7Q *Longbow*'s 255 fusion engine is a vast improvement over the original Longbow's huge VOX

340 engine. Lighter and more efficient, the new fusion engine gives the 7Q *Longbow* a slightly faster top speed while enabling the 'Mech to carry three tons of additional armor spread across the three front torsos, the arms, and the legs. The 7Q *Longbow* is fitted with twenty-two heat sinks, which allow it to keep up with advancing 'Mech forces and still deliver deadly missile fire. Two medium lasers give the 7Q *Longbow* short-range fighting ability; as the 'Mech was never intended for front-line duty, the designers felt that these short-range weapons were sufficient. The 7Q shares with its 0W model predecessor an antiaircraft targeting and tracking system widely considered to be one of the best in the Inner Sphere.

DEPLOYMENT

StarCorps factories in Marik territory are currently running at full speed to fill all the orders for 7Q *Longbow*s for the Free Worlds League military. They have no plans as yet to sell any to mercenary units. The Federated Commonwealth has sent several lances of its *Longbow*s to its Periphery border, and the Lyran Alliance has deployed several lances to its borders with the Jade Falcon occupied zone and Marik space. StarCorps factories in the Federated Commonwealth are reportedly selling the *Longbow* to mercenary units employed by the Commonwealth government, and the single StarCorps facility in the Lyran Alliance has announced its intention to sell *Longbow*s to mercenary units stationed within Alliance borders.

VARIANTS

StarCorps also offers a major upgrade of the 7Q *Longbow* known as the 7V, which replaces the fusion engine with an XL engine. The 7V also replaces the twenty-two standard heat sinks with fourteen double heat sinks, and drops the LRM-5 racks in order to accommodate one and a half tons of additional armor. To make the 7V a more potent front-line fighter, it mounts an extended-range large laser and four medium pulse lasers, plus two additional tons of ammunition for its LRM-20 racks. Both torsos are equipped with CASE to protect the pilot from ammo explosions. To

make the LRMs more accurate, each of the 'Mech's arms sports a fire-control system. The medium lasers have been dropped, and a medium pulse laser installed in the *Longbow*'s head.

Type: Longbow
Technological Base: Inner Sphere
Tonnage: 85

Equipment		Mass
Internal Structure:		8.5
Engine:	255	13
Walking MP:	3	
Running MP:	5	
Jumping MP:	0	
Heat Sinks:	22	12
Gyro:		3
Cockpit:		3
Armor Value:	232	14.5

	Internal Structure	Armor Value
Head	3	9
Center Torso	27	37
Center Torso (rear)		12
R/L Torso	18	26
R/L Torso (rear)		10
R/L Arm	14	23
R/L Leg	18	28

Weapons and Ammo	Location	Critical	Tonnage
LRM 20	RA	5	10
LRM 20	LA	5	10
LRM 5	LT	1	2
LRM 5	RT	1	2
Ammo (LRM) 12	RT	2	2
Ammo (LRM) 12	LT	2	2
Ammo (LRM) 24	CT	1	1
Medium Laser	RT	1	1
Medium Laser	LT	1	1

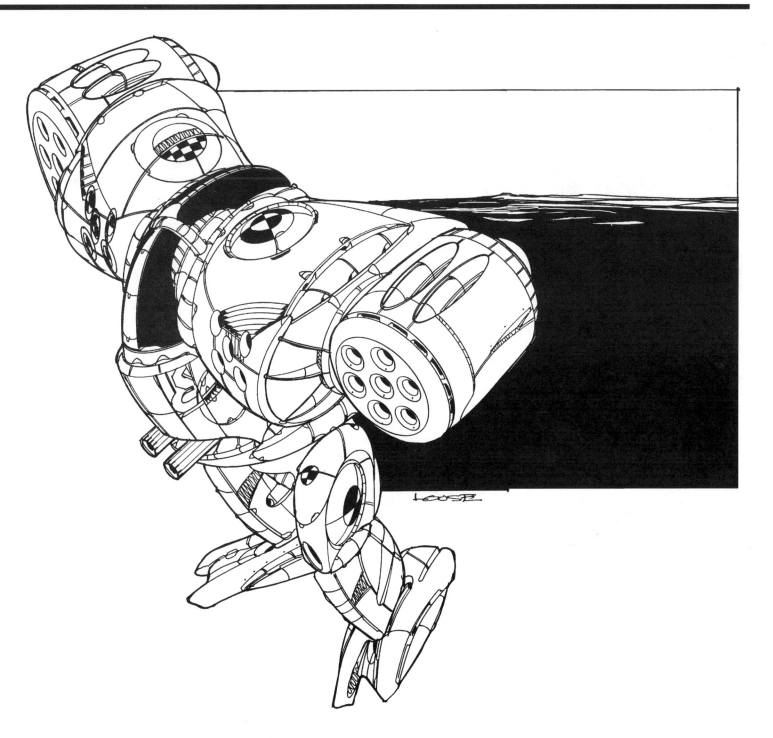

EMP-6A EMPEROR

INNER SPHERE MECHS

Mass: 90 tons
Chassis: Titan Super TZ-7EA
Power Plant: PlasmaStar 270 XL
Cruising Speed: 32 kph
Maximum Speed: 54 kph
Jump Jets: Pitban LFT-50
   Jump Capacity: 90 meters
Armor: ArcShield VII Mk 5
Armament:
   2 Imperator Code Red LB 10-X Autocannons
   2 Magna Mk III Large Lasers
   2 Defiance P5M Medium Pulse Lasers
   1 Phototech 806c Medium Laser
Manufacturer: StarCorps Industries
   Primary Factory: Son Hoa, Menke, St. Ives
Communications System: Telestar Model XTD-67A1
Targeting and Tracking System: Starlight Seeker
   LX-4K

OVERVIEW

First seen on the battlefield in 2502, the *Emperor* was the first BattleMech to use the newly developed XL engine, LB 10-X autocannon, double heat sinks, and CASE. At the time of its introduction, it was also the largest BattleMech to carry jump jets.

The *Emperor* was still in production at the start of the Second Succession War, but a Marik raid on the StarCorps plant on Son Hoa ended production of the *Emperor* in a radioactive cloud. StarCorps recently completed a new 'Mech plant near the old site and began building new *Emperor*s and *Highlander*s in the fall of 3057.

CAPABILITIES

When the SLDF High Command wanted a new 90-ton assault 'Mech incorporating the newest weapons and other components designed by the Star League's top scientists, they secretly solicited new design proposals from several BattleMech manufacturers. Per standard policy, only the Royal BattleMech units would receive these new 'Mechs—the High Command did not want the new technology to fall into the hands of the League's member-states. The SLDF High Command liked what they saw in StarCorps's *Emperor* design and awarded the company a contract.

The lightweight new XL engine lay at the heart of the new design, allowing the StarCorps design team to place additional components on the *Emperor* that would otherwise have made the 'Mech too heavy. First, they added double-strength heat sinks that enabled the *Emperor* to dissipate large amounts of heat quickly. The designers also gave the *Emperor* two state-of-the-art Imperator LB 10-X autocannons—a lighter model that took up less space than standard autocannons—and two tons of ammunition for each. When loaded with special cluster rounds, the autocannons are as deadly against aerospace fighters as they normally are against enemy BattleMechs.

Backing up the autocannons is an impressive array of energy weapons: two large lasers, two medium pulse lasers and a standard medium laser. To give the *Emperor* more maneuverability, the design team installed Pitban LFT-50 jump jets. The *Emperor* also boasts impressive armor protection—seventeen and a half tons of heavy armor cover the *Emperor*'s frame.

DEPLOYMENT

The Lyran Alliance and the St. Ives Compact have deployed several lances of *Emperor*s. The Capellan Confederation owns several but has yet to deploy them despite its desperate need for front-line assault 'Mechs. According to rumor, Chancellor Sun-Tzu Liao is displeased with McCarron's Trading Company, builders of the *Emperor* on Menke, allegedly because all *Emperor*s produced so far have ended up in McCarron's Armored Cavalry. The St. Ives Compact recently announced its decision to sell *Emperor*s to the

Federated Commonwealth, and StarCorps plants in the Lyran Alliance intend to sell a few *Emperor*s to Alliance-affiliated mercenary units.

Type: Emperor
Technology Base: Inner Sphere
Tonnage: 90

Equipment		Mass
Internal Structure:		9
Engine:	270 XL	7.5
Walking MP:	3	
Running MP:	5	
Jumping MP:	3	
Heat Sinks:	12 [24]	2
Gyro:		3
Cockpit:		3
Armor Factor:	279	17.5

	Internal Structure	Armor Value
Head	3	9
Center Torso	29	48
Center Torso (rear)		10
R/L Torso	19	30
R/L Torso (rear)		8
R/L Arm	15	30
R/L Leg	19	38

Weapons and Ammo	Location	Critical	Tonnage
LB 10-X AC	RA	6	11
Ammo (LB 10-X) 20	RT	2	2
LB 10-X AC	LA	6	11
Ammo (LB 10-X) 20	LT	2	2
Large Laser	RA	2	5
Large Laser	LA	2	5
Medium Pulse Laser	RT	1	2
Medium Pulse Laser	LT	1	2
Medium Laser	H	1	1
CASE	RT	1	.5
CASE	LT	1	.5
Jump Jet	RL	1	2
Jump Jet	LL	1	2
Jump Jet	CT	1	2

EMP-6A EMPEROR

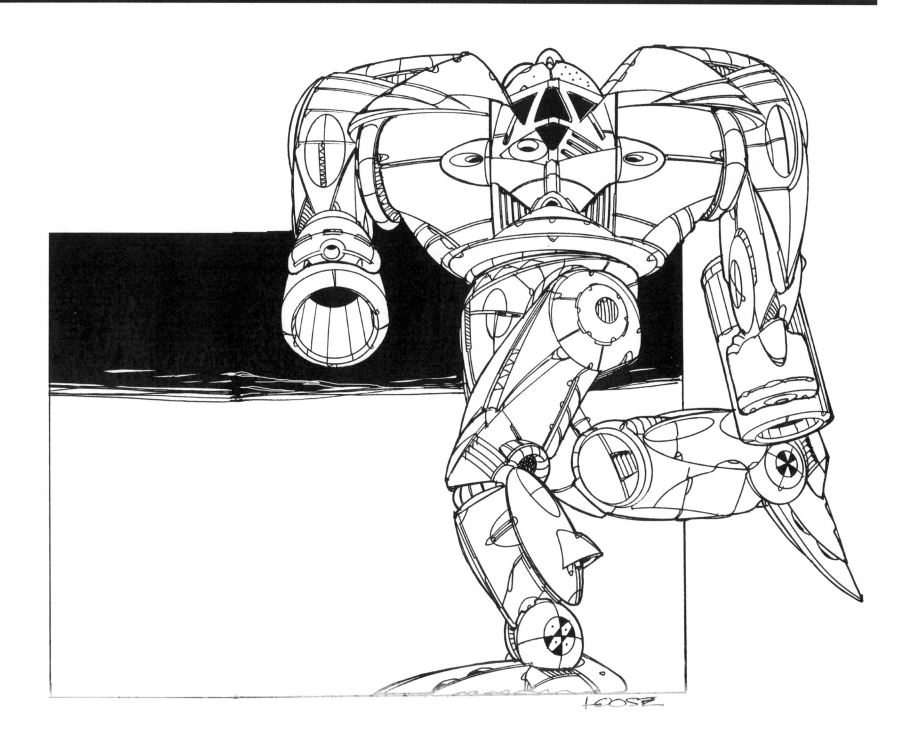

INNER SPHERE MECHS

Mass: 95 tons
Chassis: Norse-GM HeavyTRQ
Power Plant: Pitban 285 XL
Cruising Speed: 32 kph
Maximum Speed: 54 kph
Jump Jets: None
  Jump Capacity: None
Armor: Kellon Royalstar Heavy Type K
Armament:
  2 Norse-Storm Model 7D Gauss Rifles
  1 Defiance 1001 ER PPC
  2 Defiance P5M Medium Pulse Lasers
  1 Exostar Small Laser
Manufacturer: GM BattleMechs; Norse-Storm
Technologies Inc.
  Primary Factory: Kathil, Solaris VII
Communications System: Tek Battlecomm
Targeting and Tracking System: DLK Type Phased
  Array Sensors

OVERVIEW

The last of the *Marauder* series BattleMechs, the *Nightstar* was intended as a general support 'Mech for heavy companies. Its primary role was to protect unit commanders piloting *Marauder*s, who had become prime targets for Amaris troops during the early years of the Amaris Civil War. The SLDF High Command commissioned GM BattleMechs and Norse-Storm to design a heavy support 'Mech, and after eight months of intense work the companies put the *Nightstar* into production. Unfortunately, the 'Mech became a casual-

ty of the Succession Wars. Three months after the First Succession War began, Norse-Storm's primary production facility for the *Nightstar* was destroyed by Marik troops. At the same time, several members of the GM design team died in a freak accident at GM's plant on Kathil. Two hundred and fifty years would pass before GM and Norse-Storm recovered enough technological expertise to put the *Nightstar* back into production.

CAPABILITIES

The *Nightstar* shares many of the *Marauder*'s design features, such as its flexible ball-and-socket arm joints. The *Nightstar*'s reinforced *Marauder* chassis enables it to carry twenty more tons than the *Marauder*, and so it has heavier weapons and stronger armor protection. The 285 XL fusion engine makes the *Nightstar* almost as fast as the *Marauder*, and certainly as fast as most assault 'Mechs. Fourteen double heat sinks keep the *Nightstar* cool on the battlefield.

The *Nightstar*'s weapons include twin Gauss rifles with seven tons of ammunition and two medium pulse lasers, as well as an extended-range PPC. An Exostar small laser rounds out the *Nightstar*'s weaponry. The *Nightstar*'s electronics package includes the excellent Tek Battlecomm communications system, in production since the decoding of the Gray Death memory core, and the DLK Phased-Array Sensor System. The best 'Mech targeting system in the Inner Sphere, the DLK gives pilots incredible firing accuracy.

DEPLOYMENT

The *Nightstar* has seen limited combat with the mercenary units Storm's Metal Thunder and the Blackstone Highlanders, who have raided several Clan-held worlds in the Jade Falcon occupation zone. Various units in the Lyran Alliance military are reported to deploy *Nightstar*s, including the First Lyran Guards. The Federated Commonwealth has stationed several *Nightstar*s with units along the Periphery border.

VARIANTS

A variant built by General Motors, the 9FC, replaces the 285 XL engine with a 380 XL engine that

gives the *Nightstar* higher cruising and maximum speeds. Two LB 10-X autocannons replace the massive Gauss rifles, and four tons of ammo are stored in its CASE-equipped left torso. Standard medium lasers replace the medium pulse lasers, and the small laser is upgraded to a standard medium laser. One double heat sink has been removed, giving the 9FC a total of thirteen double heat sinks.

Type: Nightstar
Technology Base: Inner Sphere
Tonnage: 95

Equipment		Mass
Internal Structure:		9.5
Engine:	285 XL	8.5
Walking MP:	3	
Running MP:	5	
Jumping MP:	0	
Heat Sinks:	14 [28]	4
Gyro:		3
Cockpit:		3
Armor Factor:	293	18.5

	Internal Structure	Armor Value
Head	3	9
Center Torso	30	50
Center Torso (rear)		10
R/L Torso	20	32
R/L Torso (rear)		8
R/L Arm	16	32
R/L Leg	20	40

Weapons and Ammo	Location	Critical	Tonnage
Gauss Rifle	RA	7	15
Medium Pulse Laser	RA	1	2
Gauss Rifle	LA	7	15
Medium Pulse Laser	LA	1	2
ER PPC	RT	3	7
Ammo (Gauss) 24	RT	3	3
Ammo (Gauss) 24	LT	3	3
Small Laser	H	1	.5
Ammo (Gauss) 8	CT	1	1

NSR-9J NIGHTSTAR

DVS-2 DEVASTATOR

INNER SPHERE MECHS

Mass: 100 tons
Chassis: Star League XT
Power Plant: Vlar 300 XL
Cruising Speed: 32 kph
Maximum Speed: 54 kph
Jump Jets: None
Jump Capacity: None
Armor: Durallex Heavy
Armament:
2 Poland Main Model A Gauss Rifles
2 Donal Particle Projection Cannons
4 Intek Medium Lasers
Manufacturer: Norse-Storm BattleMechs, Inc.
Primary Factory: Loxley
Communications System: Johnston Wide Band
Targeting and Tracking System: Rander Pinpoint-HY

OVERVIEW

The *Devastator* was built from a Star League-era design, discovered in 3023 by Davion troops in the remains of a Star League base on the planet Hoff. Inner Sphere scientists and BattleMech manufacturers, however, lacked the technology to build the Gauss rifles, extra-light engines, and double heat sinks the design required. The blueprints for the *Devastator* languished in the files of the New Avalon Institute of Science for ten years, until advanced technological information uncovered in the Gray Death memory core enabled House Davion to construct a prototype of the BattleMech.

Originally designed by General Kerensky to correct the flaws in the prototype *Titan* BattleMech, the *Devastator* can deliver tremendous firepower at long range. The chaos of the Amaris Civil War disrupted the development of the original *Devastator,* though several prototypes reached General Kerensky's forces in time for the final assault on Terra. No record of the 'Mech's deployment during the Succession Wars exists; experts assume that all the prototypes accompanied General Kerensky in the Exodus.

CAPABILITIES

The relative lightness of the *Devastator*'s 300 XL engine enables the 'Mech to carry several heavy weapons and extra double heat sinks. A total of fourteen double heat sinks keep the *Devastator* cool even at the height of battle, and eighteen and a half tons of armor give the *Devastator* excellent protection.

The *Devastator*'s weapons are impressive and deadly. Two Gauss rifles and two PPCs make up the major portion of the 'Mech's arsenal, allowing the *Devastator* to inflict immense damage at long range. The 'Mech's four tons of Gauss ammunition are stored in four separate bins, eliminating the possibility of putting the Gauss rifles out of action with a single lucky hit. For short-range combat, the *Devastator* is equipped with four medium lasers, including one rear-mounted laser.

DEPLOYMENT

Norse-Storm has been producing a moderate number of *Devastators* at their Loxley facility for the past ten years. All of these units have been sold to the Federated Commonwealth. It is unknown how many *Devastators* were deployed with Lyran units when the Lyran Alliance declared its independence from the Commonwealth. Experts estimate that as many as 100 *Devastators* may be stationed along the borders of the Clan occupation zones.

VARIANTS

The only known variant of the *Devastator* is the DVS-3, which remains under development at this time.

The DVS-3 drops three of the original design's medium lasers in favor of an additional half ton of armor and two more tons of Gauss ammunition. In addition, a rear-firing small laser is mounted in the center torso. This model has not yet seen combat.

Type: **Devastator**
Technology Base: Inner Sphere
Tonnage: 100

Equipment			Mass
Internal Structure:			10
Engine:		300 XL	9.5
Walking MP:		3	
Running MP:		5	
Jumping MP:		0	
Heat Sinks:		14 [28]	4
Gyro:			3
Cockpit:			3
Armor Factor:		296	18.5
	Internal Structure	Armor Value	
Head	3	9	
Center Torso	31	47	
Center Torso (rear)		12	
R/L Torso	21	30	
R/L Torso (rear)		10	
R/L Arm	17	34	
R/L Leg	21	40	

Weapons and Ammo	Location	Critical	Tonnage
Gauss Rifle	RA	7	15
Gauss Rifle	LA	7	15
PPC	RT	3	7
PPC	LT	3	7
Medium Laser	CT (R)	1	1
Medium Laser	H	1	1
Medium Laser	RT	1	1
Medium Laser	LT	1	1
Ammo (Gauss) 8	RA	1	1
Ammo (Gauss) 8	LA	1	1
Ammo (Gauss) 8	LT	1	1
Ammo (Gauss) 8	RT	1	1

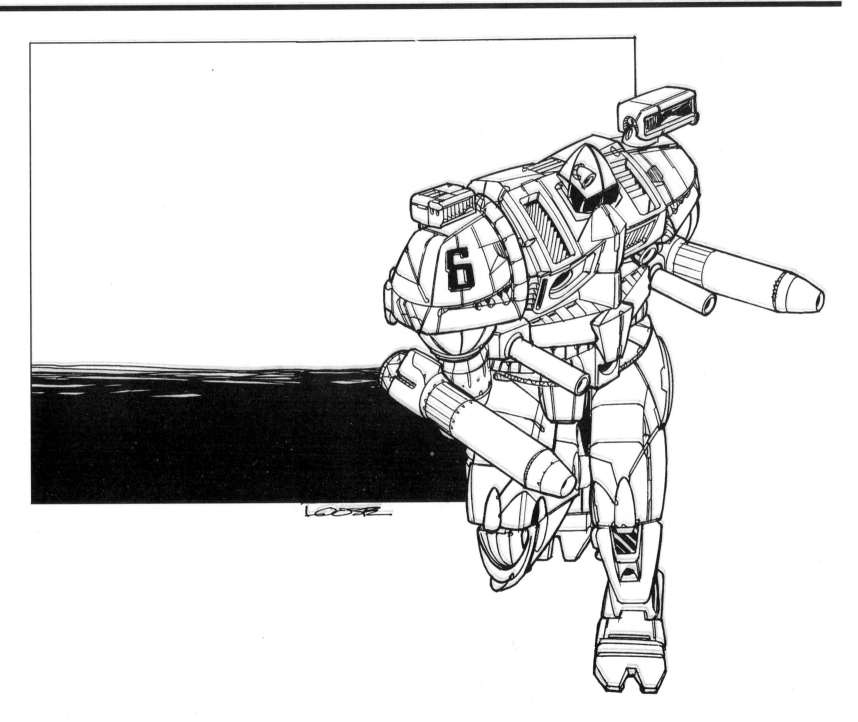

MSK-6S MACKIE

INNER SPHERE MECHS

Mass: 100 tons
Chassis: Ford Super H QWA3X
Power Plant: Hermes 360
Cruising Speed: 32 kph
Maximum Speed: 54 kph
Jump Jets: None
    Jump Capacity: None
Armor: Standard
Armament:
    1 PPC
    2 Medium Lasers
    1 Class 10 Autocannon
Manufacturer: Skobel Mechworks
    Primary Factory: None
Communications System: Unknown
Targeting and Tracking System: Unknown

OVERVIEW

"A box with legs" is how one military commander described the *Mackie* the first time he saw it. Others saw the *Mackie* as the future of warfare, and time has vindicated their judgment. Though the *Mackie* was first developed in 2439 by the Terran Hegemony, its existence and that of the Hegemony's entire BattleMech program was kept secret until 2443, when a lance of *Mackies* from the 801st Heavy Armored Regiment destroyed a company of Kurita tanks on the planet Styx.

The *Mackie* was the first BattleMech to be mass-produced on Terra, in no less than six factories. It remained the Hegemony's ultimate weapon until 2455,

when a commando unit from the Lyran Commonwealth stole the plans for BattleMech construction. The *Mackie* was produced until the start of the Amaris Civil War on Terra, and it is believed that General Kerensky took more than one hundred *Mackies* with him on his Exodus from the Inner Sphere. Three of Skobel's *Mackie* factories on Terra were destroyed in later years; the fate of the other three remains unknown.

CAPABILITIES

Built on the largest chassis available at the time, the *Mackie* used a massive 360 fusion engine that constituted a third of the 'Mech's total weight. The *Mackie*'s design team asked twenty of Terra's best weapons and support firms to help with the 'Mech's armament and electronics; as a result of the extra expertise, the *Mackie*'s sensor system was the best ever built in the Inner Sphere.

The *Mackie*'s armor, though weak for an assault 'Mech by modern standards, was more than adequate for the first 'Mech ever built. The *Mackie* has only fifteen heat sinks, and so the pilot must keep a sharp eye on the 'Mech's heat levels. The *Mackie*'s engine shielding is poor, and so its fusion engine runs hotter than normal. The *Mackie*'s weapons, like its armor, were top of the line in the mid-25th century: a PPC, two medium lasers, and a Class 10 autocannon. The *Mackie*'s cockpit canopy is unusual, made of one-way Plexiglas that allows the pilot to see out while preventing anyone from seeing in. The one-way canopy makes the 'Mech look eerily uninhabited.

Most of the *Mackie*'s records have been lost or destroyed over the six and a half centuries of the *Mackie*'s existence. General Aleksandr Kerensky is also believed to have taken a major portion of its records with him when he and the SLDF left the Inner Sphere. Many historians hope to find more information about the first BattleMech from ComStar's newly opened archives.

DEPLOYMENT

The *Mackie*'s design has been rendered obsolete by six centuries of technological development. No

House army or mercenary unit in the Inner Sphere, nor any armed forces operating in the Periphery are known to deploy this prototype 'Mech.

Type: Mackie
Technology Base: Inner Sphere
Tonnage: 100

Equipment		Mass
Internal Structure:		10
Engine:	360	33
Walking MP:	3	
Running MP:	5	
Jumping MP:	0	
Heat Sinks:	15	5
Gyro:		4
Cockpit:		5
Armor Factor:	212	20

	Internal Structure	Armor Value
Head	3	8
Center Torso	31	30
Center Torso (rear)		10
R/L Torso	21	20
R/L Torso (rear)		10
R/L Arm	17	24
R/L Leg	21	28

Weapons and Ammo	Location	Critical	Tonnage
PPC	LA	3	7
Medium Laser	CT	1	1
Medium Laser	CT	1	1
AC/10	RA	7	12
Ammo (AC) 20	RT	2	2

Game Note

Because the *Mackie* was the first BattleMech, it mounted a prototype engine, cockpit and armor. These components are heavier than standard, and so the *Mackie* does not adhere to standard **BattleTech** game rules.

MSK-6S MACKIE

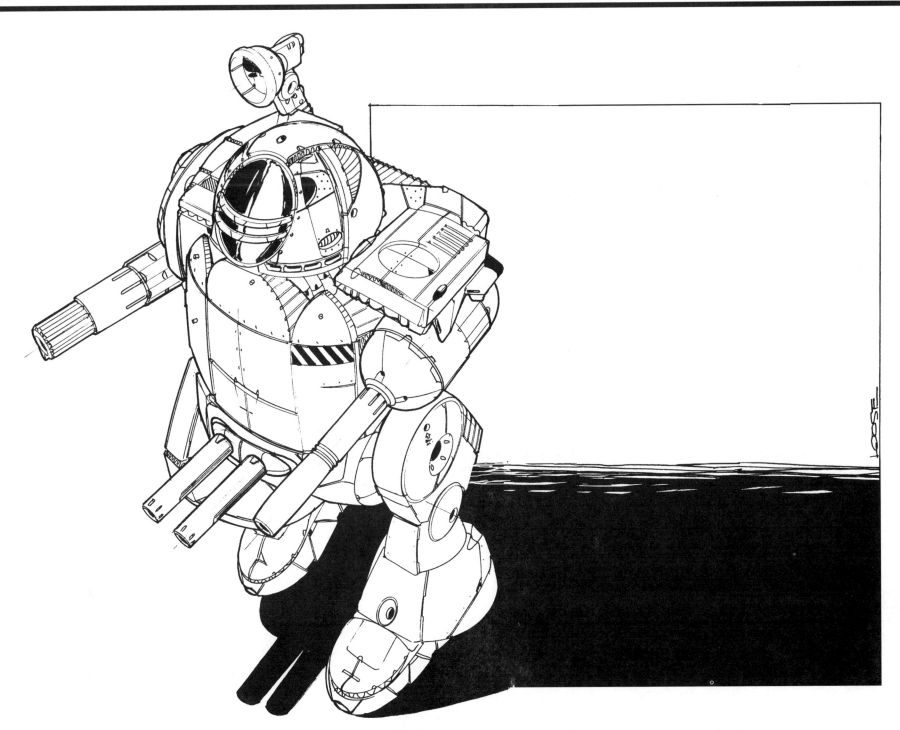

PLG-3Z PILLAGER

INNER SPHERE MECHS

Mass: 100 tons
Chassis: HildCo Heavy Type VIIQT
Power Plant: Vlar 300 XL
Cruising Speed: 32 kph
Maximum Speed: 54 kph
Jump Jets: HildCo Model 13
   Jump Capacity: 90 meters
Armor: Star Slab/9.5 Mk II
Armament:
   2 Poland Main Model A Gauss Rifle
   4 Ceres Arms Medium Laser
   1 Defiance B3L Large Laser
Manufacturer: HildCo Interplanetary Inc.
   Primary Factory: St. Ives
Communications System: CeresCom Recon Model
 12k
Targeting and Tracking System: C-Apple Churchill

OVERVIEW

The success of its *Victor* design led HildCo Interplanetary to develop a larger version of that BattleMech for city assaults and defense, either standing alone or as part of a lance. That 'Mech was the *Pillager*. Built during the Reunification War, the *Pillager* enjoyed great success with the SLDF and helped turn the tide of that conflict in the Star League's favor. The *Pillager* is the largest BattleMech ever constructed by HildCo. The destruction of the facilities that made its advanced systems kept the *Pillager* out of production from the end of the Second Succession War, but the decoding of the Gray Death memory core provided

HildCo's engineers with the knowledge their predecessors had lost. HildCo Interplanetary recently restarted production of the *Pillager* at its plant on St. Ives.

CAPABILITIES

Built on one of the largest chassis ever designed in the Inner Sphere, the *Pillager* presents an intimidating sight. The new Vlar 300 XL engine gives the *Pillager* the same top speed as the *Atlas* but at half the weight, allowing for the installation of heavier weapons and armor. The *Pillager*'s main weapons are its two Gauss rifles, a large laser and four medium lasers. The *Pillager*'s nineteen tons of armor give it excellent protection. Fourteen double heat sinks keep the modern-day *Pillager* cool—indeed, it is one of the coolest-running 'Mechs on the battlefield. The *Pillager* is also equipped with jump jets that allow it to leap up to ninety meters.

The *Pillager* has a long and colorful combat history, including action in the Reunification War, the Amaris Civil War, and the Succession Wars. According to records of those conflicts, enemy forces tended to flee from the mere sight of approaching *Pillager*s.

DEPLOYMENT

HildCo has already completed four production runs of the *Pillager* and has begun a fifth. The biggest customer so far has been the St. Ives Compact Military. The St. Ives government has announced plans to sell the *Pillager* to mercenary units in the near future.

Type: **Pillager**
Technology Base: Inner Sphere
Tonnage: 100

Equipment		Mass
Internal Structure:		10
Engine:	300 XL	9.5
Walking MP:	3	
Running MP:	5	
Jumping MP:	3	
Heat Sinks:	14 [28]	4
Gyro:		3
Cockpit:		3
Armor Factor:	307	19.5

	Internal Structure	Armor Value
Head	3	9
Center Torso	31	52
Center Torso (rear)		10
R/L Torso	21	32
R/L Torso (rear)		10
R/L Arm	17	34
R/L Leg	21	42

Weapons and Ammo	Location	Critical	Tonnage
Gauss Rifle	RT	7	15
Gauss Rifle	LT	7	15
Medium Laser	LA	1	1
Medium Laser	LA	1	1
Medium Laser	H	1	1
Medium Laser	CT	1	1
Large Laser	RA	2	5
Ammo (Gauss) 16	RT	2	2
Ammo (Gauss) 16	LT	2	2
Ammo (Gauss) 8	RL	1	1
Ammo (Gauss) 8	LL	1	1
Jump Jet	CT	1	2
Jump Jet	RL	1	2
Jump Jet	LL	1	2

PLG-3Z PILLAGER

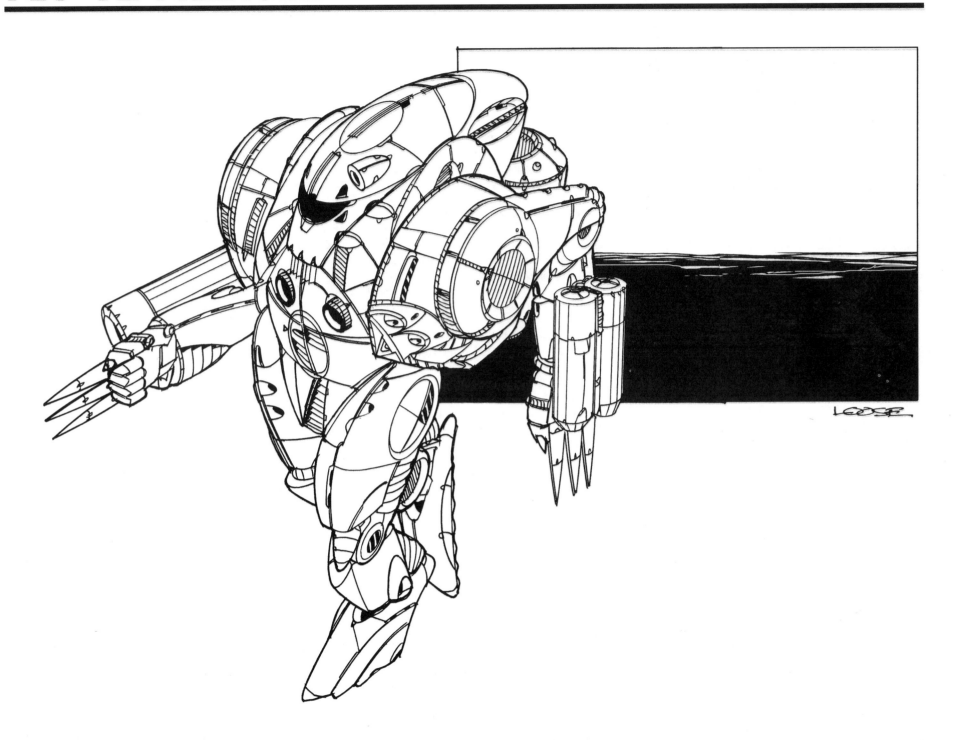

INNER SPHERE MECHS

Mass: 100 tons
Chassis: Norse Heavy XTI-4C
Power Plant: Vlar 300 XL
Cruising Speed: 32 kph
Maximum Speed: 54 kph
Jump Jets: None
  Jump Capacity: None
Armor: ArcShield Heavy Type K
Armament:
  3 Norse Model M-7D Gauss Rifles
  4 Defiance B3M Medium Lasers
Manufacturer: Norse-Storm BattleMechs Inc.
  Primary Factory: Loxley
Communications System: Tek BattleCom
Targeting and Tracking System: DLK Type Phased
  Array Sensor System

OVERVIEW

The *Thunder Hawk* is a Star League-era design developed and built for the SLDF by Norse Technologies during the final six years of the Amaris Civil War. General Aleksandr Kerensky is believed to have taken all the remaining *Thunder Hawks* with him on the Exodus. However, Norse-Storm BattleMechs Inc. recently announced its intention to produce and sell new *Thunder Hawks* to mercenary units as well as Successor State militaries.

CAPABILITIES

The *Thunder Hawk* was designed as a fire-support 'Mech for assault lances and companies, and it performs that role extremely well thanks to the devastating firepower of its three Norse Gauss rifles. One salvo from these weapons is enough to destroy a light or medium 'Mech and seriously damage a heavy or assault 'Mech. Each Gauss rifle is equipped with two tons of ammunition. Four Defiance B3M medium lasers round out the weapons array, providing the pilot with backup weapons in case the *Thunder Hawk* runs out of Gauss ammunition. To allow the *Thunder Hawk* the greatest possible staying power in combat, the design team at Norse Technologies gave it ArcShield Heavy BattleMech armor for maximum protection.

To make room for the third Gauss rifle, the design team used the newly developed, lightweight Vlar 300 XL engine. The *Thunder Hawk* is a slow 'Mech with a top speed of only 54 kph, but the engineers felt that the tremendous range and striking power of the Gauss rifles more than made up for the 'Mech's lack of speed.

DEPLOYMENT

The Lyran Alliance is the only Successor State that currently fields *Thunder Hawks*; the Alliance military has stationed several lances of them along its border with the Jade Falcon occupied zone. *Thunder Hawks* have also been spotted in the ranks of three mercenary units in Alliance employ—Storm's Metal Thunder, the Blackstone Highlanders, and the Regiment Wreckers. All of these units are long-time employees of House Steiner, and reportedly each fields at least two lances of this deadly BattleMech.

VARIANTS

Norse-Storm BattleMechs is developing two variants of the *Thunder Hawk*. The first variant removes all four medium lasers and replaces them with two medium pulse lasers. The second variant, known as the 7KMA, replaces the Gauss rifle and ammunition mounted in the left torso with a Katyusha Arrow IV missile artillery system in the left torso and arm. Two tons of missile reloads are stored in the left leg.

Type: Thunder Hawk
Technology Base: Inner Sphere
Tonnage: 100

Equipment			Mass
Internal Structure:			10
Engine:	300 XL		9.5
Walking MP:	3		
Running MP:	5		
Jumping MP:	0		
Heat Sinks:	10		0
Gyro:			3
Cockpit:			3
Armor Factor:	307		19.5

	Internal Structure	Armor Value
Head	3	9
Center Torso	31	50
Center Torso (rear)		12
R/L Torso	21	32
R/L Torso (rear)		10
R/L Arm	17	34
R/L Leg	21	42

Weapons and Ammo	Location	Critical	Tonnage
Gauss Rifle	RA	7	15
Gauss Rifle	RT	7	15
Gauss Rifle	LT	7	15
Medium Laser	LA	1	1
Medium Laser	LA	1	1
Medium Laser	H	1	1
Medium Laser	RA	1	1
Ammo (Gauss) 16	CT	2	2
Ammo (Gauss) 16	RT	2	2
Ammo (Gauss) 16	LT	2	2

TDK-7X THUNDER HAWK

CLAN BATTLEMECHS

Though outright warfare with the Clans has ceased since the Truce of Tukayyid, intelligence-gathering efforts have increased tenfold. As the truce's expiration date draws nearer, ComStar and other Inner Sphere powers are intensifying efforts to learn as much about the Clan enemy as possible before war breaks out afresh.

These efforts have been greatly aided by the release of certain classified information from the datastores of Wolfnet, one of the few storehouses of knowledge not yet penetrated by our Order. Wolfnet has given us accurate, detailed descriptions of many Clan BattleMechs and OmniMechs heretofore rarely seen in the field but which are increasingly appearing in Clan garrisons throughout the Clan-occupied zones. Some designs, once seen in limited numbers among command Stars, are becoming more and more common. In the case of certain Clans, such as the Jade Falcons, these rotations probably stem from efforts to make up for their staggering losses in their recent conflict with Clan Wolf. Other Clans may be bringing new units from their homeworlds to beef up their forces in anticipation of the renewed offensive against the Inner Sphere.

This report indicates that the Clans are moving as rapidly as we are in the development and deployment of new battlefield units. Many military experts believe that the Clans will break the Truce of Tukayyid and resume their push toward Terra before the truce expires in 3067. Given this frightening possibility, the Inner Sphere must continue to be vigilant.

—Jared Pascal
Adept XIV-Omega
ComStar Archives, Terra
4 January 3058

PIRANHA

CLAN MECHS

Mass: 20 tons
Chassis: Endo Steel
Power Plant: 180 XL
Cruising Speed: 97 kph
Maximum Speed: 151 kph
Jump Jets: None
　　Jump Capacity: None
Armor: Standard
Armament:
　　12 Machine Guns
　　2 ER Medium Lasers
　　1 ER Small Laser
Manufacturer: Unknown
Communications System: Unknown
Targeting and Tracking System: Unknown

OVERVIEW

The *Piranha*, like the Diamond Shark Clan that uses it, is something of an enigma. Though this light 'Mech offers superior speed and maneuverability, the *Piranha* is armed with a weapon load more suited to an attack unit than a recon unit. Also, this 'Mech would seem to operate at peak efficiency when using the "pack" tactics common to the Inner Sphere, as its name implies, but none have been sighted attacking in such a way. Questions about this 'Mech may never be resolved, because the last of these 'Mechs disappeared along with the rest of Clan Diamond Shark's military after the Battle of Tukayyid.

CAPABILITIES

As the *Piranha* has rarely been seen in combat, observers can only guess at its true capabilities. A large XL engine and powerful legs give the *Piranha* an astounding running speed, allowing it to close quickly with the enemy and bring its twelve heavy machine guns to bear. Such a large array of machine guns can be deadly to units twice the *Piranha*'s size, especially if the small 'Mech can run behind the enemy. At short range, a *Piranha* can chew through any opponent's back armor almost instantly. The machine guns are also extremely potent antipersonnel weapons. Because the Clans rarely use unarmored infantry, it is safe to assume the *Piranha* was created in direct response to battles with Inner Sphere forces.

Three extended-range lasers, one small and two medium, supplement the *Piranha*'s machine guns. Because the 'Mech lacks the heat sinks to use them effectively, it is likely most pilots use these energy weapons only if they run out of ammunition—a rare occurrence, because the *Piranha* is always stationed near ample supply depots. If the pilot is willing to risk a heat spike by firing all three lasers simultaneously, the 'Mech can deliver firepower greater than that offered by most medium 'Mechs.

DEPLOYMENT

A few Stars of *Piranha*s saw action in the Tukayyid campaign, acting as combination striker/recon units attached to Omega Galaxy. The *Piranha*s would rush ahead of the main unit, flushing out hidden troops by firing machine guns into the trees and undergrowth, then herding them into the waiting arms of the main attack force. They also proved quite effective as anti-infantry 'Mechs, destroying entire companies of troops in seconds.

Type: Piranha
Technology Base: Clan
Tonnage: 20

Equipment			Mass
Internal Structure:	Endo Steel		1
Engine:	180 XL		3.5
Walking MP:	9		
Running MP:	14		
Jumping MP:	0		
Heat Sinks:	10		0
Gyro:			2
Cockpit:			3
Armor Factor:	64		4

	Internal Structure	Armor Value
Head	3	8
Center Torso	6	9
Center Torso (rear)		3
R/L Torso	5	8
R/L Torso (rear)		2
R/L Arm	3	6
R/L Leg	4	6

Weapons and Ammo	Location	Critical	Tonnage
ER Medium Laser	RA	1	1
ER Medium Laser	LA	1	1
6 Machine Guns	RT	6	1.5
Ammo (MG) 100	RT	1	.5
6 Machine Guns	LT	6	1.5
Ammo (MG) 100	LT	1	.5
ER Small Laser	CT	1	.5

PIRANHA

FIRE FALCON

CLAN MECHS

Mass: 25 tons
Chassis: Endo Steel
Power Plant: 200 XL
Cruising Speed: 86 kph
Maximum Speed: 130 kph
Jump Jets: None
    Jump Capacity: None
Armor: Ferro-Fibrous
Armament:
    10 tons of pod space available
Manufacturer: Unknown
Communications System: Unknown
Targeting and Tracking System: Unknown

OVERVIEW

The *Fire Falcon* is a Clan OmniMech, seen sporadically among the Jade Falcons. They appear to be evaluating this 'Mech as a replacement for the *Koshi*, over which the *Fire Falcon* has many advantages: superior ground speed, frontal armor and heavier weapons. However, the *Fire Falcon* also suffers significant disadvantages. It does not include an active probe as part of its standard equipment, and its lack of jump jets impairs its mobility. Paper-thin rear armor also makes the *Fire Falcon* particularly vulnerable to infantry heavy weapons. None of these characteristics are desirable in a reconnaissance vehicle, which by the nature of its mission often runs into ambushes of camouflaged infantry and combat vehicles.

CAPABILITIES

The primary configuration of the *Fire Falcon* consists of two extended-range medium lasers and two improved smaller lasers mounted in the right arm. The left shoulder sports twin Streak short-range missile launchers, each capable of firing four missiles at a time. An effective medium pulse laser is mounted in the left arm. Heat build-up is significant when all these weapons are fired simultaneously, but the *Fire Falcon* can nonetheless lay down an impressive level of fire for a few minutes at a time. A second configuration appears to serve as an overwatch vehicle, providing long-range autocannon and LRM fire for advancing units of the primary-configuration *Fire Falcon*s.

A third reported configuration, spotted on a *Fire Falcon* with the markings of the Falcon Keshik, sports two long-range large lasers and a targeting computer. During the Jade Falcon withdrawal from Tukayyid, a unit of this *Fire Falcon* held up the advance of a Com Guard medium company for some time before the Com Guards put it out of action. A fourth variant seems to be configured for anti-personnel missions, with four 20mm miniguns and two SRM-6 racks, designed to break up massed infantry formations or clear out buildings in close-quarters city fighting.

The final configuration is reportedly used in conjunction with heavy missile- or Arrow IV-equipped units. With its TAG and Narc beacons, this *Fire Falcon* works perfectly as a spotter, directing fire from hidden units. As much tactical sense as this configuration makes, however, it is anathema to the traditional Jade Falcon perspective of honorable combat in one-on-one duels. Therefore, this configuration will probably never appear in front-line units.

DEPLOYMENT

The *Fire Falcon* is being deployed more frequently along Clan Jade Falcon's border with the Lyran Alliance, always accompanying *Black Lanner* OmniMechs. None have been reported in the forces of any other Clan.

Type: Fire Falcon
Technology Base: Clan OmniMech
Tonnage: 25

Equipment		Mass
Internal Structure:	Endo Steel	1.5
Engine:	200 XL	4.5
Walking MP:	8	
Running MP:	12	
Jumping MP:	0	
Heat Sinks:	10 [20]	0
Gyro:		2
Cockpit:		3
Armor Factor:	77	4

	Internal Structure	Armor Value
Head	3	9
Center Torso	8	11
Center Torso (rear)		3
R/L Torso	6	9
R/L Torso (rear)		2
R/L Arm	4	6
R/L Leg	6	10

Weight and Space Allocation

Location	Fixed	Spaces Remaining
Head		1
Center Torso		2
Right Torso	2 Engine	6
	4 Ferro-Fibrous	
Left Torso	2 Engine	6
	4 Endo Steel	
Right Arm	3 Ferro-Fibrous	5
Left Arm	3 Endo Steel	5
Right Leg	Double Heat Sink	0
Left Leg	Double Heat Sink	0

Weapons and Ammo	Location	Critical	Tonnage
Primary Weapons Configuration			
2 ER Medium Lasers	RA	2	2
2 ER Small Lasers	RA	2	1
Medium Pulse Laser	LA	1	2
2 Streak SRM 4	LT	2	4
Ammo (SRM) 25	LT	1	1

FIRE FALCON

Weapons and Ammo	Location	Critical	Tonnage
Alternate Configuration A			
Ultra AC/2	RA	2	5
Ammo (AC) 45	RT	1	1
ER Small Laser	LA	1	.5
LRM 10	LT	1	2.5
Ammo (LRM) 12	LT	1	1
Alternate Configuration B			
ER Large Laser	RA	1	4
ER Large Laser	LA	1	4
Targeting Computer	LT	2	2
Alternate Configuration C			
4 Machine Guns	RA	4	1
Ammo (MG) 100	RA	1	.5
Medium Pulse Laser	LA	1	2
Small Pulse Laser	LA	1	1
ER Small Laser	LA	1	.5
2 SRM 6	LT	2	3
Ammo (SRM) 15	LT	1	1
Active Probe	H	1	1
Alternate Configuration D			
2 SRM 4	LT	2	2
Ammo (SRM) 50	LT	2	2
ER Medium Laser	LA	1	1
Narc Missile Beacon	RA	1	2
Ammo (Narc) 12	RT	2	2
TAG	H	1	1

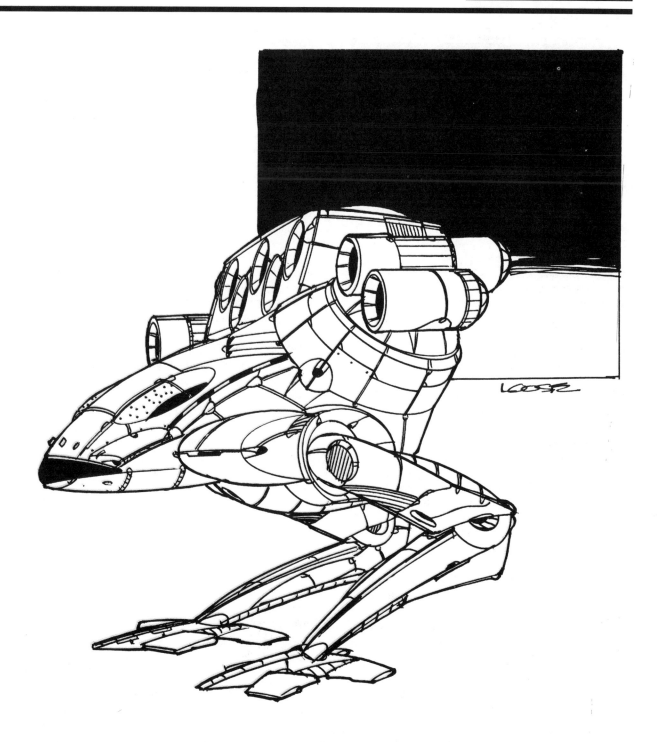

HANKYU

Mass: 30 tons
Chassis: Endo Steel
Power Plant: 240 XL
Cruising Speed: 86 kph
Maximum Speed: 130 kph
Jump Jets: 6
    Jump Capacity: 180 meters
Armor: Ferro-Fibrous
Armament:
    9.5 tons of pod space available
Manufacturer: Unknown
Communications System: Unknown
Targeting and Tracking System: Unknown

OVERVIEW

The *Hankyu*, or "Short Bow," made its first appearance in the Inner Sphere during the Battle of Luthien. Apparently the Smoke Jaguars' attempt to create a fast scout 'Mech, the *Hankyu* has somewhat lighter armor than that of comparable Inner Sphere designs, but its speed makes it a difficult target to hit.

CAPABILITIES

The *Hankyu*'s several different configurations enable it to carry a wide variety of weapons and electronics. All variants carry an anti-infantry flamer.

In its primary configuration the *Hankyu* mounts an LRM-5 pack on each arm. CASE-protected storage bins in the machine's torso hold ammunition for these weapons. Extended-range medium lasers in each wrist and the standard flamer complete the weapons array.

In addition to its impressive firepower, the primary configuration also boasts an active probe system, target-acquisition gear, and a full ECM suite.

Alternate configuration A replaces the long-range missile systems with Streak SRM-6 packs. A single, small pulse laser provides precision fire and the flamer completes the weapon load in this close-combat version.

Alternate configuration B boasts a diverse mix of long- and short-range weapons. A multibarrel LB 2-X autocannon sprouts from the machine's right hand, backed up by the flared muzzle of the standard flamer. A pair of medium lasers hang below the left wrist.

Alternate configuration C modifies the *Hankyu* for extended scouting missions. This configuration features two extended-range medium lasers in each wrist, and a medium pulse laser in both the right and left torso. The left torso also houses the standard flamer. An active probe allows the pilot to spot hidden or shut-down 'Mechs at a safe distance.

DEPLOYMENT

Clan Smoke Jaguar is the primary user of the *Hankyu*, though the Nova Cats and Steel Vipers are also rumored to employ the design.

Type: **Hankyu**
Technology Base: Clan OmniMech
Tonnage: 30

Equipment		Mass
Internal Structure:	Endo Steel	1.5
Engine:	240 XL	6
Walking MP:	8	
Running MP:	12	
Jumping MP:	6	
Heat Sinks:	10 [20]	0
Gyro:		3
Cockpit:		3
Armor Factor:	77	4

	Internal Structure	Armor Value
Head	3	9
Center Torso	10	9
Center Torso (rear)		5
R/L Torso	7	8
R/L Torso (rear)		4
R/L Arm	5	7
R/L Leg	7	8

Weight and Space Allocation

Location	Fixed	Spaces Remaining
Head	1 Ferro-Fibrous	0
Center Torso	2 Jump Jets	0
Right Torso	2 Ferro-Fibrous	4
	2 Endo Steel	
	2 Engine	
	2 Double Heat Sink	
Left Torso	2 Ferro-Fibrous	5
	3 Endo Steel	
	2 Engine	
Right Arm	1 Ferro-Fibrous	6
	1 Endo Steel	
Left Arm	1 Ferro-Fibrous	6
	1 Endo Steel	
Right Leg	2 Jump Jet	0
Left Leg	2 Jump Jet	0

Weapons and Ammo	Location	Critical	Tonnage
Primary Weapons Configuration			
LRM 5	RA	1	1
Ammo (LRM) 24	RT	1	1
LRM 5	LA	1	1
Ammo (LRM) 24	LT	1	1
ER Medium Laser	RA	1	1
ER Medium Laser	LA	1	1
Flamer	RT	1	.5
Active Probe	RT	1	1
TAG	LT	1	1
ECM Suite	LT	1	1

HANKYU

Weapons and Ammo	Location	Critical	Tonnage
Alternate Configuration A			
Streak SRM 6	RA	2	3
Ammo (SRM) 15	RT	1	1
Streak SRM 6	LA	2	3
Ammo (SRM) 15	LT	1	1
Small Pulse Laser	RA	1	1
Flamer	LA	1	.5
Alternate Configuration B			
LB 2-X AC	RA	3	5
Ammo (AC) 45	RT	1	1
Medium Pulse Laser	LA	1	2
ER Medium Laser	LA	1	1
Flamer	RA	1	.5
Alternate Configuration C			
2 ER Medium Lasers	RA	2	2
2 ER Medium Lasers	LA	2	2
Medium Pulse Laser	RT	1	2
Medium Pulse Laser	LT	1	2
Active Probe	RT	1	1
Flamer	LT	1	.5

CLAN MECHS

Mass: 40 tons
Chassis: Endo Steel
Power Plant: 240 Standard
Cruising Speed: 65 kph
Maximum Speed: 97 kph
Jump Jets: None
   Jump Capacity: None
Armor: Ferro-Fibrous
Armament:
   14 tons of pod space available
Manufacturer: Clan Steel Viper
Communications System: Bishop 400
   Holly/Meridian CTC
Targeting and Tracking System: Spanke 112-A

OVERVIEW

Like its sister 'Mech the *Crossbow*, the *Battle Cobra* is unusual in Clan OmniMech design. Only the 'Mech's arms are equipped to accept weapon pods—its legs and torso are unarmed. This design characteristic is used to date only by Clan Steel Viper, and the *Battle Cobra* is the centerpiece of this innovative design scheme.

CAPABILITIES

The *Battle Cobra's* main firepower is focused in energy-based weapons, primarily pulse lasers and PPCs. Its primary configuration and alternate configuration A both use multiple pulse lasers; alternate configuration B replaces some of the additional pulse lasers with two PPCs. The relatively small size of this 'Mech

prompted the Steel Vipers to limit ammunition carrying-space, which in turn allowed greater speed. Significant firepower and speed combine to earn the *Battle Cobra* a strong reputation within the Clans. The Jade Falcons are currently negotiating to procure a number of *Battle Cobra*s to modify to their own weapons needs.

*Battle Cobra*s are used primarily in light, fast scout or harasser Stars, fitting well into the Steel Viper's familiar hit-and-run tactics. The 'Mech's unique cobra-like hood behind the cockpit stands out on the battlefield. Though designed as a sensor array, this hood also adds to the mystique of this deadly 'Mech.

DEPLOYMENT

During the Battle for Tukayyid, the 205th Viper Striker Cluster (the Fangs of Blood) equipped a Trinary primarily with *Battle Cobra*s. During the initial thrust at Devil's Bath, the 205th's *Battle Cobra*s played a key role in skirting the flanks of the Vipers' Com Guard opponents.

At the end of the battle most of the *Battle Cobra*s were still operational, a solid testimony to the effectiveness of their design. Rumor has it that ComStar recovered one of the fallen 'Mechs of this design and may be working on a similar model, but this rumor has not been confirmed.

Type: **Battle Cobra**
Technology Base: Clan OmniMech
Tonnage: 40

Equipment		Mass
Internal Structure	Endo Steel	2
Engine:	240	11.5
Walking MP:	6	
Running MP:	9	
Jumping MP:	0	
Heat Sinks:	10 [20]	0
Gyro:		3
Cockpit:		3
Armor Factor:	125	6.5

	Internal Structure	Armor Value
Head	3	9
Center Torso	12	17
Center Torso (rear)		5
R/L Torso	10	14
R/L Torso (rear)		5
R/L Arm	6	11
R/L Leg	10	17

Weight and Space Allocation

Location	Fixed	Spaces Remaining
Head		1
Center Torso	1 Endo Steel	0
	1 Ferro-Fibrous	
Right Torso	3 Endo Steel	6
	3 Ferro-Fibrous	
Left Torso	3 Endo Steel	6
	3 Ferro-Fibrous	
Right Arm		8
Left Arm		8
Right Leg	Double Heat Sink	0
Left Leg		2

Weapons and Ammo	Location	Critical	Tonnage
Primary Weapons Configuration			
Large Pulse Laser	RA	2	6
Large Pulse Laser	LA	2	6
Small Pulse Laser	RA	1	1
Small Pulse Laser	LA	1	1
Alternate Configuration A			
2 Medium Pulse Lasers	RA	2	4
3 Small Pulse Lasers	RA	3	3
2 Medium Pulse Lasers	LA	2	4
3 Small Pulse Lasers	LA	3	3
Alternate Configuration B			
ER PPC	RA	2	6
ER PPC	LA	2	6
Small Pulse Laser	RA	1	1
Small Pulse Laser	LA	1	1

BATTLE COBRA

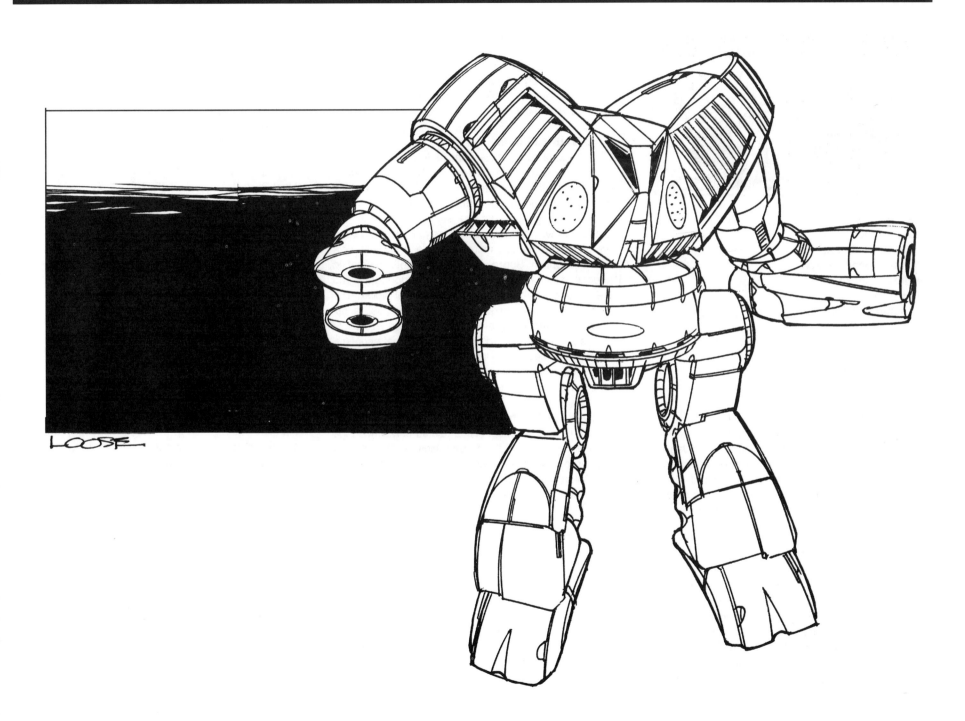

GRENDEL

CLAN MECHS

Mass: 45 tons
Chassis: Endo Steel
Power Plant: 315 XL
Cruising Speed: 76 kph
Maximum Speed: 119 kph
Jump Jets: 7
    Jump Capacity: 210 meters
Armor: Ferro-Fibrous
Armament: 13.5 tons of pod space available
Manufacturer: Unknown
Communications System: Unknown
Targeting and Tracking System: Unknown

OVERVIEW

Initially identified with Clan Diamond Shark units in the Kozice Valley and later with Clan Smoke Jaguar, all five configurations of the *Grendel* have appeared in Clan front lines, leading light 'Mechs toward distant objectives. All five configurations so far observed possess a powerful array of weapons capable of delivering a consistent attack over varying ranges.

This 'Mech, tagged *Grendel* by Inner Sphere soldiers who encountered it, was among the first units to enter the Kozice Valley and engage the ComStar defenders on Tukayyid. These 'Mechs also fought against the Com Guards in the Racice Delta. The *Grendel*'s reliance on energy-based weapons, especially in its primary configuration, simplified initial supply problems for Clans Diamond Shark and Smoke Jaguar, allowing their units to range far into the field. Had these 'Mechs been properly supported, they could have done extensive damage to the Com Guards' lines.

The large 315 XL engine produces enormous power that allows the *Grendel* to move at a steady pace over all kinds of terrain. The 'Mech's jump jets proved especially useful in the difficult ground around the edge of the Kozice Valley, allowing the *Grendel* to keep up with faster ground-based 'Mechs.

CAPABILITIES

The wide range of weapons featured in all configurations of the *Grendel* make the 'Mech an excellent choice for battling an unknown enemy. As a recon 'Mech or raider, the design performs extremely well. In the stand-and-slug-it-out fighting style common to the Clans, however, the 'Mech fares less well than some others of its type that can more easily close and deliver a knockout punch. Successful *Grendel* pilots attempt to engage at long range, then dash within short range and fire off a deadly SRM and medium laser volley. The Streak system is especially useful for this tactic, because its missiles are not wasted on careless shots as the pilots rush toward the enemy. Alternate configuration A has appeared almost exclusively as a fire-support 'Mech with mobile reserves, and fired its LRMs at long range more often than it sought to disengage.

DEPLOYMENT

To date the *Grendel* has appeared only among the Diamond Sharks and the Smoke Jaguars. Though they appear to make heavy use of it, it remains to be seen if this 'Mech is as common among these specific Clans as it seems or if it saw particularly heavy action on Tukayyid.

Type: **Grendel**
Technology Base: Clan OmniMech
Tonnage: 45

Equipment			Mass
Internal Structure:	Endo Steel		2.5
Engine:	315 XL		11
Walking MP:	7		
Running MP:	11		
Jumping MP:	7		
Heat Sinks:	10 [20]		0
Gyro:			4
Cockpit:			3
Armor Factor:	144		7.5

	Internal Structure	Armor Value
Head	3	9
Center Torso	14	18
Center Torso (rear)		9
R/L Torso	11	16
R/L Torso (rear)		6
R/L Arm	7	12
R/L Leg	11	20

Weight and Space Allocation

Location	Fixed	Spaces Remaining
Head		1
Center Torso	1 Jump Jet	1
Right Torso	3 Endo Steel	6
	2 XL Engine	
	1 Jump Jet	
Left Torso	3 Endo Steel	6
	2 XL Engine	
	1 Jump Jet	
Right Arm	1 Endo Steel	4
	3 Ferro-Fibrous	
Left Arm	4 Ferro-Fibrous	4
Right Leg	2 Jump Jets	0
Left Leg	2 Jump Jets	0

GRENDEL

Weapons and Ammo	Location	Critical	Tonnage
Primary Weapons Configuration			
ER Large Laser	RA	1	4
ER Small Laser	RA	1	.5
ER Medium Laser	H	1	1
2 ER Medium Lasers	LA	2	2
Streak SRM 6	RT	2	3
Ammo (SRM) 15	RT	1	1
Double Heat Sink	RT	2	1
Double Heat Sink	LT	2	1
Alternate Configuration A			
Medium Pulse Laser	RA	1	2
ER Small Laser	RA	1	.5
LRM 15	LT	2	3.5
Ammo (LRM) 16	LT	2	2
LRM 15	RT	2	3.5
Ammo (LRM) 16	RT	2	2
Alternate Configuration B			
Ultra AC/5	RA	3	7
ER Medium Laser	RA	1	1
Medium Pulse Laser	LA	1	2
ER Small Laser	CT	1	.5
Ammo (AC) 20	RT	1	1
Medium Pulse Laser	RT	1	2
Alternate Configuration C			
LB 10-X AC	RA	5	10
ER Medium Laser	LA	1	1
Ammo (LB 10-X) 10	RT	1	1
Anti-Missile System	LT	1	.5
Ammo (AMS) 24	LT	1	1
Alternate Configuration D			
Small Pulse Laser	RA	1	1
Medium Pulse Laser	LA	1	2
ER Medium Laser	LA	1	1
ER PPC	RT	2	6
SRM 6	LT	1	1.5
Ammo (SRM) 30	LT	2	2

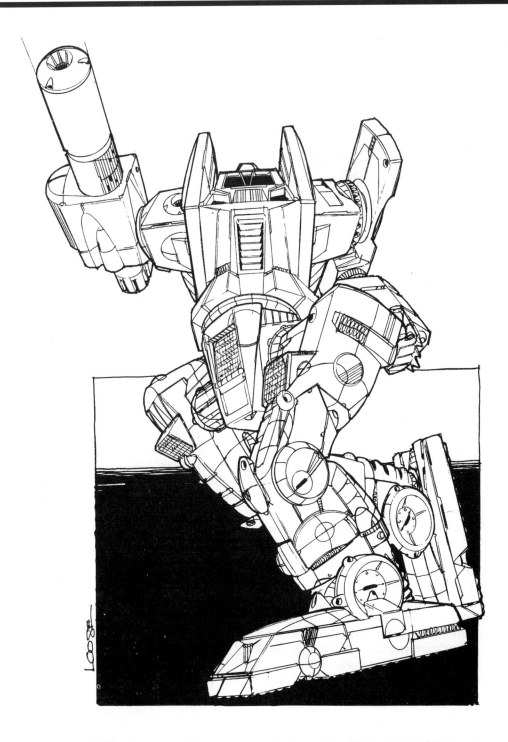

SHADOW CAT

CLAN MECHS

Mass: 45 tons
Chassis: Endo Steel
Power Plant: 270 XL
Cruising Speed: 65 kph
Maximum Speed: 97 kph, w/MASC 130 kph
Jump Jets: 6
    Jump Capacity: 180 meters
Armor: Ferro-Fibrous
Armament:
    17 tons of pod space available
Manufacturer: Unknown
Communications System: Unknown
Targeting and Tracking System: Unknown

OVERVIEW

Following sketchy initial reports from the Battle of Luthien, high-ranking sources within the DCMS confirmed observations of a new class of OmniMech, tagged the *Shadow Cat*. The Clans, primarily the Smoke Jaguars and Nova Cats, used this 'Mech extensively on Tukayyid, though Clan Steel Viper forces also used it at Hladno Springs.

CAPABILITIES

This 45-ton medium 'Mech appeared in the vanguard of the Nova Cat forces on Tukayyid. Fast and agile, the 'Mech was deployed primarily as a command vehicle for the Clan Nova Cat Stars that emerged from the Smoke Jaguars' defensive wedge formation. According to eyewitness reports at Luthien and the Racice Delta on Tukayyid, the

Shadow Cat moved at a speed of close to 130 kph over the open plains. On Luthien, the 'Mech overwhelmed the forward observation posts even as they relayed reports of the oncoming enemy forces back to the Imperial City. From the observation posts, the *Shadow Cat*s moved out in an ever-widening crescent to search for lightly defended paths to Luthien's capitol. Similar tactics brought the Clans several initial successes on Tukayyid.

The *Shadow Cat* appears to serve in Nova Cat and Smoke Jaguar forces much as the *Fenris* serves in Wolf Clan forces, even matching the Fenris's sophisticated sensor array. The *Shadow Cat*'s engine is smaller and the 'Mech has a correspondingly slower top speed, but it mounts myomer accelerator signal circuitry (MASC), which pushes its top speed beyond its opponents' expectations. The *Shadow Cat* is jump-capable, and its heat sinks are certainly double strength.

The *Shadow Cat*'s primary weapon is an arm-mounted Gauss rifle. Against the light and medium 'Mechs that normally oppose such a machine, the Gauss rifle is a devastating weapon, capable of coring most light 'Mechs with a single shot. Even the heavy 'Mechs of the Com Guards were staggered by the rain of shells the *Shadow Cat*s' Gauss rifles produced.

Backing up the Gauss rifle is a pair of medium lasers. As with most Clan weapons, these lasers demonstrate increased range and accuracy when compared with Inner Sphere weapons. Though incapable of bringing down an enemy 'Mech with a single shot, these weapons work very well as secondary armaments to the rifle.

DEPLOYMENT

To date, confirmed observations place the *Shadow Cat* only among Clans Nova Cat, Smoke Jaguar and Steel Viper. Initial analysis suggests that the 'Mech serves as a reconnaissance unit, probably teamed with other light or medium 'Mechs or as part of a command Star.

Type: Shadow Cat
Technology Base: Clan OmniMech
Tonnage: 45

Equipment			Mass
Internal Structure:	Endo Steel		2.5
Engine:	270 XL		7.5
Walking MP:	6		
Running MP:	9 (12)		
Jumping MP:	6		
Heat Sinks:	10 [20]		0
Gyro:			3
Cockpit:			3
Armor Factor:	134		7

	Internal Structure	Armor Value
Head	3	8
Center Torso	14	20
Center Torso (rear)		6
R/L Torso	11	18
R/L Torso (rear)		4
R/L Arm	7	10
R/L Leg	11	18

Weight and Space Allocation

Location	Fixed	Spaces Remaining
Head	1 Endo Steel	0
Center Torso	2 MASC	0
Right Torso	2 XL Engine	4
	4 Ferro-Fibrous	
	1 Jump Jet	
	1 Endo Steel	
Left Torso	2 XL Engine	5
	3 Ferro-Fibrous	
	1 Jump Jet	
	1 Endo Steel	
Right Arm	2 Endo Steel	6
Left Arm	2 Endo Steel	6
Right Leg	2 Jump Jets	0
Left Leg	2 Jump Jets	0

SHADOW CAT

Weapons and Ammo	Location	Critical	Tonnage
Primary Weapons Configuration			
Gauss Rifle	RA	6	12
Ammo (Gauss) 16	RT	2	2
ER Medium Laser	LA	1	1
ER Medium Laser	RT	1	1
Active Probe	LT	1	1
Alternate Configuration A			
ER Large Laser	LA	1	4
ER Large Laser	RA	1	4
Streak SRM 6	RT	2	3
Ammo (SRM) 30	RT	2	2
Double Heat Sink	LA	2	1
Double Heat Sink	RA	2	1
Double Heat Sink	LT	2	1
Active Probe	LT	1	1
Alternate Configuration B			
LRM 15	LA	2	3.5
Ammo (LRM) 16	LT	2	2
Artemis IV FCS	RT	1	1
LRM 15	RA	2	3.5
Ammo (LRM) 16	RT	2	2
Artemis IV FCS	RA	1	1
ER Medium Laser	LA	1	1
ER Medium Laser	RA	1	1
ECM Suite	LT	1	1
Active Probe	RT	1	1

HUNCHBACK IIC

Mass: 50 tons
Chassis: Endo Steel
Power Plant: 200 XL
Cruising Speed: 43 kph
Maximum Speed: 65 kph
Jump Jets: 4
    Jump Capacity: 120 meters
Armor: Standard
Armament:
    2 Ultra 20 Autocannons
    2 ER Medium Lasers
Manufacturer: Unknown
Communications System: Unknown
Targeting and Tracking System: Unknown

OVERVIEW

The *Hunchback* IIC is a reworking of the venerable Star League-era HBK-2, a basic design that has remained largely unchanged since its inception. Initial hardware assessments of this new version observed among the Clan forces suggest that Clan technicians incorporated into this machine more compact and technologically sophisticated components, allowing the installation of two rapid-fire autocannons rather than a single AC-20. The higher tech also allows room for the installation of jump jets, which greatly enhance the *Hunchback*'s effectiveness as an urban and woodland fighter.

CAPABILITIES

This version of the tried and true *Hunchback* is similar to its Inner Sphere counterpart in at least one respect: the 'Mech is lightly armored for a unit of its weight class. Indeed, the *Hunchback*'s overall design makes it ill-suited to endure a protracted engagement with hostile forces. In addition to the weakness of its armor, the BattleMech's main weapons—its Ultra autocannons—only carry sufficient ammunition for about 20 seconds of sustained fire. The addition of jump jets has done much to improve the usefulness of this design in long-term battles by giving it extra mobility, but the jump capability may not compensate for the design's apparent flaws. Even with the ability to jump out of weapons locks and crossfires, the *Hunchback* IIC remains only an average heavy weapons platform. Given the advanced materials and systems observed in other Clan 'Mechs, the question of why this design is still among their front-line units continues to provide a point of contentious debate. One school of thought holds that, regardless of the rhetoric, the Clans are human and therefore make mistakes. As with the CGR-1A1 *Charger*, the Clan designers may have decided that overemphasizing one aspect of the battlement would give the unit an advantage. And like all military projects, the *Hunchback* IIC program took on a life of its own, and by sheer bureaucratic inertia the 'Mech made it into production and distribution to the troops.

The other school of thought attempts to explain the *Hunchback* IIC's design by placing it in the context of the warrior caste culture. The Clans practice the ultimate "up or out" personnel policy. Warriors who do not prove exemplary in combat are weeded out, denied the opportunity to assume leadership roles or contribute to the next generation of their caste. Warriors who fail to be identified as *ristars* become more and more desperate and begin taking more risks in combat, looking for that one glorious fight that will place them back on the path to a Bloodname. For these types of warriors, the *Hunchback* IIC, with its all-or-nothing design, is a perfect match.

DEPLOYMENT

The *Hunchback* IIC serves in the front lines of nearly all the invading Clans. Reports indicate that *Hunchback* pilots attached to front-line units seem to fight with a desperate ferocity unique even among the Clans, evidence that supports the idea that the *Hunchback* IIC is a last-chance 'Mech for Clan pilots.

Type: Hunchback IIC
Technology Base: Clan
Tonnage: 50

Equipment		Mass
Internal Structure:	Endo Steel	2.5
Engine:	200 XL	4.5
Walking MP:	4	
Running MP:	6	
Jumping MP:	4	
Heat Sinks:	12 [24]	2
Gyro:		2
Cockpit:		3
Armor Factor:	96	6

	Internal Structure	Armor Value
Head	3	8
Center Torso	16	18
Center Torso (rear)		4
R/L Torso	12	12
R/L Torso (rear)		3
R/L Arm	8	6
R/L Leg	12	12

Weapons and Ammo	Location	Critical	Tonnage
Ultra AC/20	RT	8	12
Ammo (AC) 5	RT	1	1
ER Medium Laser	CT	1	1
Ultra AC/20	LT	8	12
Ammo (AC) 5	LT	1	1
ER Medium Laser	CT	1	1
Jump Jets	RL	2	1
Jump Jets	LL	2	1

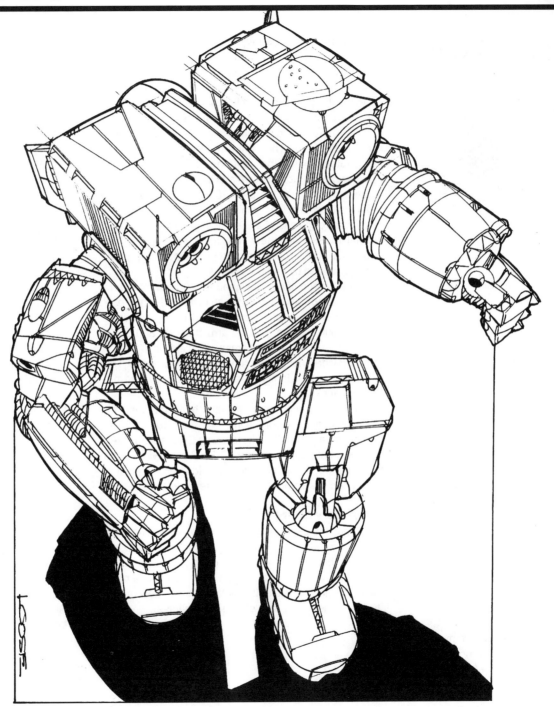

NOBORI-NIN

CLAN MECHS

Mass: 50 tons
Chassis: Endo Steel
Power Plant: 250 XL
Cruising Speed: 54 kph
Maximum Speed: 86 kph
Jump Jets: 5
    Jump Capacity: 150 meters
Armor: Ferro-Fibrous
Armament:
    23.5 tons of pod space available
Manufacturer: Unknown
Communications System: Unknown
Targeting and Tracking System: Unknown

OVERVIEW

The first *Nobori-nin*, or "Banner-bearer," appeared during the Battle of Luthien in the colors of the 119th Nova Cat Striker Cluster. The single finlike projection sprouting from its back gave this humanoid 'Mech its name. Apparently it reminded a DCMS intelligence officer of the banner samurai sometimes wore on their backs in feudal Japan. This design is known as the *Huntsman* among the Clans. It exemplifies the OmniMech concept, as it fills a variety of roles depending on its pod configuration.

CAPABILITIES

In its primary configuration, the *Nobori-nin* makes a superb prolonged-combat 'Mech. The right arm mounts an AC-5 Ultra autocannon, the left a Streak SRM-6. Each arm also holds a pair of medium lasers.

An LRM-10 slaved to an Artemis IV fire-control system provides the *Nobori-nin* with accurate long-range fire capability. An anti-missile system and A-pods provide close defense, and an active probe/TAG combination provides the pilot with his electronic eyes. A standard flamer rounds out the primary weapons array.

Alternate configuration A mounts a large pulse laser in each arm. The right arm also supports an LB 2-X autocannon, the left an LRM-10 system. Apparently, the *Nobori-nin* A's LRM launcher uses the same technology as the LRM-20 found on the *Atlas*. A rapid-cycle ammo feed allows the weapon to fire five missiles through each tube in the same amount of time normal missile launchers require to cycle once. Two additional double heat sinks help dissipate the great heat generated by these weapons.

The *Nobori-nin* B, designed for sudden raids and rapid strike operations, mounts an extended-range particle cannon in its right arm backed up by a pair of medium pulse lasers. The left arm supports an LB 10-X autocannon. Two tons of ammunition stored in the left torso provide enough ammunition for a fast strike. The B variant's anti-infantry weapons include two 11mm rotary machine guns.

The C variant seems to have been intended for long-range fire support. It mounts an LRM-20 in its right torso, an LRM-15 in its left. One ER medium laser, an ER small laser and an AC-5 Ultra provide more accurate fire. A Streak SRM-4 provides heavy striking power, while a flamer handles close-in defense.

DEPLOYMENT

Since the Battle of Luthien, the *Nobori-nin* has been spotted in striker Clusters all along the Draconis Combine border. It is seen more often among Nova Cat units than any other, but is uncommon even among them. This indicates that the design is either new or that its use carries some sort of inherent dishonor.

Type: **Nobori-nin**
Technology Base: Clan OmniMech
Tonnage: 50

Equipment			Mass
Internal Structure:	Endo Steel		2.5
Engine:	250 XL		6.5
Walking MP:	5		
Running MP:	8		
Jumping MP:	5		
Heat Sinks:	10 [20]		0
Gyro:			3
Cockpit:			3
Armor Factor:	169		9

	Internal Structure	Armor Value
Head	3	9
Center Torso	16	25
Center Torso (rear)		7
R/L Torso	12	18
R/L Torso (rear)		6
R/L Arm	8	16
R/L Leg	12	24

Weight and Space Allocation

Location	Fixed	Spaces Remaining
Head	1 Ferro-Fibrous	0
Center Torso	1 Jump Jet	0
	1 Endo Steel	
Right Torso	2 Engine	6
	1 Endo Steel	
	2 Ferro-Fibrous	
	1 Jump Jet	
Left Torso	2 Engine	5
	1 Endo Steel	
	3 Ferro-Fibrous	
	1 Jump Jet	
Right Arm	2 Endo Steel	6
Left Arm	1 Ferro-Fibrous	5
	2 Endo Steel	
Right Leg	1 Jump Jet	1
Left Leg	1 Jump Jet	1

NOBORI-NIN

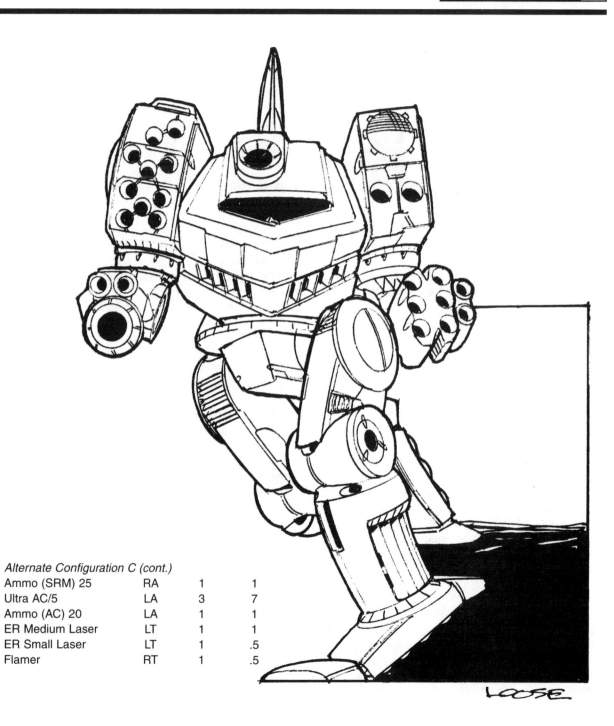

Weapons and Ammo	Location	Critical	Tonnage
Primary Weapons Configuration			
2 ER Medium Lasers	RA	2	2
2 ER Medium Lasers	LA	2	2
Ultra AC/2	RA	2	5
Ammo (AC) 45	RA	1	1
Streak SRM 6	LA	2	3
Ammo (SRM) 15	LA	1	1
LRM 10	RT	1	2.5
Ammo (LRM) 12	RT	1	1
Artemis IV FCS	RT	1	1
Anti-Missile System	LT	1	.5
Ammo (AMS) 24	LT	1	1
Active Probe	RT	1	1
TAG	LT	1	1
A-Pod	RL	1	.5
A-Pod	LL	1	.5
Flamer	LT	1	.5
Alternate Configuration A			
Large Pulse Laser	RA	2	6
Large Pulse Laser	LA	2	6
LB 2-X AC	RA	3	5
Ammo (AC) 45	RT	1	1
LRM 10	LA	1	2.5
Ammo (LRM) 12	LT	1	1
Double Heat Sink	RT	2	1
Double Heat Sink	LT	2	1
Alternate Configuration B			
ER PPC	RA	2	6
LB 10-X AC	LA	5	10
Ammo (AC) 20	LT	2	2
2 Medium Pulse Lasers	RA	2	4
2 Machine Guns	RT	2	.5
Ammo (MG) 200	RT	1	1
Alternate Configuration C			
LRM 15	LT	2	3.5
Ammo (LRM) 8	LT	1	1
LRM 20	RT	4	5
Ammo (LRM) 6	RT	1	1
Streak SRM 4	RA	1	2
Alternate Configuration C (cont.)			
Ammo (SRM) 25	RA	1	1
Ultra AC/5	LA	3	7
Ammo (AC) 20	LA	1	1
ER Medium Laser	LT	1	1
ER Small Laser	LT	1	.5
Flamer	RT	1	.5

BLACK LANNER

CLAN MECHS

Mass: 55 tons
Chassis: Endo Steel
Power Plant: 385 XL
Cruising Speed: 76 kph
Maximum Speed: 119 kph, 151 kph w/MASC
Jump Jets: None
    Jump Capacity: None
Armor: Ferro-Fibrous
Armament:
    13 tons of pod space available
Manufacturer: Unknown
Communications System: Unknown
Targeting and Tracking System: Unknown

OVERVIEW

The *Black Lanner* OmniMech was first sighted with the Jade Falcon Keshik during the Battle of Tukayyid. Fast for its weight class, the *Black Lanner* acts as a direct fire-support 'Mech for light reconnaissance Stars. The majority of the various configurations sighted mount primarily long-range weapons, though other configurations equipped mainly with close-range weapons have also been spotted.

CAPABILITIES

The most common configuration of the *Black Lanner* features one rack each of long- and short-range missiles as well as extended-range lasers. This configuration also contains an ECM suite that can significantly degrade the effectiveness of active Inner Sphere targeting and communications systems such as the newly deployed C[3].

A second common configuration appears on *Black Lanner*s operating for extended periods of time without any direct support—for example, when a Star is bid down to one or two 'Mechs. With an improved PPC and pulse lasers, this *Black Lanner* configuration offers less firepower than the primary configuration. Its electronics suite, however, is significantly enhanced with an active probe, ECM, and TAG for long-range Arrow IV support.

A third configuration consists of two massive long-range missile launchers, capable of launching forty missiles in a single salvo for devastating firepower. However, this 'Mech carries a relatively small number of rounds—it can only keep up a sustained rate of fire for 90 seconds before its ammunition supply is exhausted. A fourth *Black Lanner* carries what appears to be a *Blackhawk* arm, equipped with extra heat sinks and six medium lasers. Only one example of this configuration has been seen, a single 'Mech with the Turkina Strikers on Tukayyid.

The final variant has appeared in urban and other infantry-heavy battlefield environments. Bristling with flamers, machine guns and small-bore lasers, this configuration can deliver devastating short-range firepower.

DEPLOYMENT

The *Black Lanner* is currently deployed only with the Jade Falcon Clan. Its deployment scheme derives from the bird for which it is named—a Terran falcon from the Mediterranean region. The lanner was successfully transplanted to a Jade Falcon planet, where it developed a symbiotic hunting relationship with the smaller, indigenous fire falcon. Though the fire falcon was too small to bring down larger prey, it could see animals cowering in the ground cover far better than the larger lanner. The fire falcon learned to flush out larger game for the lanner to dispatch—then both birds would feed on the carcass. The *Black Lanner* and *Fire Falcon* OmniMechs hunt their prey on the battlefield in a similar way. Working in mixed Stars, *Fire Falcon*s scout for hidden enemies and the supporting *Black Lanner*s attack.

Type: Black Lanner
Technology Base: Clan OmniMech
Tonnage: 55

Equipment			Mass
Internal Structure:	Endo Steel		3
Engine:	385 XL		22
Walking MP:	7		
Running MP:	11 (14)		
Jumping MP:	0		
Heat Sinks:	10 [20]		0
Gyro:			4
Cockpit:			3
Armor Factor:	154		8

	Internal Structure	Armor Value
Head	3	9
Center Torso	18	26
Center Torso (rear)		7
R/L Torso	13	16
R/L Torso (rear)		5
R/L Arm	9	13
R/L Leg	13	22

Weight and Space Allocation

Location	Fixed	Spaces Remaining
Head		1
Center Torso	2 MASC	0
Right Torso	2 Engine	7
	3 Ferro-Fibrous	
Left Torso	2 Engine	7
	3 Endo Steel	
Right Arm	2 Endo Steel	6
Left Arm	2 Ferro-Fibrous	6
Right Leg	2 Ferro-Fibrous	0
Left Leg	2 Endo Steel	0

Weapons and Ammo

Weapons and Ammo	Location	Critical	Tonnage
Primary Weapons Configuration			
LRM 10	LT	1	2.5
Ammo (LRM) 12	LT	1	1
SRM 6	RT	1	1.5
Ammo (SRM) 15	RT	1	1
2 ER Medium Lasers	LA	2	2

BLACK LANNER

Weapons and Ammo	Location	Critical	Tonnage
ER Large Laser	RA	1	4
ECM Suite	H	1	1
Alternate Configuration A			
ER PPC	RA	2	6
2 Medium Pulse Lasers	LA	2	4
ECM Suite	H	1	1
TAG	LT	1	1
Active Probe	RT	1	1
Alternate Configuration B			
LRM 20	RA	4	5
Ammo (LRM) 6	RT	1	1
LRM 20	LA	4	5
Ammo (LRM) 12	LT	2	2
Alternate Configuration C			
6 ER Medium Lasers	LA	6	6
Streak SRM 6	RA	2	3
Ammo (SRM) 15	RA	1	1
3 Double Heat Sinks	LT	6	3
Alternate Configuration D			
Medium Pulse Laser	LA	1	2
ER Small Laser	LA	1	.5
2 Machine Guns	LA	2	.5
Medium Pulse Laser	RA	1	2
ER Small Laser	RA	1	.5
2 Machine Guns	RA	2	.5
Ammo (MG) 100	LT	1	.5
SRM 6	RT	1	1.5
SRM 6	LT	1	1.5
Ammo (SRM) 30	RT	2	2
Flamer	LT	1	.5
Active Probe	H	1	1

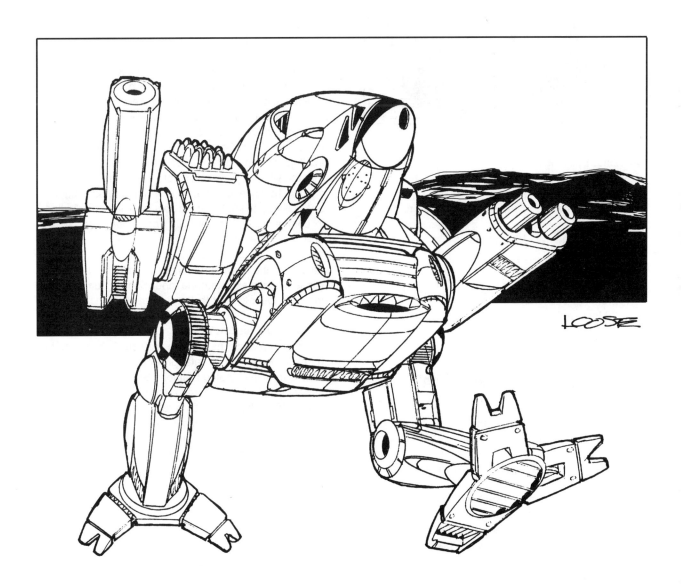

THRESHER

CLAN MECHS

Mass: 60 tons
Chassis: Endo Steel
Power Plant: 300 XL
Cruising Speed: 54 kph
Maximum Speed: 86 kph, w/MASC 108 kph
Jump Jets: 5
   Jump Capacity: 150 meters
Armor: Standard
Armament:
   1 Ultra Class 10 Autocannon
   2 SRM-6 Launchers
   2 Medium Pulse Lasers
   1 ER Medium Laser
Manufacturer: Unknown
Communications System: Unknown
Targeting and Tracking System: Unknown

OVERVIEW

Similar in many ways to the heavier *Thor* favored by Clan Jade Falcon, the *Thresher* is a Clan Diamond Shark 'Mech ideally suited to garrison duty. With a versatile selection of weapons and excellent maneuverability, the 60-ton *Thresher* can adapt to a variety of terrain. Circumstances prevent the Diamond Sharks from fielding a significant garrison force, so the *Thresher* has yet to be deployed in the Inner Sphere. Little data exists about this unusual 'Mech design.

CAPABILITIES

Obviously intended to fill a number of different battlefield roles, the *Thresher* seems to excel at none.

Jump jets and myomer acceleration signal circuitry give the 'Mech superior speed and maneuverability for its class, but its weapons fail to take full advantage of this swiftness. An Ultra-10 autocannon in the right torso is a solid weapon at all ranges, but lacks the punch of larger models. Each arm mounts a medium pulse laser and a standard SRM-6 launcher. Along with an ER medium laser in the torso, these weapons do well at short range, but fall short of the firepower expected of a heavy Clan 'Mech. All in all, this design neither succeeds spectacularly nor fails completely.

One Inner Sphere commander made an interesting observation about this 'Mech. After looking at the intelligence reports on the *Thresher,* he commented that the whole design is "one big compromise, just like a bill in the Assembly that no one wants to pass but no one is willing to kill. The thing gets modified and diddled in committee until it's equally unacceptable to everyone. The *Thresher* looks like its designers went through the same process." Considering the "democratic" nature of the Diamond Sharks relative to the other Clans, it is possible that the Inner Sphere commander may be closer to right than he might suspect.

DEPLOYMENT

No *Thresher*s have been sighted in battle or in garrison forces. The data provided in this briefing comes from intercepted Diamond Shark transmissions as well as intelligence gathered from classified debriefing of Phelan Kell's Wolf Clan refugees. Field commanders should anticipate inconsistencies between the information given in this briefing and the actual 'Mech, should they ever encounter one.

Type: Thresher
Technology Base: Clan
Tonnage: 60

Equipment			Mass
Internal Structure:	Endo Steel		3
Engine:	300 XL		9.5
Walking MP:	5		
Running MP:	8 (10)		
Jumping MP:	5		
Heat Sinks:	13 [26]		3
Gyro:			3
Cockpit:			3
Armor Factor:	152		9.5
	Internal	*Armor*	
	Structure	*Value*	
Head	3	9	
Center Torso	20	22	
Center Torso (rear)		7	
R/L Torso	14	17	
R/L Torso (rear)		5	
R/L Arm	10	14	
R/L Leg	14	21	

Weapons and Ammo	Location	Critical	Tonnage
Ultra AC/10	RT	4	10
Ammo (AC) 20	RT	2	2
MASC	LT	2	2
ER Medium Laser	LT	1	1
SRM 6	RA	1	1.5
Medium Pulse Laser	RA	1	2
Ammo (SRM) 15	RA	1	1
SRM 6	LA	1	1.5
Medium Pulse Laser	LA	1	2
Ammo (SRM) 15	LA	1	1
Jump Jet	CT	1	1
Jump Jets	RL	2	2
Jump Jets	LL	2	2

CAULDRON-BORN

CLAN MECHS

Mass: 65 tons
Chassis: Endo Steel
Power Plant: 325 XL
Cruising Speed: 54 kph
Maximum Speed: 86 kph
Jump Jets: None
    Jump Capacity: None
Armor: Ferro-Fibrous
Armament:
    30 tons of pod space available
Manufacturer: Unknown
Communications System: Unknown
Targeting and Tracking System: Unknown

OVERVIEW

First seen during the battle of Luthien, this OmniMech soon earned the name *Cauldron-Born*, after the unstoppable zombies of Irish myth, because of its ability to take immense damage and remain operational.

CAPABILITIES

The *Cauldron-Born* arsenal is built around a massive Gauss rifle, which occupies the 'Mech's entire right arm. A dual-purpose autocannon occupies the left arm. The *Cauldron-Born* carries two tons of ammunition for each of these weapons. An LRM-10 launcher juts above the birdlike 'Mech's left shoulder, while an SRM-2 launcher in an over-and-under mount fills the machine's right breast. A single ER medium laser is the *Cauldron-Born*'s only energy weapon.

Alternate configuration A carries a mammoth autocannon in its right torso. Three tons of ammunition ensure the pilot will not run out of close-range firepower too early in the fight. ER large lasers and heavy machine guns are mounted in each arm. The right arm also supports a medium pulse laser, while the left carries an anti-infantry flamer. A trio of ER medium lasers sprout from the machine's left torso. Two of these weapons fire into the 'Mech's rear arc.

The *Cauldron-Born* B carries an arsenal of energy weapons. Each arm carries an ER PPC and a large pulse laser in side-by-side mounts. The machine's torso mounts a pair of medium pulse lasers, and an active probe and target acquisition gear allow the pilot to detect hidden enemy units.

Alternate configuration C boasts a pair of LRM-15 launchers and a pair of SRM-6 launchers, with two tons of ammo provided for each. A pair of Ultra autocannons allows the *Cauldron-Born* C to place accurate, effective fire on an enemy's position.

DEPLOYMENT

So far, only the First Jaguar Guard Cluster appears to use the *Cauldron-Born*. Because only three machines have been engaged by Inner Sphere warriors, most believe the design is so new that the other Clans have not yet deployed this 'Mech. Clan warriors taken prisoner in the Kado-guchi Valley provided the information on the B and C variants.

Type: Cauldron-Born
Technology Base: Clan OmniMech
Tonnage: 65

Equipment		Mass
Internal Structure:	Endo Steel	3.5
Engine:	325 XL	12
Walking MP:	5	
Running MP:	8	
Jumping MP:	0	
Heat Sinks:	13 [26]	3
Gyro:		4
Cockpit:		3
Armor Factor:	182	9.5

	Internal Structure	Armor Value
Head	3	9
Center Torso	21	32
Center Torso (rear)		9
R/L Torso	15	22
R/L Torso (rear)		8
R/L Arm	10	17
R/L Leg	15	19

Weight and Space Allocation

Location	Fixed	Spaces Remaining
Head	1 Ferro-Fibrous	0
Center Torso	1 Endo Steel	0
	1 Ferro-Fibrous	
Right Torso	2 Engine	9
	1 Endo Steel	
Left Torso	2 Engine	8
	1 Endo Steel	
	1 Ferro-Fibrous	
Right Arm	2 Ferro-Fibrous	6
Left Arm	2 Ferro-Fibrous	6
Right Leg	2 Endo Steel	0
Left Leg	2 Endo Steel	0

Weapons and Ammo	Location	Critical	Tonnage
Primary Weapons Configuration			
Gauss Rifle	RA	6	12
Ammo (Gauss) 16	RT	2	2
LB 5-X AC	LA	4	7
Ammo (AC) 40	LA	2	2
LRM 10	LT	1	2.5
Ammo (LRM) 24	LT	2	2
ER Medium Laser	LT	1	1
SRM 2	RT	1	.5
Ammo (SRM) 50	RT	1	1
Alternate Configuration A			
Ultra AC/20	RT	8	12
Ammo (AC) 15	LT	3	3
ER Large Laser	RA	1	4
ER Large Laser	LA	1	4
ER Medium Laser	LT	1	1

CAULDRON-BORN

Weapons and Ammo	Location	Critical	Tonnage
2 ER Medium Lasers	LT (R)	2	2
Medium Pulse Laser	RA	1	2
Flamer	LA	1	.5
Machine Gun	RA	1	.25
Machine Gun	LA	1	.25
Ammo (MG) 200	LT	1	1

Alternate Configuration B

ER PPC	RA	2	6
ER PPC	LA	2	6
Large Pulse Laser	RA	2	6
Large Pulse Laser	LA	2	6
Medium Pulse Laser	RT	1	2
Medium Pulse Laser	LT	1	2
Active Probe	RT	1	1
TAG	LT	1	1

Alternate Configuration C

SRM 6	RA	1	1.5
Ammo (SRM) 30	RT	2	2
SRM 6	LA	1	1.5
Ammo (SRM) 30	LT	2	2
LRM 15	RT	2	3.5
Ammo (LRM) 16	RT	2	2
LRM 15	LT	2	3.5
Ammo (LRM) 16	LT	2	2
Ultra AC/2	RA	2	5
Ammo (AC) 45	RA	1	1
Ultra AC/2	LA	2	5
Ammo (AC) 45	LA	1	1

CROSSBOW

CLAN MECHS

Mass: 65 tons
Chassis: Standard
Power Plant: 325 Standard
Cruising Speed: 54 kph
Maximum Speed: 86 kph
Jump Jets: None
    Jump Capacity: None
Armor: Standard
Armament:
    16 tons of pod space available
Manufacturer: Clan Steel Viper
Communications System: Bishop 211 Meridian
Targeting and Tracking System: Spanke 112-A

OVERVIEW

Clan Steel Viper originally developed the *Crossbow* after Viper warriors captured several members of Clan Snow Raven's scientist caste in a Trial of Possession. They set the Snow Raven scientists to work with their own technical engineers and, using Snow Raven expertise, developed an excellent missile-carrying OmniMech. The *Crossbow* and its sister 'Mech, the *Battle Cobra*, mount weapons pods only in their arms, with no additional weaponry—a striking contrast with other Clan OmniMechs.

CAPABILITIES

Similar in many ways to the Star League-era *Longbow*, the *Crossbow* has a more rounded shape and a sleeker overall appearance. Though its short, squat profile lacks elegance, the 'Mech's reliable and punishing performance makes the *Crossbow* a favorite among sec-

ond-line Clan warriors, and its shape has become a familiar one to Inner Sphere MechWarriors after extensive confrontations with it in combat. The *Crossbow* has earned a fierce reputation, especially in Configuration B, which is used for close-support fighting.

The *Crossbow* was developed specifically to deliver a missile-based offensive, a rare goal within the Clans. This 'Mech has given Clan Steel Viper MechWarriors a unique edge in several trials. Several Stars of the elite Viper Guards make heavy use of the *Crossbow*, combining it with Elemental Points to devastating effect in close combat.

DEPLOYMENT

During the Trial of Possession for Firebase Climax on the planet Homer, Clan Steel Viper unveiled the *Crossbow* for the first time against an enclave of Clan Smoke Jaguar. Several Viper Stars were equipped with the new Omni in its primary configuration, and the unique 'Mechs used their long-range missiles to whittle away at their opponents. The Vipers were able to hold back until they had expended their long-range ammunition, then charge up to close range and finish off their work with Streak SRMs. The Smoke Jaguar forces, after only an hour of fighting, conceded the firebase to their opponents.

Type: **Crossbow**
Technology Base: Clan OmniMech
Tonnage: 65

Equipment		Mass
Internal Structure:		6.5
Engine:	325	23.5
Walking MP:	5	
Running MP:	8	
Jumping MP:	0	
Heat Sinks:	10 [20]	0
Gyro:		4
Cockpit:		3
Armor Factor:	192	12

	Internal Structure	Armor Value
Head	3	9
Center Torso	21	26
Center Torso (rear)		13
R/L Torso	15	19
R/L Torso (rear)		9
R/L Arm	10	18
R/L Leg	15	26

Weight and Space Allocation

Location	Fixed	Spaces Remaining
Head		1
Center Torso		2
Right Torso		12
Left Torso		12
Right Arm		8
Left Arm		8
Right Leg		2
Left Leg		2

Weapons and Ammo	Location	Critical	Tonnage
Primary Weapons Configuration			
LRM 20	RA	4	5
Artemis IV FCS	RA	1	1
Ammo (LRM) 12	RA	2	2
LRM 20	LA	4	5
Artemis IV FCS	LA	1	1
Ammo (LRM) 12	LA	2	2

CROSSBOW

Weapons and Ammo	Location	Critical	Tonnage
Alternate Configuration A			
LRM 5	RA	1	1
Ammo (LRM) 24	RA	1	1
Streak SRM 6	RA	2	3
Ammo (SRM Streak) 15	RA	1	1
Medium Pulse Laser	RA	1	2
LRM 5	LA	1	1
Ammo (LRM) 24	LA	1	1
Streak SRM 6	LA	2	3
Ammo (SRM) 15	LA	1	1
Medium Pulse Laser	LA	1	2
Alternate Configuration B			
2 Streak SRM-6	RA	4	6
Ammo (SRM) 30	RA	2	2
2 Streak SRM-6	LA	4	6
Ammo (SRM) 30	LA	2	2

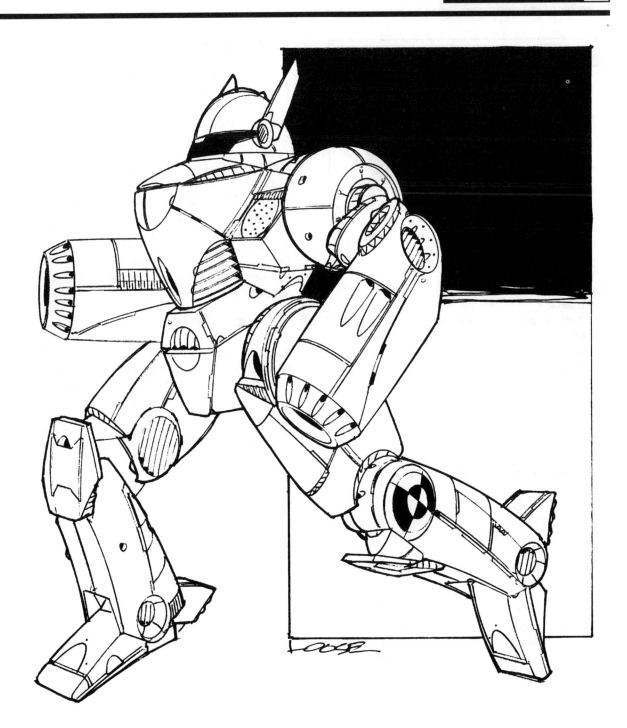

GRIZZLY

CLAN MECHS

Mass: 70 tons
Chassis: Endo Steel
Power Plant: 280 Standard
Cruising Speed: 43 kph
Maximum Speed: 65 kph
Jump Jets: 4
    Jump Capacity: 120 meters
Armor: Standard
Armament:
    1 Gauss Rifle
    1 LRM-10 Launcher
    1 Large Pulse Laser
    1 Medium Pulse Laser
    1 Small Pulse Laser
Manufacturer: Unknown
Communications System: Unknown
Targeting and Tracking System: Unknown

OVERVIEW

So far observed only in Ghost Bear garrison Clusters, the *Grizzly* is a multirole heavy 'Mech that shares design concepts with Clan Ghost Bear's two favorite Omnis, the *Vulture* and the *Gladiator*. Though slower than other 'Mechs in its class, the *Grizzly* makes up for its lack of speed with jump jets and effective long-range weapons. Though the *Grizzly* is a unit with many potential uses, it has thus far failed to find a niche among the Ghost Bear forces, in part because it lacks the focus of its parent designs on a single combat role.

CAPABILITIES

Ghost Bear Provisional Garrison Cluster commanders use the *Grizzly* for roles that other Clans tend to fill with *Thor*s and *Loki*s. The 'Mech's heavier armor and standard engine give it a much higher survival rate than the *Thor* and *Loki* models, which is fortunate because it is difficult to repair. The *Grizzly* has layers of sloped armor that tend to lodge in place when damaged, and its bulky leg actuators are apparently unique and hard to obtain.

The *Grizzly* is jump-capable and mounts a deadly array of weapons, featuring a massive Gauss rifle in the right arm. The 'Mech's left arm sports a trio of pulse lasers similar to but smaller than the array featured in Configuration D of the *Gladiator*. The 'Mech's long-range firepower is supplemented by a ten-pack of long-range missiles in the left torso.

DEPLOYMENT

Though the *Grizzly* has been in service for more than a hundred years, it apparently has never been a popular design. Hundreds of these 'Mechs are still on active duty in Ghost Bear PGCs, even though the *Grizzly* has not been manufactured since 3013. These numbers are a strong testament to the *Grizzly*'s excellent survivability rate in combat. Current intelligence shows *Grizzly*s scattered throughout the Ghost Bear occupation zone.

Type: **Grizzly**
Technology Base: Clan
Tonnage: 70

Equipment			Mass
Internal Structure:	Endo Steel		3.5
Engine:	280		16
Walking MP:	4		
Running MP:	6		
Jumping MP:	4		
Heat Sinks:	11 [22]		1
Gyro:			3
Cockpit:			3
Armor Factor:	208		13

	Internal Structure	Armor Value
Head	3	9
Center Torso	22	31
Center Torso (rear)		10
R/L Torso	15	23
R/L Torso (rear)		7
R/L Arm	11	22
R/L Leg	15	27

Weapons and Ammo	Location	Critical	Tonnage
Gauss Rifle	RA	6	12
Ammo (Gauss) 16	RA	2	2
Large Pulse Laser	LA	2	6
Medium Pulse Laser	LA	1	2
Small Pulse Laser	LA	1	1
LRM 10	LT	1	2.5
Ammo (LRM) 12	LT	1	1
Jump Jets	RL	2	2
Jump Jets	LL	2	2

GRIZZLY

NIGHT GYR

CLAN MECHS

Mass: 75 tons
Chassis: Endo Steel
Power Plant: 300 XL
Cruising Speed: 43 kph
Maximum Speed: 65 kph
Jump Jets: 4
    Jump Capacity: 120 meters
Armor: Ferro-Fibrous
Armament:
    38 tons of pod space available
Manufacturer: Unknown
Communications System: Unknown
Targeting and Tracking System: Unknown

OVERVIEW

The *Night Gyr* is seen most often among Clan Jade Falcon, though the 'Mech also appears in Smoke Jaguar units. Like other new Jade Falcon OmniMech designs, the *Night Gyr* was first spotted within the Jade Falcon Keshik.

CAPABILITIES

The most interesting feature of the *Night Gyr* is its innovative heat-sink design. Standard heat sinks use radiators and heat-conductive fluids to cool the 'Mechs. The *Night Gyr*'s heat sinks use lasers to excite the hot exhaust gases into a higher-energy state, effectively converting the IR energy of the gases to the visual spectrum. The light is then shunted out of the 'Mech via mirrors and highly polished surfaces rather than the usual collection of pipes and tubing.

While these laser-based heat sinks have no

weight or size advantage over the current generation of conventional heat sinks, they appear to be blazing the trail for future improvements in heat sink technology. These laser heat sinks also have an interesting side effect that the Jade Falcons, of all the Clans, surely must appreciate. When firing its weapons at night, the *Night Gyr* appears to be shrouded in plumage of light beams as the 'Mech exudes its converted heat. The efficiency of modern targeting sensors means that this spectacular visual display does not carry any significant disadvantage—indeed, the sight of it can be extremely frightening to green troops.

The primary configuration includes a good mix of long- and short-range firepower; two improved PPCs, three small pulse lasers and a Ultra autocannon make up its weapons array. To cope with the extreme heat build-up caused by using these weapons, the *Night Gyr* carries an additional six laser heat sinks. Another variant reflects the Jade Falcons' new focus on close combat, in urban environments and rough or mountainous terrain. The combination of two Streak short-range missile racks, a heavy Ultra autocannon, three pulse lasers and a long-range large laser give this variant of the *Night Gyr* tremendous punch, especially at shorter ranges.

The *Night Gyr* has two configurations that both appear to serve as long-range snipers. The first is equipped with two Gauss rifles and two long-range LB-X autocannons, allowing it to dispatch its opponents long before most 'Mechs can move into effective weapons range. The second mounts an array of three Ultra autocannons in the left arm and two extended-range lasers in the right. Its weapons paired with a sophisticated targeting computer, this configuration lacks the firepower of other *Night Gyrs* but is unmatched in range and accuracy.

The remaining known configuration is a superior fire-support platform. A total of four long-range missile racks, each capable of launching twenty missiles in a single salvo, are tied to an improved targeting system. Like most missile boats, this configuration can only maintain a sustained barrage for barely a minute, but the results of that minute of hell prove deadly for any target.

DEPLOYMENT

This new design has been seen in increasing numbers among Jade Falcon units, most likely fielded to fill the Falcon ranks in the wake of the devastation wreaked by the so-called Refusal War against Clan Wolf.

Type: **Night Gyr**
Technology Base: Clan OmniMech
Tonnage: 75

Equipment			Mass
Internal Structure:	Endo Steel		4
Engine:	300 XL		9.5
Walking MP:	4		
Running MP:	6		
Jumping MP:	4		
Heat Sinks:	12 [24]		2
Gyro:			3
Cockpit:			3
Armor Factor:	221		11.5

	Internal Structure	Armor Value
Head	3	9
Center Torso	23	34
Center Torso (rear)		10
R/L Torso	16	22
R/L Torso (rear)		10
R/L Arm	12	24
R/L Leg	16	28

Weight and Space Allocation

Location	Fixed	Spaces Remaining
Head		1
Center Torso		2
Right Torso	2 Engine	5
	5 Ferro-Fibrous	
Left Torso	2 Engine	5
	5 Endo Steel	
Right Arm	2 Endo Steel	6
Left Arm	2 Ferro-Fibrous	6
Right Leg	2 Jump Jets	0
Left Leg	2 Jump Jets	0

NIGHT GYR

Weapons and Ammo	Location	Critical	Tonnage
Primary Weapons Configuration			
2 ER PPC	LA	4	12
2 Double Heat Sinks	LA	4	2
Ultra AC/10	RA	4	10
Ammo (AC) 20	RA	2	2
Double Heat Sink	RA	2	1
Medium Pulse Laser	LT	1	2
2 Double Heat Sinks	LT	4	2
Medium Pulse Laser	RT	1	2
2 Double Heat Sinks	RT	4	2
Medium Pulse Laser	H	1	2
Double Heat Sink	CT	2	1
Alternate Configuration A			
Ultra AC/20	RA	8	12
Ammo (AC) 15	RT	3	3
Streak SRM 6	RT	2	3
Streak SRM 6	LT	2	3
Ammo (SRM) 15	LT	1	1
Double Heat Sink	LT	2	1
Large Pulse Laser	LA	2	6
2 Medium Pulse Lasers	LA	2	4
2 Double Heat Sinks	LA	4	2
Double Heat Sink	CT	2	1
Medium Pulse Laser	H	1	2
Alternate Configuration B			
Gauss Rifle	LA	6	12
Ammo (Gauss) 8	LT	1	1
LB 2-X AC	LT	3	5
Ammo (LB 2-X) 45	LT	1	1
Gauss Rifle	RA	6	12
Ammo (Gauss) 16	RT	2	2
LB 2-X AC	RT	3	5
Alternate Configuration C			
3 Ultra AC/2	LA	6	15
Ammo (AC) 90	LA	2	2
2 ER Large Lasers	RA	2	8
3 Double Heat Sinks	RA	6	3
ER Medium Laser	LT	1	1
2 Double Heat Sinks	LT	4	2
Targeting Computer	RT	5	5
Double Heat Sink	CT	2	1
ER Medium Laser	H	1	1

Weapons and Ammo	Location	Critical	Tonnage
Alternate Configuration D			
LRM 20	LA	4	5
Artemis IV FCS	LA	1	1
Ammo (LRM) 18	LA	3	3
LRM 20	RA	4	5
Artemis IV FCS	RA	1	1
Ammo (LRM) 18	RA	3	3
LRM 20	LT	4	5
Artemis IV FCS	LT	1	1
LRM 20	RT	4	5
Artemis IV FCS	RT	1	1
Medium Pulse Laser	H	1	2
Large Pulse Laser	CT	2	6

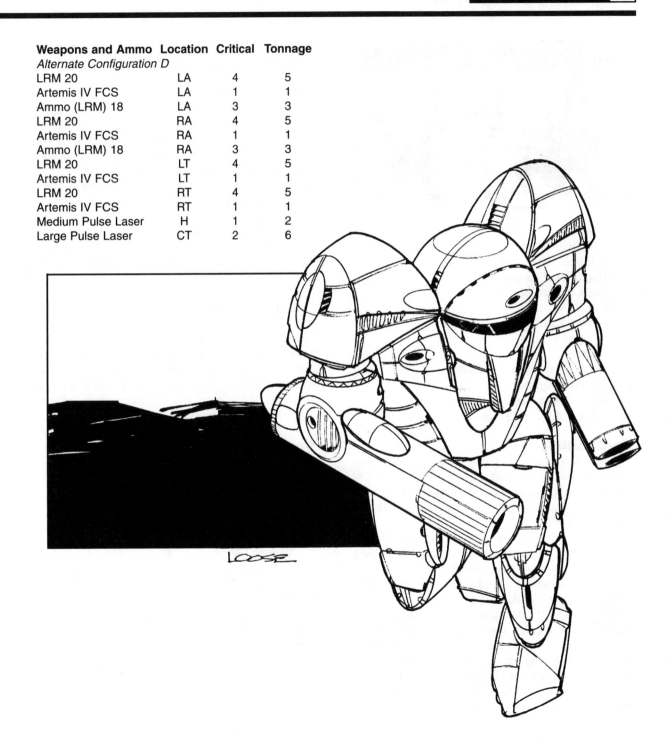

KINGFISHER

CLAN MECHS

Mass: 90 tons
Chassis: Endo Steel
Power Plant: 360 Standard
Cruising Speed: 43 kph
Maximum Speed: 65 kph
Jump Jets: None
    Jump Capacity: None
Armor: Ferro-Fibrous
Armament:
    24 tons of pod space available
Manufacturer: Unknown
Communications System: Unknown
Targeting and Tracking System: Unknown

OVERVIEW

Though not built for great speed, the *Kingfisher* has the stamina to stick with other assault 'Mechs and slug it out toe to toe. Designed to seize the high ground and hold it, the *Kingfisher* is a welcome addition to Clan assault units.

The *Kingfisher* is one of the few OmniMechs not built around an XL engine, which makes it something of an oddity among Clan machines. The standard engine, though heavy, still leaves a lot of room in this giant 'Mech for a wide range of weapons, and the lower engine cost often gives unit commanders the opportunity to bid the 'Mech into forces where they might have to bargain away a more conventional assault 'Mech. The remainder of the *Kingfisher*'s design follows standard Clan patterns. The ferro-fibrous armor provides more than fourteen tons of protection, and the double heat sinks combat the cooling

problems caused by the wide range of weapons that are carried in all configurations.

CAPABILITIES

Each of the five known *Kingfisher* configurations centers around a single heavy weapon or a matched pair of lighter weapons. All weapons configurations are designed to meet a wide range of tactical considerations with a good mix of long- and short-range capability. Standard practice calls for the *Kingfisher* to close with its opponents as quickly as possible, bringing as many weapons to bear as it can. Pilots who prefer the 'Mech's primary configuration, however, have the luxury of delaying their rush until they have softened up their opponents with the firepower of their large lasers and LRMs.

DEPLOYMENT

The five *Kingfisher* configurations seen at the Battle of Tukayyid appeared among the Ghost Bear forces in the fighting at Spanac and Luk and among the Smoke Jaguars in the Dinju Mountains and Racice Delta. Though not as common as the *Gladiator* or *Masakari*, the *Kingfisher* often fights in the company of those OmniMechs.

Type: Kingfisher
Technology Base: Clan OmniMech
Tonnage: 90

Equipment		Mass
Internal Structure:	Endo Steel	4.5
Engine:	360	33
Walking MP:	4	
Running MP:	6	
Jumping MP:	0	
Heat Sinks:	17 [34]	7
Gyro:		4
Cockpit:		3
Armor Factor:	278	14.5

	Internal Structure	Armor Value
Head	3	9
Center Torso	29	44
Center Torso (rear)		13
R/L Torso	19	28
R/L Torso (rear)		10
R/L Arm	15	30
R/L Leg	19	38

Weight and Space Allocation

Location	Fixed	Spaces Remaining
Head	1 Ferro-Fibrous	0
Center Torso		2
Right Torso	3 Endo Steel	4
	3 Ferro-Fibrous	
	2 Double Heat Sinks	
Left Torso	4 Endo Steel	5
	3 Ferro-Fibrous	
Right Arm		8
Left Arm		8
Right Leg	2 Double Heat Sinks	0
Left Leg	2 Double Heat Sinks	0

Weapons and Ammo	Location	Critical	Tonnage
Primary Weapons Configuration			
Large Pulse Laser	RA	2	6
Streak SRM 6	LA	2	3
Ammo (SRM) 15	LA	1	1
ER Small Laser	LA	1	.5
Large Pulse Laser	CT	2	6
Medium Pulse Laser	RT	1	2
LRM 10	LT	1	2.5
Ammo (LRM) 12	LT	1	1
Medium Pulse Laser	LT	1	2
Alternate Configuration A			
LB 10-X AC	RA	5	10
ER Medium Laser	LA	1	1
Medium Pulse Laser	LA	1	2
ER PPC	CT	2	6
Ammo (LB 10-X) 20	RT	2	2
ER Small Laser	RT	1	.5
SRM 6	LT	1	1.5
Ammo (SRM) 15	LT	1	1

KINGFISHER

Weapons and Ammo	Location	Critical	Tonnage
Alternate Configuration B			
Ultra AC/20	RA	8	12
ER Large Laser	LA	1	4
ER Medium Laser	LA	1	1
ER Small Laser	LA	1	.5
Anti-Missile System	CT	1	.5
Ammo (AMS) 24	CT	1	1
Ammo (AC) 10	RT	2	2
ER Medium Laser	RT	1	1
2 ER Medium Lasers	LT	2	2
Alternate Configuration C			
ER PPC	RA	2	6
ER Medium Laser	RA	1	1
2 Double Heat Sinks	RA	4	2
ER PPC	LA	2	6
ER Medium Laser	LA	1	1
2 Double Heat Sinks	LA	4	2
2 ER Medium Lasers	CT	2	2
2 Double Heat Sinks	RT	4	2
2 Double Heat Sinks	LT	4	2
Alternate Configuration D			
Ultra AC/10	RA	4	10
2 ER Large Lasers	LA	2	8
ER Large Laser	CT	1	4
Ammo (AC) 20	RT	2	2

SUPERNOVA

Mass: 90 tons
Chassis: Standard
Power Plant: 270 Standard
Cruising Speed: 32 kph
Maximum Speed: 54 kph
Jump Jets: 3
  Jump Capacity: 90 meters
Armor: Standard
Armament:
  6 ER Large Lasers
Manufacturer: Unknown
Communications System: Unknown
Targeting and Tracking System: Unknown

OVERVIEW

Mounting a menacing array of lasers, the *Supernova* is every bit the big brother of the *Black Hawk*, which is known as the *Nova* among the Clans. Though most designers would assume that the *Supernova* was developed in the mold of its smaller brother, evidence suggests that its design actually predated the *Black Hawk*. The *Supernova*'s design replaces the autocannon of the *King Crab* with clusters of large lasers, a choice that stemmed from a shortage of ammunition. Though this design met with little success due to the *Crab*'s integral ferro-fibrous armor, it gave rise to a lighter and leaner design functioning on a similar principle. It is unknown if the *Supernova* was actually produced at the same time as the *Black Hawk* or if it was shelved in favor of the *Black Hawk* OmniMech.

CAPABILITIES

Slow-moving but surprisingly agile, the *Supernova* counts on destroying its enemies before they get close enough for mobility to be a factor. It accomplishes this task with frightening regularity using its array of six extended-range large lasers, three in each arm. Provided that the pilot has a clear line of sight to the enemy, a single *Supernova* can often eliminate an entire Star of approaching 'Mechs before they get off a shot in return. Like the *Black Hawk*, the *Supernova* suffers from severe overheating if all its lasers are fired repeatedly. Even the 26 double-strength freezers mounted in the 'Mech's roomy chassis can only dissipate 75 percent of the heat generated by its weapons.

DEPLOYMENT

Despite problems with overheating, the *Supernova* has become a mainstay of Nova Cat garrison forces. The *Supernova* is rarely seen outside of Clan Nova Cat, and then always serves a defensive role. Garrisons throughout the Nova Cat occupation zone have one or two of these 'Mechs stationed at most major bases, factories and cities. Reports also place a few *Supernova*s in the PGCs of Clans Wolf and Ghost Bear.

Type: **Supernova**
Technology Base: Clan
Tonnage: 90

Equipment		Mass
Internal Structure:		9
Engine:	270	14.5
Walking MP:	3	
Running MP:	5	
Jumping MP:	3	
Heat Sinks:	26 [52]	16
Gyro:		3
Cockpit:		3
Armor Factor:	232	14.5

	Internal Structure	Armor Value
Head	3	9
Center Torso	29	33
Center Torso (rear)		10
R/L Torso	19	26
R/L Torso (rear)		8
R/L Arm	15	26
R/L Leg	19	30

Weapons and Ammo	Location	Critical	Tonnage
3 ER Large Lasers	RA	3	12
3 ER Large Lasers	LA	3	12
Jump Jet	CT	1	2
Jump Jet	RT	1	2
Jump Jet	LT	1	2

SUPERNOVA

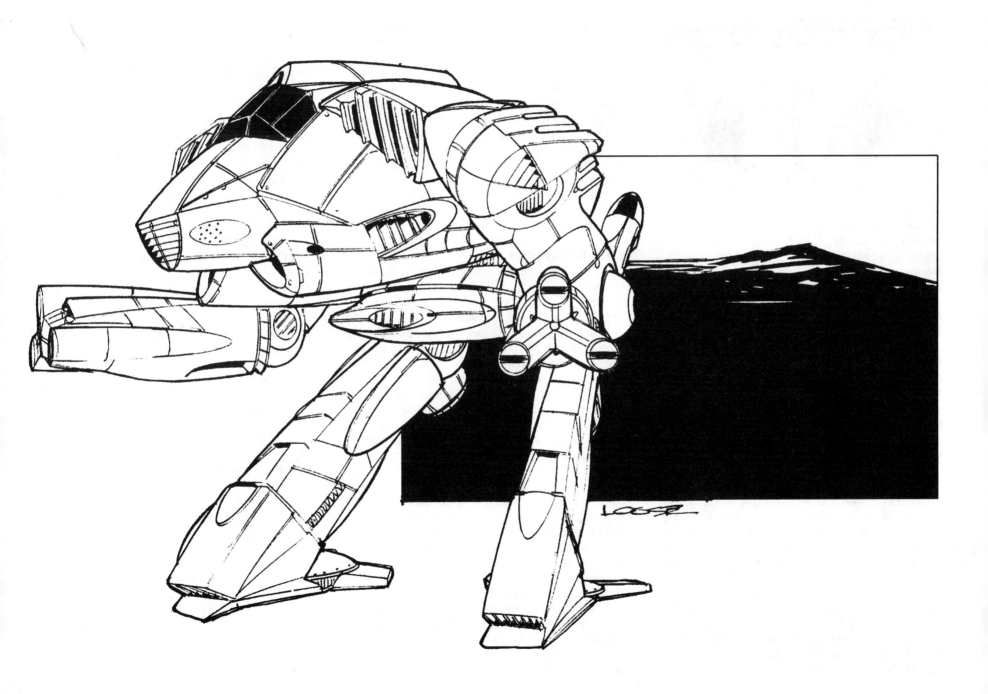

TURKINA

CLAN MECHS

Mass: 95 tons
Chassis: Standard
Power Plant: 285 XL
Cruising Speed: 32 kph
Maximum Speed: 54 kph
Jump Jets: 3
  Jump Capacity: 90 meters
Armor: Standard
Armament:
  42 tons of pod space available
Manufacturer: Unknown
Communications System: Unknown
Targeting and Tracking System: Unknown

OVERVIEW

Clan Jade Falcon uses the massive, jump-capable assault OmniMech named the *Turkina* in situations other Clans might address with a *Dire Wolf (Daishi)*. The addition of jump jets as standard equipment marks this OmniMech as unique among the Clans. The Clans build few jump-capable 'Mechs, instead taking advantage of the OmniMech's modular nature to add jump jets when required by the current mission and configuring extra weapons when jump jets are not necessary.

The most plausible explanation for this radical departure from standard design parameters is that the younger MechWarriors find themselves overwhelmed by the panoply of choices they confront in 'Mech training. While most Inner Sphere warriors stay with one type of 'Mech for most of their careers, Clan warriors

must face the task of mastering what is effectively an infinite variety of systems. To misquote an old saying, Clan warriors possess the potential to become jacks of all trades and masters of none. On the homeworlds, the sibko training regime was rigorous enough to insure that the graduates could rise to this challenge and still maintain their edge. In the Jade Falcon Clan, it seems that the losses suffered at Tukayyid and during the Refusal War have forced the Clan to relax its strict standards in this matter and allow new cadets to gain the benefits of a certain level of standardization. The *Turkina* may represent a minor concession to the need for Clan MechWarriors to spend more training time in a standard platform.

CAPABILITIES

The most common configuration of the *Turkina* is equipped with two racks of long-range missile launchers, two LB-X class autocannon and two improved PPCs. This flexible mix of weapons systems gives the *Turkina* exactly twice the punch packed by the primary configuration of the *Thor* and adds just more than 40 percent the *Thor*'s weight.

For situations likely to result in long-range engagements, the first alternate configuration carries two Gauss rifles and two massive racks of LRMs.

Configuration B of the *Turkina* demonstrates that the Clans learned from their defeats on Tukayyid and other planets. The extended campaigns the Clans fought on Tukayyid placed great stress on ammo resupply efforts. In those thirty terrible days, many Clan units found their firepower significantly reduced through the failure of their supply system to provide them with sufficient ammo. Rather than beef up their logistical units, the Clans now field more 'Mechs equipped solely with energy weapons. The *Turkina* B mounts all laser weapons combined with a deadly accurate targeting computer.

The *Turkina* C represents another lesson learned from the ongoing struggle between the Clans and the people of the Inner Sphere. This 'Mech is configured for close-in city fighting against swarms of infantry, both standard and power suit-equipped.

DEPLOYMENT

Current reports show the Turkina to be deployed only with Clan Jade Falcon, though earlier reports claimed that Smoke Jaguar units were also using this 'Mech.

Type: **Turkina**
Technology Base: Clan OmniMech
Tonnage: 95

Equipment			Mass
Internal Structure:			9.5
Engine:	285 XL		8.5
Walking MP:	3		
Running MP:	5		
Jumping MP:	3		
Heat Sinks:	15 [30]		5
Gyro:			3
Cockpit:			3
Armor Factor:	288		18
		Internal Structure	Armor Value
Head		3	9
Center Torso		30	45
Center Torso (rear)			10
R/L Torso		20	30
R/L Torso (rear)			10
R/L Arm		16	32
R/L Leg		20	40

Weight and Space Allocation

Location	Fixed	Spaces Remaining
Head		1
Center Torso	1 Jump Jet	1
Right Torso	2 Engine	5
	1 Jump Jet	
	2 Double Heat Sinks	
Left Torso	2 Engine	5
	1 Jump Jet	
	2 Double Heat Sinks	
Right Arm		8
Left Arm		8
Right Leg		2
Left Leg		2

TURKINA

Weapons and Ammo	Location	Critical	Tonnage
Primary Weapons Configuration			
2 LB 5-X AC	LA	8	14
Ammo (LB 5-X) 40	LA	2	2
2 ER PPC	RA	4	12
2 Double Heat Sinks	RA	4	2
LRM 15	LT	2	3.5
Ammo (LRM) 16	LT	2	2
LRM 15	RT	2	3.5
Ammo (LRM) 8	RT	1	1
Double Heat Sink	LL	2	1
Double Heat Sink	RL	2	1
Alternate Configuration A			
Gauss Rifle	RA	6	12
Ammo (Gauss) 16	RA	2	2
Ammo (LRM) 6	RA	1	1
Gauss Rifle	LA	6	12
Ammo (Gauss) 16	LA	2	2
Ammo (LRM) 6	LA	1	1
LRM 20	RT	4	5
Ammo (LRM) 6	RT	1	1
LRM 20	LT	4	5
Ammo (LRM) 6	LT	1	1
Alternate Configuration B			
2 Large Pulse Lasers	LA	4	12
3 Double Heat Sinks	LA	6	3
2 ER Large Lasers	RA	2	8
Double Heat Sink	RA	2	1
Targeting Computer	RA	6	6
ER Medium Laser	LT	1	1
2 Double Heat Sinks	LT	4	2
ER Medium Laser	RT	1	1
2 Double Heat Sinks	RT	4	2
Medium Pulse Laser	H	1	2
Medium Pulse Laser	CT	1	2
Double Heat Sink	LL	2	1
Double Heat Sink	RL	2	1
Alternate Configuration C			
LB 20-X AC	LA	9	12
Ammo (LB 20-X) 5	LA	1	1
2 Large Pulse Lasers	RA	4	12
2 Double Heat Sinks	RA	4	2

Weapons and Ammo	Location	Critical	Tonnage
2 Medium Pulse Lasers	LT	2	4
2 Flamers	LT	2	1
Ammo (LB 20-X) 15	LT	3	3
2 Machine Guns	RT	2	.5
Ammo (MG) 100	RT	1	.5
3 Double Heat Sinks	RT	6	3
Active Probe	H	1	1
A-Pod	LL	1	.5
A-Pod	RL	1	.5

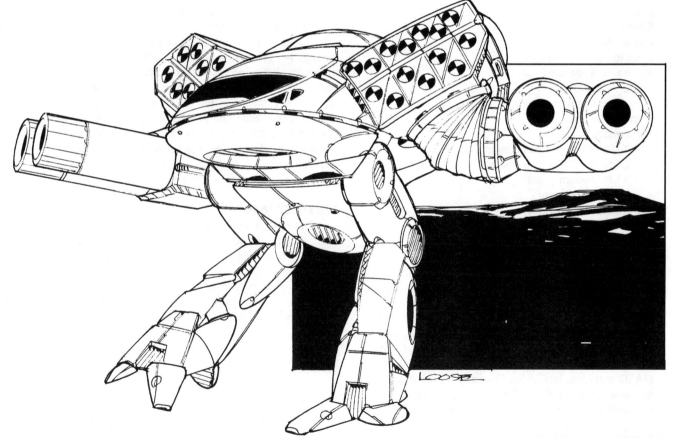

KODIAK

CLAN MECHS

Mass: 100 tons
Chassis: Endo Steel
Power Plant: 400 XL
Cruising Speed: 43 kph
Maximum Speed: 65 kph
Jump Jets: None
    Jump Capacity: None
Armor: Standard
Armament:
    1 Ultra Class 20 Autocannon
    2 Streak SRM-6 Launchers
    8 ER Medium Lasers
    1 ER Large Laser
Manufacturer: Unknown
Communications System: Unknown
Targeting and Tracking System: Unknown

OVERVIEW

The *Kodiak* is a large, fast-moving assault 'Mech that carries impressive medium-range firepower. Clan Ghost Bear technicians most likely designed it as the second-line equivalent to the popular *Gladiator* OmniMech, once again demonstrating the Ghost Bears' tendency to stick with the familiar. Trading the MASC and jump jets of the *Gladiator* for more armor and weaponry, the *Kodiak* has gained a fearsome reputation in the short time it has been in service.

CAPABILITIES

A complete *Kodiak* has yet to be salvaged from a battlefield, and so a comprehensive study cannot be done. However, certain assumptions about the *Kodiak's* capabilities can be made based solely on its known weapon load. A devastating Ultra-20 autocannon occupies the entire right side of its torso. Opposite the autocannon is a pair of Streak SRM-6 launchers. Combined, these weapons provide ample close-in firepower but lack the ammunition to fight an extended battle. Because the 'Mech is intended for garrison use close to supply lines, its designers probably regarded this drawback as negligible. The diminutive ammunition load also reflects the Clan mode of war, in which the campaign is decided in a quick, decisive clash on a field of honor rather than in a slugging match dragged out over the course of weeks or months.

Above each hand is a clawlike array of four extended-range medium lasers, which give the *Kodiak* impressive hitting power even if it runs out of ammunition. Supplementing these weapons is a single ER large laser mounted in the torso directly beneath the engine. Likely added as an afterthought, this weapon gives the 'Mech a single long-range weapon with which to harass a closing enemy, but it generates too much heat to be used in conjunction with the other weapons once the target is within 250 meters.

DEPLOYMENT

The *Kodiak* is believed to be unique to Clan Ghost Bear, though one odd report cites a *Kodiak* operating with a Smoke Jaguar Binary. It is a relatively new design—Inner Sphere troops have thus far seen very few and encountered even fewer. *Kodiak*s spotted among provisional garrison Clusters always serve as the command vehicle of assault Trinaries and Clusters.

Type: Kodiak
Technology Base: Clan
Tonnage: 100

Equipment			Mass
Internal Structure:	Endo Steel		5
Engine:	400 XL		26.5
Walking MP:	4		
Running MP:	6		
Jumping MP:	0		
Heat Sinks:	20 [40]		10
Gyro:			4
Cockpit:			3
Armor Factor:	280		17.5

	Internal Structure	Armor Value
Head	3	9
Center Torso	31	40
Center Torso (rear)		15
R/L Torso	21	32
R/L Torso (rear)		10
R/L Arm	17	32
R/L Leg	21	34

Weapons and Ammo	Location	Critical	Tonnage
Ultra AC/20	RT	8	12
Ammo (AC) 10	RT	2	2
ER Large Laser	CT	1	4
2 Streak SRM 6	LT	4	6
Ammo (SRM) 30	LT	2	2
4 ER Medium Lasers	RA	4	4
4 ER Medium Lasers	LA	4	4

KODIAK

LOOSE

INDEX/APPENDIX

BattleMechs and vehicles arranged alphabetically.

Alacorn Mk VI Heavy Tank 75
Avatar 92
Badger Tracked Transport 22
Bandit Hovercraft 44
Battle Cobra 162
Black Hawk-KU 90
Black Lanner 172
Blackjack II 88
Blizzard Hover Transport 16
Brutus Assault Tank 64
Bushwacker 114
Cauldron-Born 176
Cavalry Attack Helicopter 18
Centipede Scout Car 12
Cestus 122
Challenger XMBT 72
Chameleon 106
Crossbow 178
Devastator 146
Dragon Fire 128
Emperor 142
Enfield 108
Excalibur 124
Falcon Hawk 98
Fire Falcon 158
Firestarter II 86
Fulcrum Heavy Hovercraft 46
Galleon Light Tank 24
Goblin Infantry Support Vehicle 40
Grand Crusader 132
Grendel 164
Grizzly 180
Hankyu 160
Hunchback IIC 168
Hunter Light Support Tank 32
Karnov UR Transport 26
Kestrel VTOL 20
Kingfisher 184
Kodiak 190
Lineholder 116
Longbow 140
Lynx 118
Mackie 148
Maelstrom 130
Manticore Heavy Tank 54
Maultier Hover APC 10
Maxim Heavy Hover Transport 48
Merlin 120
Nexus 96
Night Gyr 182
Night Hawk 100
Nightstar 144
Nobori-nin 170
O-Bakemono 134
Ontos Heavy Tank 76

Owens 82
Padilla Heavy Artillery Tank 66
Partisan Air Defense Tank 70
Pegasus Scout Hovertank 34
Peregrine Attack VTOL 28
Pillager 150
Pilum Heavy Tank 60
Piranha 156
Plainsman Medium Hovertank 36
Po Heavy Tank 56
Raijin 110
Raptor 80
Regulator Hovertank 42
Shadow Cat 166
Shootist 126
Spartan 136
Spector 102
Sprint Scout Helicopter 8
SRM/LRM Carrier 52
Starslayer 112
Strider 84
Striker 138
Striker Light Tank 38
Sunder 94
Supernova 186
Talon 104
Thresher 174
Thunder Hawk 152
Tokugawa Heavy Tank 58
Turkina 188
Typhoon Urban Assault Vehicle 62
Vedette Medium Tank 50
Warrior H-8 Attack Helicopter 14
Yellow Jacket Gunship 30
Zhukov Heavy Tank 68

BattleMechs and vehicles listed by tons.

10
Sprint Scout Helicopter 8

15
Maultier Hover APC 10

20
Centipede Scout Car 12
Piranha 156
Warrior H-8 Attack Helicopter 14

25
Blizzard Hover Transport 16
Cavalry Attack Helicopter 18
Fire Falcon 158
Kestrel VTOL 20
Nexus 96
Raptor 80

30
Badger Tracked Transport 22
Galleon Light Tank 24
Hankyu 160
Karnov UR Transport 26
Peregrine Attack VTOL 28
Yellow Jacket Gunship 30

35
Falcon Hawk 98
Hunter Light Support Tank 32
Night Hawk 100
Owens 82
Pegasus Scout Hovertank 34
Plainsman Medium Hovertank 36
Spector 102
Striker Light Tank 38
Talon 104

40
Battle Cobra 162
Strider 84

45
Firestarter II 86
Goblin Infantry Support Vehicle 40
Grendel 164
Regulator Hovertank 42
Shadow Cat 166

50
Bandit Hovercraft 44
Blackjack II 88
Chameleon 106
Enfield 108
Fulcrum Heavy Hovercraft 46
Hunchback IIC 168
Maxim Heavy Hover Transport 48
Nobori-nin 170
Raijin 110
Starslayer 112
Vedette Medium Tank 50

55
Black Lanner 172
Bushwacker 114
Lineholder 116
Lynx 118

60
Black Hawk KU 90
Manticore Heavy Tank 54
Merlin 120
Po Heavy Tank 56
SRM/LRM Carrier 52
Thresher 174
Tokugawa Heavy Tank 58

65
Cauldron-Born 176
Cestus 122
Crossbow 178

70
Avatar 92
Excalibur 124
Grizzly 180
Pilum Heavy Tank 60
Shootist 126
Typhoon Urban Assault Vehicle 62

75
Brutus Assault Tank 64
Dragon Fire 128
Maelstrom 130
Night Gyr 182
Padilla Heavy Artillery Tank 66
Zhukov Heavy Tank 68

80
Grand Crusader 132
O-Bakemono 134
Partisan Air Defense Tank 70
Spartan 136
Striker 138

85
Longbow 140

90
Challenger XMBT 72
Emperor 142
Kingfisher 184
Sunder 94
Supernova 186

95
Alacorn Mk VI Heavy Tank 75
Nightstar 144
Ontos Heavy Tank 76
Turkina 188

100
Devastator 146
Kodiak 190
Mackie 148
Pillager 150
Thunder Hawk 152